The Royal Commission on His

Guides to Sources for British History
based on the National Register of Archives
8

Records of
BRITISH BUSINESS
AND INDUSTRY
1760 – 1914
Textiles and Leather

London   Her Majesty's Stationery Office

©Crown copyright 1990
First published 1990

British Library Cataloguing in Publication Data

A CIP catalogue record for this book is available from the British Library

ISBN 0 11 440226 4

HMSO publications are available from:

HMSO Publications Centre
(Mail and telephone orders only)
PO Box 276, London, SW8 5DT
Telephone orders 071-873 9090
General enquiries 071-873 0011
(queuing system in operation for both numbers)

HMSO Bookshops
49 High Holborn, London, WC1V 6HB   071-873 0011 (counter service only)
258 Broad Street, Birmingham, B1 2HE   021-643 3740
Southey House, 33 Wine Street, Bristol, BS1 2BQ   (0272) 264306
9-21 Princess Street, Manchester, M60 8AS   061-834 7201
80 Chichester Street, Belfast, BT1 4JY   (0232) 238451
71 Lothian Road, Edinburgh, EH3 9AZ   031-228 4181

HMSO's Accredited Agents
(see Yellow Pages)

and through good booksellers

Preface

This volume, the first of a group describing the records of business and industry, is based like its companions in the series of *Guides to sources for British history* on the resources of the National Register of Archives. In planning a series of guides concentrating initially on sources for nineteenth-century history it was apparent from the beginning that the Register was rich in information not only about the papers of individuals eminent in areas of public life but also about corporate and institutional records, and that scholars of business, social, technical and urban history and kindred disciplines were in need of such information. The rapid growth of the Register's Companies Index from the 1970s reflected both the Commission's response to this demand and the increasing quantity of business records finding their way into record offices, libraries and museums. A preliminary survey soon established that the amount of material required a number of guides, probably four in all, each concentrating on a different sector of industrial activity. As a key industry for nineteenth-century commercial and urban development, textiles was the chosen subject for the first of these; the equally important engineering industry will feature in the next volume.

At the outset of the survey there were many gaps in the Commission's knowledge, and considerable research has been carried out in order to check, amplify and supplement the information already in the Register. This would not have been possible without the assistance of numerous companies and other private owners, many of whom gladly gave much time to the Commission's staff, and of individual scholars, curators, librarians and archivists who so readily responded to requests for information. Their valuable contribution, evident from the text, is most gratefully acknowledged. Many users of this volume will also find it helpful to consult the complementary textile surveys being undertaken by the Royal Commission on the Historical Monuments of England (Yorkshire, Greater Manchester and East Cheshire Textile Mills Surveys) and the Pasold Research Fund (Clothes, Fashion and the English Economy 1660-1820 and the Pasold Dictionary of Surviving Costume). These concentrate mainly on archaeological and bibliographical material but their editors have generously shared with the Commission knowledge of relevant manuscript material gained from their own enquiries.

The investigatory work and the compilation of the guide were undertaken by Mr LA Ritchie, Dr SG Roberts and Dr Anita Travers under the direction of Dr Eileen Scarff.

BS SMITH
Secretary
31 October 1989

Quality House, Quality Court,
Chancery Lane, London WC2A 1HP

Contents

Introduction

This guide describes the records of 1,200 textile, clothing and leather firms in Great Britain and Northern Ireland between 1760 and 1914. Its chosen period begins with the cotton masters and others who pioneered the Industrial Revolution, and ends with the industrial watershed marked by the beginning of the first world war.

In most branches of textiles the period 1760 to 1860 saw an immense concentration of capital and resources, generated by changes in technology, ownership and the organisation of raw materials, production, markets and marketing. By contrast, production in the clothing and leather industries remained in the hands of individual craft workers or very small enterprises throughout most of the nineteenth century. The guide therefore deals with the records produced by many different kinds of business concerns, some surviving and some defunct, ranging from those of individuals, partnerships and independent private companies, to the loose amalgamations of companies that were coming into existence in some areas of textiles at the end of the nineteenth century. The main focus is on manufacturing rather than distributive enterprises, although textile and leather merchants, commission agents, factors and brokers have been included. Drapers, shoe retailers and other firms whose functions were wholly retail, cloth halls, research associations, design guilds, and many individuals working in collaboration with manufacturing firms, such as pattern drawers and designers, have all been excluded.

Within the category of business firm as thus described, the guide includes all those known to the Commission that have left a significant quantity of papers relating to the period 1760 to 1914, or whose records for that period are of particular importance either in terms of date or in shedding light on various aspects of industrial organisation and development. On this basis most single volumes and the slight, personal records of many individual handloom weavers, tanners, craftsmen and traders noted in the National Register of Archives have had to be excluded. Within the collections noticed in the guide, records later than 1914 have been included for the sake of completeness. Records of subsidiaries have been omitted where no pre-1914 material survives, since in most cases these were found to amount to little more than miscellaneous corporate and financial records. Personal and family papers have been included where they provide insights into business activities.

The main emphasis, therefore, is on records generated by business firms and their proprietors that are readily available to scholars, generally in record offices, libraries and museums, although in the case of important, old-established firms the Commission has attempted to locate and describe records that remain in private hands. An initial trawl of the National Register of Archives produced some 600 textile and leather firms which had left records of some description but this list was substantially enlarged during subsequent research and investigation. Eventually over 2,000 concerns were identified of which 1,200 qualified for inclusion.

Among the subjects of the guide are companies that were the life-force of a town or factory community. They include most of the textile firms listed among the largest manufacturing employers at the end of the period. Some played a decisive role in the organisation of a particular branch of textiles, such as the amalgamations formed by the Bleachers, Bradford Dyers, the Calico Printers, English Sewing Cotton and the Fine Spinners & Doublers. Some undertook technical innovation, which transformed the operation of their industry, and often had to be defended in lengthy lawsuits. Many came to overshadow their rivals through the quality of their management and their efficiency in production and marketing, such as Patons & Baldwins (the largest wool yarn spinning company), Templetons (the largest carpet producers), Tootal Broadhurst Lee (cotton), Baxter Brothers (the largest flax firm), Cox Brothers (jute), Michael Nairn and James Williamson (linoleum), the Belfast Ropeworks (the largest rope manufacturers), Courtaulds, Grouts and Hindes (crape), United Turkey Red (Turkey-red dyeing), and Morton Sundour and associated companies (textile printing, lace, carpet manufacture and dyeing). J & P Coats, the largest firm in British textiles by 1913, with some forty associated and subsidiary companies and around 39,000 employees throughout the world, is a prime example of the several ambitious mergers to be found in the guide. A few large companies, for example, William Hollins, Rylands and Tootals, became virtually integrated firms carrying out all the processes of production. Many were involved in international trade. The large numbers of overseas order and sales books amongst the records of Irish linen firms chart the development of world wide connections that were of vital importance to that industry.

Records of factory communities include those of the Ashworths at New Eagley, the Clarks at Street, the Gregs at Styal, Robert Owen at New Lanark, JN Richardson at Bessbrook and the Strutts at Belper. A great deal of information survives regarding employees, their housing, welfare and recreations, in such sources as the statutory registers of employment preserved by many firms, the records of the factory doctor at Styal, the sickness benefit club at Cash's, the chapel, school and hospital papers at AC Bealey and the brass band papers at RV Marriner and John Murgatroyd. Examples of early profit-sharing schemes for employees are to be found in the collections of Samuel Slater, JT & J Taylor and William Thomson & Sons.

Alongside the factory communities are numerous small-scale operations and many family-owned firms moving late into private limited liability status. To some extent the mergers in the textile industry threatened the family managerial autonomy, yet even in the case of J & P Coats, which had some 25,000 shareholders in 1913, about half the shares were still in family hands, and the whole period remains dominated by family partnerships. There are examples in the guide of families developing a whole network of partnerships, like the Philips family in Manchester (J & N Philips, JL Philips & Brother and Philips & Lee). Many instances occur of firms remaining in the hands of founder families for 150 to 200 years, sometimes still operating from the same site, the Gurteens of Haverhill, whose records begin in 1784, being a notable example. In contrast, some sites changed hands frequently, leaving little trace of their occupants, although in a few cases records survive of successive businesses on the same site that between them span around 200 years, as at the Merton Abbey Works from Robert Maxwell and John Leach, Bennett & Co in the late eighteenth century to Liberty & Co in the twentieth. Finally, some of the most important collections relate to pioneering firms that ultimately failed, like Marshall & Co (the largest flax spinning company in 1828), Samuel Oldknow, and Samuel Crompton's ill-fated ventures.

The richest and most varied collections are mainly concentrated in the woollen, worsted, cotton, linen, jute, silk and finishing industries. Disappointingly little survives for the early leather industries. In hosiery and lace, where survivals are also few, important collections have nevertheless been traced for some key firms. In the clothing industries there is little information available on the large-scale manufacture of suits, overcoats and other outerwear in the late nineteenth and early twentieth centuries, but there are important early records of wig and hat making, gold and silver lace and military uniform manufacture, and ecclesiastical, academic and court robe making. Overall, there are 254 collections containing eighteenth-century material. Frequently these early survivals take the form of design records, sometimes acquired by a firm from many different sources, and often physically separated from the rest of the archive. Most of the records remaining with companies were entirely uncatalogued and invariably unknown to the potential researcher. Many papers held by record offices, libraries and museums were also wholly or partly unlisted, often on account of their sheer bulk. Uncatalogued collections were surveyed by the Commission's staff when practicable, and altogether 205 entries are based on knowledge acquired through such personal inspections.

Papers were traced for 1,054 textile firms and 146 leather firms. For these 1,200 firms a total of 1,586 groups of papers have been identified. They are to be found in 196 repositories and 194 private collections, making a total of 390 locations. Of the repositories, 87 are national and local record offices, 20 university and college libraries and departments, 29 public libraries and 50 museums. Only 10 are overseas.

The economic depression of the 1930s, the second world war, and the widespread recent collapse of manufacturing firms have led to the destruction of many records. Some collections that were noted by antiquarians in the last century, or were listed by the National Register of Archives Committees in the 1940s and 1950s or even more recently by the Business Archives Council (Scotland), have since disappeared altogether or are known to have been destroyed. But collections of business records continue to emerge unexpectedly and undoubtedly other material remains to be discovered or made available for historical research. The Commission would welcome further information from owners, custodians and scholars to add to that uncovered by this survey.

Access to privately owned papers

Privately owned collections of papers deposited on loan in libraries, record offices and other public institutions are normally available for research without restriction. Special conditions, however, may sometimes apply, particularly if a collection is as yet uncatalogued, and advice on access and related matters should be sought from the institutions concerned.

Permission to study papers that remain with a company or other private owner should be sought from the owner in writing, either direct or, where indicated, through an intermediary. Applicants are reminded that such papers can normally be made available only at considerable inconvenience to their owners, and that access for the purposes of research is a privilege and not a right. The conditions of access cited in the guide are those that prevailed in October 1989. Details of the present location of collections whose ownership or whereabouts is not specified in the guide may, where appropriate, be obtained from the Commission.[1]

Those wishing to study papers in private hands are also advised to consult catalogues or other finding aids available in the Commission's search room or elsewhere before approaching owners or custodians.

1. Enquiries to the Commission should be addressed to the Secretary, The Royal Commission on Historical Manuscripts, Quality House, Quality Court, Chancery Lane, London WC2A 1HP. Where indicated, enquiries about Scottish collections should be addressed to the Secretary, National Register of Archives (Scotland), West Register House, Charlotte Square, Edinburgh EH2 4DF. For addresses of repositories generally, see the Commission's *Record Repositories in Great Britain, a geographical directory*, eighth edition, HMSO 1987.

Editorial note

Textile firms are assigned to sub-sections on the basis of their main business activity. The name of the firm given is that by which it was known for the longest period covered by its surviving records. The geographical location relates to the head office or the particular factories from which records emanate. The county names used for identification are those of the pre-1974/5 counties. Where a collection has been the subject of a large-scale printed survey, only a brief description of the records is given with a reference to the work. The records are normally described in the following order: partnership deeds, minutes and other corporate records, accounting, order, sales, production, staff, property, and miscellaneous records.

The following abbreviations are used in the text.

BAC *Company Archives*   L Richmond and B Stockford, *Company archives: the survey of the records of 1,000 of the first registered companies in England and Wales*, Business Archives Council, 1986.

Hudson   P Hudson, *The West Riding wool textile industry: a catalogue of business records from the sixteenth to the twentieth century*, Pasold Research Fund Ltd, Edington, Occasional Papers no. 3, 1975.

NRA   Lists available for consultation in the National Register of Archives.

NRA(S)   Surveys produced by the National Register of Archives (Scotland).

Ulster textile industry   *Public Record Office of Northern Ireland. The Ulster textile industry: a catalogue of business records in P.R.O.N.I. relating principally to the linen industry in Ulster*, 1978.

Records of British Business and Industry 1760-1914 Textiles and Leather

WOOL

[1] **WILLIAM ACKROYD LTD**, worsted spinners, Otley, Yorks

Private and nominal ledgers (10) 1919-54, cash book 1919-24, trial balances, etc 1916-23, sales and purchase records (7 vols) 1919-59, wool and yarn notebook 1844-1919, spinning book 1925-36, drawing books (5) 1916-63, wages books (30) 1845-1947, stock inventory and valuation 1853-72, misc deeds and papers 1817-69. *Brotherton Library, Leeds University*. NRA 1099, NRA 16072.

[2] **AIREDALE MILLS CO LTD**, commission scribblers, spinners and finishers, Rodley, Yorks

Directors' and shareholders' minutes 1860-1912, shareholding records 1861-1916, creditors' and debtors' ledgers 1872-1923, accounting records 1872-1931, wages books 1903-18. *Brotherton Library, Leeds University*: see Hudson.

[3] **JAMES AKROYD & SON LTD**, stuff mfrs, worsted spinners and merchants, Halifax, Yorks

Minutes 1893-1932, private ledger 1893-1911, wages books (12) 1891-1932. *West Yorkshire Archive Service, Calderdale* (BM). NRA 26200.

[4] **JONATHAN AKROYD**, clothier, Halifax, Yorks

Account books (5) 1770-1802. *Brotherton Library, Leeds University*: see Hudson.

[5] **ALDAM, PEASE, BIRCHALL & CO**, woollen merchants, Leeds

Sales and general ledgers (19) 1738-1839, cash book 1760-85, bank book 1833-9, day book 1838, purchase and disbursement ledgers (3) 1809-25, stock books (2) 1811-18, 1832-9. *Doncaster Archives Department* (DD.Wa/B). NRA 30826.

Trade accounts 1799-1831, notes of profit and capital 1763-1810, papers and corresp rel to dyestuffs, exportation of wool, education of children in woollen mills, etc 1763-1844, Aldam family and business papers 1755-1923. *Wakefield Libraries Department of Local Studies* (Goodchild Loan MSS). NRA 23091.

[6] **JEREMIAH AMBLER & SONS LTD**, wool combers, spinners and weavers, Bradford, Yorks

Letter book and corresp 1828-98, journal 1861-1933, purchase and sales books 1849-1929, stock books 1888-1919. *Brotherton Library, Leeds University*: see Hudson.

[7] **JOHN AMBLER & SONS LTD**, worsted spinners, Luddenden, Yorks

Memorandum and articles of association 1875, account book 1828-37, cash ledger 1856-65, private ledger 1884-1901, plans of machinery 1893-5, patent 1879. *West Yorkshire Archive Service, Calderdale* (HAS 397-405). NRA 6546.

[8] **PETER ANDERSON LTD**, woollen mfrs, Galashiels, Selkirkshire

Standard pattern books (15) 1901-46; L Anderson plaid order book 1874-7, pattern books and misc records (16 vols and bundles) 1909-51, nd. *Scottish College of Textiles, Galashiels*. NRA 31124.

[9] **APPERLEY, CURTIS & CO LTD**, woollen mfrs, Stroud, Glos

Registers of members, shares and stock (6 vols) 1895-1933, history of firm, brochures, etc (7 items) 1910. *Gloucestershire RO* (D2209). NRA 11424.

[10] **APPLEGATE BROTHERS**, woollen cloth mfrs, Bradford-on-Avon, Wilts

Pattern books (3) 1833, 1886, nd. *Wiltshire RO* (WRO 604). NRA 3523.

Private ledger 1870-1906. *Wiltshire RO* (WRO 2020). NRA 3523.

[11] **J & R ARCHIBALD**, woollen mfrs, Tillicoultry, Clackmannanshire

Statements of account, profit and loss accounts, etc 1898-1902, summary ledgers (2) 1877-97, cash book 1898-1906, day books and sales books (4) 1822-56, 1891-2, 1908-9, sales ledger nd, purchase ledger nd, wages books (2) 1838-43, 1901-6, inventories of mill and furnishings 1898, misc papers 1883-95, 1915. *Public Record Office of Northern Ireland* (D 1933/14). NRA 31476.

[12] JOSEPH ASHTON, woollen mfrs, Tranwell, Northumb

Corresp 1896-1949, material record book 1929-36, invoices c1891-1948, War Office circulars and vouchers 1916-18, Wool Control circulars, etc 1939-48, wool samples incl pattern cards, trade circulars.
Northumberland RO (ZBA).

[13] G ATKIN & CO LTD, stuff merchants, Bradford, Yorks

Ledgers (2) 1881-4, 1898-1901, account books for goods sold (3 vols) 1911-45, price lists 1893-5, register of young employees 1913, misc corresp and papers 1883-1951.
West Yorkshire Archive Service, Bradford (37D87). NRA 31949.

[14] GEORGE AUSTIN & CO, clothiers and bankers, Wotton-under-Edge, Glos

Articles of partnership 1811, account book 1805-20, list of debtors 1820, inventory of stock 1820, lease of factory 1822, deeds and family papers 17th-19th cent.
Gloucestershire RO (D2078). NRA 23791.

[15] ALBERT BAILEY & SONS LTD, worsted spinners, Elland, Yorks

Share register 1915-73, ledgers and cash books (9 vols) 1915-79, day book 1913-33, sales and purchase books (13) 1911-76, salaries books (2) 1974-5.
West Yorkshire Archive Service, Calderdale (AB). NRA 27864.

[16] T & M BAIRSTOW LTD, worsted spinners and mfrs, Sutton-in-Craven, Yorks

Records 1801-1964 incl accounts, corresp, purchase and sales records, production records of outworker firms, employment and wages records, building accounts, legal papers, and insurance valuations.
West Yorkshire Archive Service, Leeds: see Hudson.

[17] BAKER'S MILL, cloth mfrs and flour millers, Bisley, Glos

Ledgers (2) 1808-26, weavers' output record (1 vol) 1811-20.
Gloucestershire RO (D5685).

[18] BALDWIN & WALKER LTD, knitting yarn mfrs, Halifax, Yorks

Account books (2) 1876-81, ledgers (2) 1888-94, 1899-1925, cash book 1879-81, bank book 1877-84, reference books (2) 1863-97, wool receipt book 1836-40, details of orders and prices (2 vols, etc) 1882-1929, notebook 1901 incl collections for relief of Mafeking, register of advertisements 1907-18, misc papers rel to closure 1974.
West Yorkshire Archive Service, Calderdale (BW). NRA 18519.

[19] D BALLANTYNE BROS & CO LTD, woollen mfrs, Peebles

Contract of copartnery, etc 1904-20, minute book 1948-80, agenda books (3) 1920-74, share certificate books (3) 1917-50, balance sheets and profit and loss accounts, etc 1904-51, letter books (3) 1884-1920, private ledgers and journals (5 vols) 1884-95, 1907-67, partners' ledger 1904-19, private cash books and other financial records (6 vols) 1913-69, standard pattern books from 1880, inventories and valuations 1880-1927, photographs 20th cent.
Henry Ballantyne & Sons Ltd. Enquiries to NRA (Scotland) (NRA(S) 1990). NRA 22834.

[20] HENRY BALLANTYNE & SONS LTD, tweed mfrs, Walkerburn, Peeblesshire

Corresp and letter books (2 boxes, 4 vols) 1845-60, 1878-1912, nd, balance sheets and profit and loss accounts (2 vols) 1883-1904, ledgers (19) 1841-1940, cash books (27) 1829-1952, day books (32) 1844-1912, journals (24) 1887-94, 1902-5, balance books (12) 1888, 1895-1915, cash contract book 1828-39, bill books (3) 1861-1939, bank books (5) 1836-56, invoice books (52) 1847-1925, order books (7) 1888-1953, purchase and sales books (5) 1917-49, handloom books (2) 1826-31, 1865-93, batch books (44) 1855-1941, number books (6) 1918-29, stock books (3) 1893-1941, wool books (24) 1858-1940, carders' books (5) 1920-5, staff and wages records (30 vols) 1846-1954, inventories and valuations (4 vols) 1908-50, misc records (8 vols) 1865-1954.
Edinburgh University Library (Gen 921–1209). NRA 29821.

Directors' minutes (6 vols) 1904-50, general meeting minutes (1 vol) 1904-38, agenda books (4) 1904-54, directors' attendance books (6) 1904-77, register of members, etc (2 vols) 1904-44, misc share records 1921-47, balance sheets, profit and loss accounts and annual reports 1904-67, private ledgers (2) 1904-64, ledger 1904-66, private journals (2) 1919-42, cash book 1967-72, cross entry book 1965-70, bill books (2) 1936-69, papers rel to plant register and investment grants, etc 1932-70, plans and photographs; Wilson & Glenny Ltd minutes 1921-69, private ledgers (2) 1931-76, misc financial papers and corresp 1919-56, trade mark registration papers 1902-50.
The Company. Enquiries to NRA (Scotland). NRA 22834.

[21] BALLYGARVEY SPINNING & WEAVING CO, woollen mfrs, Ballymena, co Antrim

Private ledger 1901-9, cash book 1908-9, sales ledgers and journals (5 vols) 1908-31, wool stock book 1929-30.
Public Record Office of Northern Ireland (D 1933/16). NRA 31476.

[22] BALLYMENAGH WOOLLEN FACTORY, woollen mfrs, Ballymena, co Antrim

Memorandum and articles of association 1904, general meeting minutes and balance sheet 1908, cash book 1904-9, bank books (3) 1901-13, sales ledgers and journal (3 vols) 1901-9, 1923-34.
Public Record Office of Northern Ireland (D 1933/15). NRA 31476.

[23] **JOHN BANCROFT & CO LTD**, worsted spinners, Oxenhope, Yorks

Letter books 1900-14, day books 1877-1914, wages books 1863-1914, factory registers 1885-1938.
Brotherton Library, Leeds University. NRA 1099; and see Hudson.

[24] **FW BANISTER & CO LTD**, worsted spinners, Bradford, Yorks

Letter books 1894-1913, cash books 1893-1933, purchase and sales records 1886-1950, production and technical books 1889-1919, wages books 1887-1904.
West Yorkshire Archive Service, Bradford: see Hudson.

[25] **THOMAS BRADBURY BARNES**, woollen cloth merchant, Trowbridge, Wilts

Ledger 1876-c1881, day book c1866-8, business and domestic corresp and invoices (1 vol) c1884-6, receipts for cloth purchases, etc (1 vol, 1 packet) c1890-1, 1899-1902.
Wiltshire RO (WRO 2153). NRA 32193.

[26] **ROBERT BATTERSBY & SONS**, woollen mfrs, Bury, Lancs

Records 1782-1886 (32 composite vols) incl letter book 1782-6, day books 1782-1867, cash book 1829-31, customers' accounts 1782-1866, order books 1782-1853, piece books 1823-73, carding accounts 1821-32, fulling accounts 1840-63, and wages books 1791-1848.
Bury Archive Service. NRA 30195.

[27] **JOHN & JOSEPH BEAUMONT**, clothiers, Kirkheaton, Yorks

Account book 1794-6, sales journals (3) 1791-1807, misc family papers 1774-1862 incl valuation of goods of John Beaumont 1814.
West Yorkshire Archive Service, Wakefield Headquarters (C296/14). NRA 24402.

[28] **SIR JACOB BEHRENS & SONS**, stuff merchants and commission agents, Bradford, Yorks and Manchester

Letter book 1853.
Manchester Central Library (MISC 783).

Export stamp impressions book 1901-23.
Quarry Bank Mill, Styal.

[29] **ARTHUR BELL (SCOTCH TWEEDS) LTD**, tweed mfrs, Langholm, Dumfriesshire

Ledger incl misc corresp and costings 1912-22, cash books and other accounting records (6 vols) 1919-72, travellers' order books (7) 1919-24, cloth design books (5) 1889-1912, wages book 1911-17, corresp, papers, drawings, etc (7 bundles and envelopes) rel to wool contracts, machinery and premises c1880, 1903-20.
The Company. Enquiries to NRA (Scotland) (NRA(S) 1776). NRA 21893.

[30] **TOM BERRY**, wool, noils and waste dealers, Bradford, Yorks

Cash book 1906-15, purchase, sales and trade books 1906-22.
Brotherton Library, Leeds University: see Hudson.

[31] **W & R BEVERIDGE & CO**, woollen mfrs, Kinross

Receipts and pattern order books 1869-95.
National Library of Scotland (Acc 5596).

[32] **JOHN BINNS & SONS LTD**, worsted mfrs and merchants, and cotton and rayon weavers, Bradford, Yorks

Cash books and misc financial records 1852-c1892, wages book 1881-4, machinery and insurance records 1861-85, corresp 1865-1915, deeds 1811-71, misc papers 1845-1952.
West Yorkshire Archive Service, Leeds: see Hudson.

[33] **DAVID BLACK & CO** (afterwards **DEBLAX LTD**), textile mfrs and woollen warehousemen, Glasgow and Edinburgh

Balance sheets, etc 1911, 1919-59, ledger 1886-9, cash books (2) 1860-74, 1888-1914, trading ledgers (9) 1873-1900, customers' account books (2) 1857-65, carriers' parcel book 1829-31, catalogues and price lists 1896-1939, wages book 1915-34, slump notebook 1920, misc printed material.
In private possession. Enquiries to NRA (Scotland) (NRA(S) 724). NRA 16079.

[34] **JOHN BLACKBURN & CO LTD**, worsted mfrs, Batley, Yorks

Balance sheets and accounts 1895-1937, nominal ledgers (5) 1899-1932, 1962-73, cash books (2) 1914-22, 1930-40, bank books (2) 1937-51, balance book 1927-32, bought and sales ledgers (4) 1912-33, purchase day books (3) 1932-43, returns day books (2) 1924-52, wages analysis books (2) 1933-52, schedule of deeds 1839-1921, misc records incl dyeing book of RH Parker, Crayford, Kent 1852.
West Yorkshire Archive Service, Kirklees (KC 197). NRA 29742.

[35] **BLACKBURN, TOLSON & CO LTD**, woollen mfrs, Heckmondwike, Yorks

Patterns of cloth weaves produced (24 vols, 6 bundles) 1891-2, 1898-9, 1901-56.
Leeds University, Department of Textile Industries. NRA 32464.

[36] **THOMAS BLAND & SON LTD**, worsted spinners, Keighley, Yorks

Records 1871-1947 incl letter books, ledgers, cash and day books, invoice and purchase books, production books, and wages books.
West Yorkshire Archive Service, Leeds (Acc 1391): see Hudson. Several volumes retained in private possession are believed to have been destroyed.

[37] **BLENKHORN, RICHARDSON & CO LTD,** tweed and woollen mfrs, Hawick, Roxburghshire

Minute book 1898-1925, registers of directors and annual returns (6 vols) 1893-1954, letter books (4) 1898-1933, private ledgers (3) 1881-1910, nominal ledgers (7) 1893-1953, journals and balance books (11) 1893-1964, sales ledgers (6) *c*1925-1950, purchase day books (2) 1934-51, wages sheets (4 vols) 1944-67; Keddie, Darling & Co Ltd minute book 1898-1912. *Scottish College of Textiles, Galashiels.* NRA 31124.

Stock transfer book 1910-32, photographs of mill. *Hawick Museum.* NRA 17662.

[38] **WILLIAM BLISS & SON LTD,** woollen mfrs, Chipping Norton, Oxon

Minute book 1917-58, annual returns 1933-50, share transfers 1917-25, letter books, ledgers and accounts (*c*50 vols) late 19th cent-*c*1970, valuation 1917. *Fox Brothers & Co Ltd.* Not available for research. NRA 30948.

[39] **BONLINIKON FELT CO LTD,** Aberdeen

General meeting minutes 1891-1905. *C Davidson & Sons Ltd.* Enquiries to NRA (Scotland) (NRA(S) 1460). NRA 20687.

[40] **HENRY BOOTH & SONS LTD,** woollen cloth mfrs, Gildersome, Yorks

Composite ledger 1859-67. *Brotherton Library, Leeds University*: see Hudson.

[41] **LJ BOOTH & SONS LTD,** woollen mfrs, Leeds

Minute book 1915-58, private ledgers (3) 1897-1965, nominal ledger 1915-46, employees' address book 1908-62, estimates, insurance receipts, etc *c*1912-52, leases and agreements 1792-1956, inventory 1886, valuation 1887, catalogues of machinery 1886, 1892. *West Yorkshire Archive Service, Leeds* (Acc 2243). NRA 22820.

[42] **BRAITHWAITE & CO LTD,** woollen mfrs, Kendal, Westmorland

Articles of association 1888, minute books (3) 1891-1964, shareholders' register 1889-1967, share certificate books (4) 1889-1963, liquidation papers (2 boxes) 1966, misc administrative papers 1844-1965, balance sheets, departmental manufacturing accounts, etc 1852-1964, ledgers (9) 1830-66, 1888-1973, day books (9) 1920-65, cash books (6) 1888-1973, journal 1958-65, bank books and statements 1954-66, misc purchase, sales, invoice and stock records 1920-66, notebooks (2) rel to cloths 1837-54, pattern book nd, misc technical records (7 bundles and items) 1863-1911, 1963-4, salaries, wages and national insurance records (9 vols) 1859-1966, property valuations, plans, etc (*c*23 vols and items) 1834-1963. *Cumbria RO, Kendal* (WDB/10). NRA 30973.

[43] **BRAMLEY family,** woollen mfrs, Leeds

Notes rel to orders 1774, nd, journal of travels in Europe seeking orders for cloth 1784-5, order book for calicoes, etc 1847-50. *Yorkshire Archaeological Society, Leeds* (DD81). NRA 12895.

[44] **BRIERLEY BROS LTD,** woollen yarn spinners, Huddersfield, Yorks

Private ledger 1896-1924, cash books (5) 1890-1936, balance books (4) 1882-1945, bank book 1939-43, sold ledgers (3) 1884-1961, sold day books (10) 1883-1955, bought ledgers (4) 1883-1962, invoice books (5) 1928-65, lot book 1954-61, commission book 1954-63, stock books (3) 1881-5, 1894-1948, wage books (5) 1933-52; Hollingworth, Wood & Co private ledger 1896-1941; Ben Lawton ledger 1881-5; George C Orrah & Co private ledger 1896-9. *West Yorkshire Archive Service, Kirklees* (KC 302). NRA 32014.

[45] **JOHN BRIGG & CO,** worsted spinners and weavers, Keighley, Yorks

Wages books, bills and accounts 1822-1900. *Keighley Central Library*: see Hudson.

Bills 1822-38. *West Yorkshire Archive Service, Leeds* (Acc 1612).

[46] **BRIGG & SONS,** woollen and worsted mfrs, Batley, Yorks

Account book 1797-1814, cash book 1882-5, sales ledger 1792-1829, stock book 1873-92, wool books (4) 1861-1902, mill books (2) 1872-9, costing book 1874-80, weft book 1893, pattern books (13) 1880-97, blend books (4) 1889-91, nd (possibly Brigg & Sons). *West Yorkshire Archive Service, Kirklees* (KC 73). NRA 27914.

[47] **WILLIAM BRIGGS & CO LTD,** wholesale art needlework and hand knitting wool specialists, Manchester

Minutes (3 vols) 1895-1959, share ledger and annual summary 1895-*c*1939. *Coats Patons plc.* Enquiries to NRA (Scotland) (NRA(S) 3088). NRA 20914.

[48] **BRINTONS LTD,** carpet mfrs, Kidderminster, Worcs

Memorandum and articles of association 1891, prospectus 1891, board minutes (8 vols) 1896-1959, conference minutes (1 vol) 1907, various committee minutes (3 vols) 1937-9, internal corresp mainly 1920-30, monthly accounts (1 vol) 1870-99, London accounts (1 file) 1936-9, carpet sales, quotations, etc (1 vol) 1907-33, sales corresp, invoices, etc (6 files) *c*1930-56, memoranda incl London warehouse 1903, corresp with Wolfe & Hollander (1 file) 1909, price lists and catalogues 1907-70, stock book 1828-33, stock lists (1 file, etc) 1934-7, calculations, trials and memoranda (1 vol) 1872-1905, production records,

Axminster and Brussels (6 vols) 1895-1938, pattern numbers books (2) 1898-1908, 1922-50, patent specifications, etc (2 files, 1 envelope, etc) 1857-1928, abridgement of specifications (4 vols) 1877-1904, weekly production report (1 vol) 1935-9, wages book 1908-14, valuations of machinery (2 vols) 1890-1, plans 1830, 1974, deeds 19th-20th cent incl schedule 1884, photographs, press cuttings (8 vols, etc) 1895-1960, notebooks containing copies of indentures and leases and extracts from the company and Brinton family records, draft history of company and related corresp, pamphlets, CC Brinton's accounts (4 vols) 1926-53; Brintons Carpet Co of Canada Ltd minutes (2 vols) 1906-10.
The Company. Not normally available for research. Enquiries to the Publicity Manager, Brintons Ltd. NRA 30836.

[49] **JOHN BROADBENT & SON (LONGWOOD) LTD**, woollen mfrs and merchants, Longwood, Yorks

Cash and bank books 1841-1918, sales and purchase records 1817-1904, stock records 1826-73, mill ledgers 1848-93, wages books 1848-88, rent books 1849-81, mill and building accounts 1848-71, misc papers 1825-*c*1915.
Brotherton Library, Leeds University: see Hudson.

Memorandum and articles of association 1920, directors' and general meeting minute book 1920-36, share corresp file 1895-1927, share registers (2) 1920-33, ledgers (2) 1916-36, cash books (9) 1915-35, stocktaking book 1927-36, insurance register 1924-6, wages books (7) 1892-1924, family ledger 1876-95, household expenses book 1886-96.
West Yorkshire Archive Service, Kirklees (KC 17). NRA 31065.

[50] **JOHN BROOKE & SONS LTD**, woollen mfrs, Armitage Bridge, Yorks

Agreement 1861, inventory, valuations and insurance policies 1825-89, solicitors' bills 1809-14, plans, etc 1886-1932, extract from accounts 1897, family corresp 1863-89.
In private possession.

[51] **ROBERT BROOKS & CO**, merchants and wool importers, London

Letter book 1841-3, ledgers (2) 1826-32, journal 1822-8, acceptance book 1846-53, cash book 1855-6.
National Library of Australia, Canberra: see *Australian Joint Copying Project Handbook*, part 8, 1984.

Corresp, etc 1862-90.
In private possession. A microfilm is in the National Library of Australia (M582-3).

[52] **J & H BROWN & CO**, woollen mfrs, Galashiels, Selkirkshire

Journal of Henry Brown 1828-9 incl details of manufacturing methods, costs and wool production.
Scottish College of Textiles, Galashiels. C Gulvin ed, 'Journal of Henry Brown, woollen manufacturer, Galashiels 1828-9', *Scottish industrial history: a miscellany*, Scottish History Society 1978.

[53] **WILLIAM BROWN, SONS & CO LTD**, woollen mfrs, Galashiels, Selkirkshire

Memorandum and articles of association 1913, 1951, annual accounts 1949-75, misc papers and corresp (*c*40 items) 1895-1973 incl trade figures for European customers and notes on scheme for a limited company 1911-13 and engine plans 1895.
Borders Region Archive (SC/S/7). NRA 32396.

Minute book 1913-38, private ledger 1965-78.
Henry Ballantyne & Sons Ltd. Enquiries to NRA (Scotland). NRA 22834.

[54] **ROBERT R BUCK & SONS LTD**, woollen mfrs, Carlisle and Dalston, Cumberland

Draft and copy minutes (1 vol, 2 files) 1934-59, deeds, agreements and other administrative records (30 vols, bundles and items) 1872-1961, ledgers (6) 1871-1936, ledger balances (2 vols) 1915, 1923-4, bill books (4) 1882-1929, bank books (28) 1866-9, 1897-1952, cash books (10) 1922-64, vouchers and other accounts (7 bundles, etc) 1863-1958, travellers' sales books (23) 1849-68, carriage day book 1931-60, customers' accounts ledgers (9) 1941-61, sales and despatch records (6 vols) 1950-62, stock books and inventories (32 vols) 1909-46, wages and salaries records (53 vols, 2 bundles) 1848-55, 1895-1967, misc corresp and papers (18 vols, bundles and items) 1877-1960, Buck family papers (18 vols, bundles and items) 1869-1946.
Cumbria RO, Carlisle (DB/43). NRA 30975.

[55] **BUCKLEY BROS**, woollen mfrs, Newtown, Montgom

Agreements, bills, etc 1742-1896.
Welsh Folk Museum, Cardiff (MS 2690). NRA 31986.

[56] **JOHN BUCKLEY & SONS**, woollen mfrs and dyers, Saddleworth, Yorks

Business corresp and papers 19th cent incl letters rel to American trade 1805-22, minute book 1830-69, and bills of sale ledger 1870-80.
In private possession. CA Jones, *Britain and the Dominions*, 1978, p71; *Guide to manuscripts relating to America in Great Britain and Ireland*, ed JW Raimo, 1979, p173.

[57] **THOMAS BURNLEY & SONS LTD**, wool spinners, Gomersal, Yorks

Minutes from 1893.
Coats Viyella plc. Enquiries to the Company Secretary. NRA 32377.

[58] **BUSBY SPINNING CO LTD**, worsted spinners, Kilwinning, Ayrshire

Minute book 1925-72, register of directors and shareholders 1925-72, corresp 1895, 1909-10, 1915, wages notebook 1889-1916, plans, specifications and valuations of machinery 1875, 1883, 1895-6.
The Company. Enquiries to NRA (Scotland) (NRA(S) 1589). NRA 21410.

[59] **RICHARD BYROM (DELPH)**, woollen mfr, Delph, Yorks

Pattern books (5) 1866, 1890s, 1950s-1960s, nd.
Saddleworth Museum (M/GX/T/BA/19-23). NRA 11134.

[60] **THOMAS CABLE & ROBERT CLARKE PAUL**, clothiers, Minchinhampton and Tetbury, Glos

Deed of partnership 1801, cash book 1801-12, business corresp and papers (7 bundles) *c*1801-14.
Gloucestershire RO (D589, box 22). NRA 24232.

[61] **CALEDONIAN CARPET CO LTD**, carpet mfrs, Stirling

Minute books (2) 1898-1933, register of debentures 1903-28, balance sheets 1899-1933, private ledgers (2) 1898-1919, general ledgers (2) 1919-33.
Stoddard Carpets Ltd. Enquiries to NRA (Scotland) (NRA(S) 283). NRA 10833.

[62] **I & I CALVERT LTD**, worsted spinners, Halifax, Yorks

Purchase, order, credit and debit records 1876-1950, lot and sample books 1880-1968, wages and employment records 1875-*c*1940, machinery and property records 1877-1946, deeds 1637-1920.
West Yorkshire Archive Service, Calderdale (WA). Formerly in Bradford University Library. NRA 18344; and see Hudson.

Deeds 1803-1910, plan 1900.
West Yorkshire Archive Service, Calderdale (MISC 166). NRA 21161.

[63] **CARPET MANUFACTURING CO LTD**, Kidderminster, Worcs

Agenda books (2) from 1894, annual returns from 1890, registers of members, shares, etc from 1922, transfers from 1890, mortgages and bonds 1908, letter book from 1934, ledgers and cash books (12 vols) from 1908, private ledgers (2) from 1890, private journals (4) from 1879, order books (2) 1913-14 and from 1956, sales ledgers (2) from 1908, sales credits from 1923, booklet of net sales 1903-37, stocktaking details 1779, 1780, 1784, stock sheets 1893, agents' stocks from 1909, Axminster setting books (6) 1919-54, department books (5) from 1928 and nd, rotation books, etc (31 vols) from 1914, pattern books nd, wages books, etc (24 vols, etc) from 1923, apprenticeship indentures 1887, and other employment records (7 vols, etc) from 1920, inventory of office equipment 1889-90, valuations 1939, photographs of premises and manufacturing processes *c*1900, history of the company *c*1959; Kidderminster Spinning Co Ltd register of members from 1908.
Kidderminster Library. NRA 28020.

[64] **CEIRIOG VALLEY WOOLLEN MILLS**, Glynceiriog, Denbighs

Ledgers (3) 1896-1931, cash books (2) 1911-34, journal 1910-14, account books (7) 1911-30, bank book 1915-19, sales books (3) 1914-34, order books (3) 1916-27, weaving books (2) 1907-20, wool book 1925-9, wages books (4) 1905-31.
University College of North Wales, Bangor (MSS 4182, 6423-48). NRA 29838.

[65] **WILLIAM CHAFFERS**, wool and woollen factor, London

Accounts, books and deeds (1 box) 1813-41.
Public Record Office, Chancery Lane (J 90/311).

[66] **JOHN & THOMAS CLARK LTD**, woollen cloth mfrs, Trowbridge, Wilts

Articles of partnership 1801, 1859, 1893, minute book 1963-7, registers of members, shares, etc (10 vols) 1896-1944, nd, papers rel to extraordinary general meetings from 1908, annual summaries, reports and accounts 1916-1960s, general corresp and papers (several boxes) 1940s-1970s, calculations of value of firm and shares of members 1893, account books (3) showing firm's dealings with Clark family 1842-97, ledgers (7 vols, 1 packet) 1922-68, nd, cash books (3) 1941-68, bill book 1900-52, misc payments book 1941-50, order books (6) 1927-70, bought day books (5) 1914-68, sales books (11) 1938-69, invoice books (7) 1960s, returns books (4) 1896-1976, stock books (8) 1804-25, 1961-70, annual stocktaking figures 1896-1921, 1940s, stocktaking and production records 1934-68, costing record 1812, record of cloths made (14 vols) 1929-*c*1963, calculations books (9) 1952-70, blend books (8) 1946-68, pattern books (10) *c*1850-1945, wages analysis (1 vol) 1944-68, employees' address book 1940s-1950s, valuations of machinery *c*1860-1892, deeds 1716-1886 and misc property records 1817-94, Clark family papers 1803-1950; pattern books, recipe books, etc (14 vols) of predecessor partnerships 1707-96.
Wiltshire RO (WRO 454, 927, 1393, 1573, 1958). NRA 6650.

Misc corresp, bills and leases 1905, 1941-67.
Wiltshire RO (WRO 1387). NRA 18828.

[67] **WILLIAM & JONATHAN CLARKSON**, woollen cloth mfrs, Pudsey, Yorks

Composite ledger 1855-62.
Brotherton Library, Leeds University: see Hudson.

[68] **JT CLAY & SONS LTD**, worsted and woollen mfrs, Rastrick, Yorks

Cash books 1799-1919, profit and loss accounts and balance sheets 1874-92, purchase book 1800-18, order, pattern, production and sample books 1834-1931, employment papers 1846-1930, inventories, valuations and technical papers 1814-*c*1930.
West Yorkshire Archive Service, Calderdale (MISC 244): see Hudson.

Letters from customers with cloth samples (13 vols, *c*45 items) 1831-73, cloth samples with weaving particulars (1 vol) nd, cloth samples (2 folders) 1853-9, details of operatives 1914, nd, misc papers 1824-*c*1910.
Saddleworth Museum (M/JTC). NRA 11134.

Orders with samples (1 bundle) 1841, pattern books (4) 1847-58, nd, sample books (9) 1845, nd; James Oridge & Sons order book 1836-8; WM Morley order book 1853-5.
Bankfield Museum, Halifax. NRA 5855.

Day book 1804-7, order books (3) 1804-6, 1837-8, 1840-3, samples and patterns *c*1837-43, 1857, stock inventory 1812.
Tolson Memorial Museum, Huddersfield. NRA 13680.

Copy stock valuation 1812, 1814, scrapbook incl letters and papers 1842-*c*1920.
Brotherton Library, Leeds University: see Hudson.

Copy deeds (1 vol) with valuations and balance sheets 1742-1921.
Yorkshire Archaeological Society, Leeds (MD 350): see Hudson.

[69] **ROBERT CLOUGH (KEIGHLEY) LTD**, worsted spinners and mfrs, Keighley, Yorks

Ledgers, day books, cash books and other accounts 1811-1939, bought day books and ledgers 1833-1915, sales day books and ledgers 1833-1917, invoice books 1843-1910, returns books 1884-1914, wages books 1815-1912, plans 1846-1913, misc letters, etc 1806-1925.
Brotherton Library, Leeds University: see Hudson.

[70] **THOMAS & WILLIAM COLFOX**, chandlers and wool merchants, Bridport, Dorset

Account books (2) 1776-92, receipts 1774-8, loose accounts 1782-4, cash book 1816-23, stock book 1792-1816, papers and corresp (137 items) rel to wool business and shares in ships 1805-47.
Dorset RO (D 43). NRA 9548.

[71] **S COLLIER & CO LTD**, woollen cloth merchants and clothing mfrs, Trowbridge, Wilts

Memorandum and articles of association 1935, minute books (3) 1902-69, register of directors' interests 1967, misc corporate records (3 files) *c*1913-74, letter book 1893, transfer books (4) and other share records *c*1959-60, ledgers (8) *c*1912-1937, 1958-71, journal 1866-87, day books (3) 1891-6, 1912-27, cash book 1972-3, order books (5) 1892-5, 1927-46, 1961-6, sales ledgers (5) 1902-1930s, purchase book 1925-37, credit journals (6) 1925-59, claims register 1929-67, returns book 1892-5, record of returns, overcharging, etc (3 vols) 1959-70, overseas agencies' address book *c*1940s, sample books (5) nd, stock books (7) 1902-3, 1937-44, stock and cost sheets *c*1930s-*c*1960s, misc advertisements, etc 20th cent; Apperley, Bidlake & Co Ltd misc corporate, financial and bankruptcy records (3 vols, 1 file) *c*1909-1966.
Wiltshire RO (WRO 1218). NRA 32199.

Collier family cloth pattern book 1774-*c*1787, business accounts 1848-53.
Wiltshire RO (WRO 719). NRA 11451.

[72] **COOK family**, wool brokers, Liverpool

Records *c*1850-*c*1920 incl papers rel to Cook & Hepworth, woollen mfrs, Yorks.
National Museums & Galleries on Merseyside, Merseyside Maritime Museum: see *Merseyside County Archives preliminary brief descriptive guide*, p10.

[73] **JOHN COOPER**, clothier, Trowbridge, Wilts

Ledger 1829-38, order book 1837-8, calculations book for cassimeres, etc *c*1829, bills and receipts (1 bundle) nd.
Wiltshire RO (WRO 2153). NRA 32193.

[74] **T CRAIG-BROWN & CO**, woollen yarn spinners, Selkirk

Letter book 1869-1937.
In private possession. Enquiries to NRA (Scotland) (NRA(S) 328). NRA 10976.

[75] **THOMAS CRESSWELL & CO**, woollen merchants, Huddersfield, Yorks

Private ledger, balance account and journal account (3 vols) 1872-85.
Hereford & Worcester RO, Hereford (G100). NRA 14843.

[76] **CROISDALE BROS**, cloth mfrs, Leeds

Account books (2) 1827-56.
West Yorkshire Archive Service, Leeds (Acc 2986).

[77] **J & J CROMBIE LTD**, woollen mfrs, Aberdeen

Directors' minutes (3 vols) 1883-1932, letter books (4) 1861-1932, account books (3) 1882-90, 1906, general ledger 1829-40, small-debt ledger 1871-1918, private journals (5) 1863-1925, cash book 1883-6, day book 1936-52, purchase ledger 1918-23, sales ledgers (4) 1868-1919, stock records 1913, memoranda books (2) 1866-1958, cloth design books (18) 1928-45, yarn manufacturing and dyeing account 1882-1924, misc production, stock and purchase records (1 file) 1913-47, plans of Grandholm flax works, etc 1785-1817, scrapbook 1924-55.
The Company. Enquiries to NRA (Scotland) (NRA(S) 1444). NRA 20432.

Time books (3) 1871-4.
Scottish Record Office (CS 96/4855-7).

[78] **JOHN CROSSLEY & SONS LTD**, carpet mfrs, Halifax, Yorks

Records 1809-1982 incl minutes, share records, annual reports and accounts, letter books, ledgers, journals, cash books, order books, sold and bought ledgers, carpet despatch books, records rel to overseas business interests and overseas agencies, stock sheets, design agreements, print records, sample books, wages and salaries books, factory registers, and Crossley family estate papers; Russian Carpet Co corresp and papers rel to shares and trading *c*1887-*c*1933, warp order books 1883-1911.
West Yorkshire Archive Service, Wakefield Headquarters (C300). BAC *Company Archives* no 66; and see *West Yorkshire Archive Service Report 1984-5*, pp26-7 and *1986-7*, p36.

Directors' minutes 1864-1918.
Debron Investments plc. A microfilm is in West Yorkshire Archive Service, Wakefield Headquarters.

Prospectus and other misc records 1864-1930.
West Yorkshire Archive Service, Calderdale (HAS/B:5/13/1). NRA 6546.

[79] **GEORGE CROWTHER & CO**, woollen mfrs, Churwell, Yorks

Cash and bill books 1863-83, weaving details 1882-3; invoice book, accounts and weave pattern book of unidentified firm 1832-40, nd.
Brotherton Library, Leeds University: see Hudson.

Bill book 1863-78.
West Yorkshire Archive Service, Leeds: see Hudson.

Crowther family business and personal corresp (*c*100 items) and misc papers 1769-1825, incl letters from David Crowther while agent for the firm in New York 1811-24.
In private possession: see *Guide to manuscripts relating to America in Great Britain and Ireland*, ed JW Raimo, 1979, pp116-17.

[80] **W & E CROWTHER LTD**, woollen mfrs, Slaithwaite, Yorks

Minute books (2) 1898-1976, returns of allotments 20th cent, letter book 1873-4, private ledgers (12) 1898-1976, ledgers (2) 1882-97, 1961-76, day book 1872-8, cash books (4) 1872-1976, sales and purchase books (8) 1875-81, 1958-77, order book 1875-80, lot book 1891-6, memoranda book 1881-93, invoice book 1918-29, stocktaking book 1899-1975, costing ledgers, etc (3 vols, etc) 1906-75, wages books (8) 1874-1940, employees' registers nd, inventories and valuations 1872-1966, papers rel to sale of Brook Mill 1901, press cuttings 1930-1.
Brotherton Library, Leeds University. NRA 1099; and see Hudson.

Lot books (19) 1900-65, order book 1919-52, stock books (2) 1919-23, 1947-59, wool pile books (2) 1916-71, blend books (11) 1902-10, 1977, nd, dyewear book 1910-54, pattern and range books and indexes 1925-72, old standard books nd, property plans (10) 1862-1947.
West Yorkshire Archive Service, Kirklees (B/WEC). NRA 31067.

[81] **DALGETY LTD**, wool brokers, merchants and stock, station and shipping agents, London

Records 1848-1961 incl directors' and general meeting minutes, account committee minutes and letter book, annual reports and accounts, letter books 1874-1919, corresp 1898-1940, register of clients, reports, photographs, press cuttings, and FG Dalgety's letter books, ledgers, journals and cash books.
Australian National University, Archives of Business & Labour Sciences, Canberra. NRA 26554; BAC *Company Archives* no 462.

Directors' and general meeting minutes from 1961, annual reports and accounts from 1946.
The Company. BAC *Company Archives* no 462.

[82] **THOMAS DAY**, worsted mfr, Newsome, Yorks

Pattern book 1876, design book 1882.
Tolson Memorial Museum, Huddersfield.

[83] **EDWARD DENISON (YEADON) LTD**, woollen mfrs, Yeadon, Yorks

Weekly and quarterly balance sheets 1891-1914, ledgers (4) 1891-1922, cash book 1927-35, purchase day books (2) 1949-61, sales day books and ledgers (6) 1901-60, invoice book 1896-1901, making and costing book 1919-20, cost books (3) 1920-5, loom books (2) 1927-8, nd, blend books (5) 1887-1961, wages books (5) 1894-1917, 1940-6, commission book 1945-57, inventories and valuations 1933-5, 1940.
West Yorkshire Archive Service, Leeds (Acc 1706). NRA 20243.

[84] **DENISON & SHARMAN** (afterwards **DOBROYD MILLS CO LTD**), woollen mfrs, Huddersfield, Yorks

Order books (2) 1912-17, making books (3) 1924-8, home and export trade record nd, sample books (*c*88) 1893-1916, 1929-1960s.
Royal College of Art, London. Enquiries to the Textile Design Department. NRA 32469.

[85] **ARTHUR DICKSON & CO LTD**, woollen mfrs, Galashiels, Selkirkshire

Ledger incl cloth samples 1805-24, notes on wool purchased 1924-57, inventory of machinery 1879, plans of mills and machinery (30) 1863-1949, nd.
The Company. Enquiries to NRA (Scotland) (NRA(S) 845). NRA 17583.

[86] **JOHN DINSMORE LTD**, woollen mfrs, Kells, co Antrim

Cloth account book 1804-6, wages book 1887-8.
In private possession. Photocopies are in the Public Record Office of Northern Ireland (T 1589): see *Ulster textile industry.*

[87] **DAVID DIXON & SONS LTD**, woollen mfrs, Leeds

Day books (8) 1929-37, cash books (4) 1894-1901, 1904-10, balance book 1921-30, sales ledgers (4) 1903-30, agents' sales book 1935-9, bought day book 1932-8, production records (14 vols) 1917-59, wages books (12) 1914-15, 1919-20, 1928-40, 1951-5, time books (9) 1942-72, inventory of machinery 1903-7, valuations of mills and machinery (6 vols) 1925-41, nd, rent book 1946-58.
West Yorkshire Archive Service, Leeds. NRA 31583.

[88] **DONISTHORPE & CO LTD**, worsted spinners, Leicester

Records 19th-20th cent incl letter book 1880-1901, production details 1908, schedule of deeds 1845-1907, and photographs.
The Company: see S Ellis, *A Mill on the Soar*, Leicester 1978.

[89] **DOVER, YOUNGHUSBAND & CO**, woollen mfrs, Millbeck, Cumberland

Sales ledger 1823-55, purchase and sales day book 1830-41, title deeds, agreements, plans, etc (5 bundles) 1760-1903.
Cumbria RO, Carlisle (D/NT 39). NRA 21925.

[90] **JAMES DRUMMOND & SONS LTD,**
worsted spinners and mfrs, Bradford, Yorks

Cash books (14) 1886-1939, bill books (4) 1921-40,
misc accounting records 1916-48, sales ledgers (7)
1846-1914, bought ledgers (3) 1864-1923, consignment
ledger 1896-1903, order books (3) 1913-40 and other
purchase, sales and production records (45 vols)
1924-66, wages books (6) 1886-1938, 1953-4 and other
employment records 1939-63, repairs, renewals and
mill furnishings day books (3) 1940-67, photographs
and drawings (57) 1918-24.
West Yorkshire Archive Service, Bradford (52D80).
NRA 28266.

[91] **DYSON, HALL & CO LTD**, plush mfrs,
Huddersfield, Yorks

Memorandum and articles of association 1907, bank
book 1896-1901, wages book 1905-10, misc reports,
balance sheets, etc (*c*12 items) 1924-69, plans and
photographs of Greenside Mills 1901-66.
Tolson Memorial Museum, Huddersfield (DH). NRA
13680.

[92] **CHARLES EARLY & CO**, blanket mfrs,
Witney, Oxon

Letter book 1848, account book 1819-23, bills,
accounts, etc (many bundles) 18th-19th cent, order
books (2) 1819-28, invoice book 1848-59, chain book
1848, papers and notes rel to blanket trade 19th cent,
deeds and misc records; Company of Blanket Weavers
in Witney foundation charter 1711, meeting book
1791-1847, account rolls and books 18th cent, ledger
1783-4, apprenticeship indentures 18th cent, deeds,
vouchers and misc papers 17th-18th cent.
In private possession. NRA 72.

[93] **BENJAMIN EASTWOOD & NEPHEW LTD**,
shoddy, mungo and waste dealers, Dewsbury, Yorks

Letter books 1885-1942, ledgers, accounts, cash and
bank books 1879-1949, sales and purchase records
1860-1948, wages and employment records 1914-39,
rent books, etc *c*1890-1929.
West Yorkshire Archive Service, Kirklees (B/BE): see
Hudson.

[94] **WILLIAM EDLESTON LTD**, woollen mfrs,
Sowerby Bridge, Yorks

Memorandum and articles of association, notices and
agenda of meetings, etc *c*1919-1950, corresp (22 files,
etc) 1884-1915, bank account (1 vol) 1876-85,
statements of account (41 files) 1895-1951, copy bank
ledger 1892-1928, rent accounts 1894-1916, receipts
and invoices (1 file) 1856-1935, summaries of accounts
1914-24, particulars of patterns sent 1916, misc
employment records 1919-48, plans 19th-20th cent,
photographs *c*1930-1950, Edleston family deeds,
financial papers, etc 18th-20th cent.
Durham County RO (D/Ed/9/3). NRA 24753.

Copy bank ledger 1892-1928, accounts 1929-57,
Edleston family papers 1880-1971.
Durham County RO (D/HH/8/5-7,9). NRA 18998.

[95] **EDWARDS & RAWSON LTD**, woollen mfrs,
Halifax, Yorks

John Edwards & Son valuation of foreign stocks and
abstracts of sales ledger 1871, abstract of invoices,
specifications, etc 1863-9, cloth manufacture
statements 1860-8, costing book 1865-9, blend book
*c*1870; WH Rawson & Co ledgers (2) 1842-76,
1896-1904, account book index *c*1845, petty sales and
disbursements account book 1898-1905, cash book
1897-1906; Edwards & Rawson Ltd corresp rel to
formation 1900-12, directors' minute book 1900-16,
cheques received book 1901-10, sales accounts (1 vol)
1900-10, notebook of orders *c*1910, corresp with agents
and vouchers 1905-10, notebook of manufacturing
costs 1905-6, cloth specifications (1 vol) *c*1930, record
of blends and pieces woven 1909, blend book 1898-9,
pattern book for blankets, etc *c*1900, delivery notebook
1899-1906, publicity brochures 1931; Rawson family
deeds and papers.
In private possession. Enquiries to West Yorkshire
Archive Service, Leeds. NRA 9568.

[96] **ELDER, SMITH & CO LTD**, wool brokers
and general merchants, London

Annual reports, balance sheets and profit and loss
accounts 1940-66, signature books (2) 1898-1953, letter
book 1957-61, ledgers and ledger sheets (8 boxes, 12
vols) 1886-1951, journals (9 boxes, 11 vols) 1888-1935,
invoices (1 vol) 1959-62, insurance contributions
(1 vol) 1950-6.
*Australian National University, Archives of Business &
Labour Sciences, Canberra.* NRA 26555.

[97] **JOHN EMSLEY LTD**, worsted mfrs, Bradford,
Yorks

Records *c*1840-20th cent incl minutes, annual reports
and accounts, corresp, ledgers, stock book, and
account of fixtures at Ashfield and Cliffe Mills.
West Yorkshire Archive Service, Bradford (25D89).

[98] **WILLIAM EYRES & SONS**, woollen mfrs and
merchants, Leeds

Day book 1891-1903, mungo, oil and cloth account
books (3) 1891-1906, order book 1891-1906, cost books
(2) 1894-1906, wool books (2) 1884-1906, test book
1888-1906, warpers' book 1903-5, sample book
1898-1905, weavers' wages book 1898-1906.
West Yorkshire Archive Service, Wakefield Headquarters
(C487). NRA 27904.

[99] **FARM INDUSTRIES LTD**, woolstaplers and
agricultural merchants, Truro, Cornwall

Financial and other corresp (227 files) mainly
1890-1920, letter books (7) 1904, 1922-6, 1929-30.
Cornwall RO (DDX 401).

[100] **FARRAR BROS LTD**, worsted spinners and
mfrs, Halifax, Yorks

Bill book 1780-2, cash book 1912-24, purchase and
sales books 1873-1923, dyeing books 1909-36, wages
book 1873-9.
West Yorkshire Archive Service, Calderdale (MISC 84):
see Hudson.

[101] **FAWCETT & FIRTH LTD**, merino mfrs, Ossett, Yorks

Register of directors, members, shares, etc 1898-1927, share certificate book 1898-1925.
Wakefield Libraries Department of Local Studies (Goodchild Loan MSS). NRA 23414.

[102] **FIELD & BOTTRILL LTD**, fancy woollen mfrs, Skelmanthorpe, Yorks

Register of employees and certificates of fitness c1886-1902.
West Yorkshire Archive Service, Kirklees: see *West Yorkshire Archive Service Report 1984-5*, p41.

[103] **FIELDING & JOHNSON LTD**, worsted spinners, Leicester

Records c1760-1966 incl minutes, corresp, private ledger, sales book, specifications, bills, inventories, valuation, and deeds.
Lister & Co plc. NRA 28631; BAC *Company Archives* no 661.

Private ledger 1864-1905, receipts and payments 1813-35, sales ledger 1816-34, wages book 1882-93, inventory 1852.
Leicestershire RO (18 D 61). NRA 6263.

[104] **FIRTH, DALLEY & COX LTD**, woollen rag merchants, Dewsbury, Yorks

Order and stock books 1904-57.
West Yorkshire Archive Service, Kirklees (B/FDC).

[105] **ISAAC, SAMUEL & JOHN FIRTH**, worsted mfrs, Halifax, Yorks

Bank book 1864-8, schedule and valuation 1868, deeds and papers 19th cent.
West Yorkshire Archive Service, Calderdale (FW 7): see Hudson.

[106] **TF FIRTH & SONS LTD**, carpet mfrs, Heckmondwike and Brighouse, Yorks

Prospectus 1889, directors' minutes 1889-1912, price list 1896, statistical note on sales 1913-14, wages summary book 1889-1913.
The Company: see JN Bartlett, *Carpeting the millions*, 1977.

[107] **WILLIAM FISON & CO LTD**, worsted spinners, Burley-in-Wharfedale, Yorks

Memorandum and articles of association 1907, board, general and committee meeting minutes (7 vols) 1907-67, register of members and share records 1907-66, reports of directors, etc (2 vols) 1907-66, seal books (3) 1907-68, secretary's rough notebook 1907-37, corresp 1851-1965, account books (2) 1886-1931, 1937-64, ledgers (2) 1907-52, private ledger 1925-37, private journals (3) 1898-1943, private cash books (5) 1893-1939, misc accounts 1849-1968, purchase and sales books (10) 1952-68, wages book 1964-8, deeds and legal papers 1641-1964, valuation

(1 vol) 1907, maps and plans 1848-95, nd, misc papers 1714-1967, nd.
West Yorkshire Archive Service, Bradford (16D84). NRA 31064.

[108] **FLEMING, REID & CO LTD**, woollen mfrs, Greenock, Renfrewshire

Articles of association and contracts of copartnery 1862-1918, papers rel to winding up 1945-61, directors' minutes (8 vols) 1899-1955, registers of directors, trustees and shareholders (24 vols) 1899-1962, dividend books (5) 1900-60 and other share records 1889-1960, corresp (14 files and bundles) 1824-1953, balance sheets and trading accounts (2 vols, 6 files, 3 bundles) 1894-1960, ledgers (17) 1872-1967, journals (35) 1861-1969, cash books (68) 1899-1970, purchase and sales books (36) 1903-70, stock books (6) 1910-62, salaries and wages records (6 vols, etc) 1906-58, inventories, valuations and agreements 1880-1963, deeds and papers rel to mills and retail shops 1704-1974, plans and photographs 1839-1966, scrapbooks, albums and printed history 1899-1957; inventory, corresp, etc rel to purchase of Robert Houston & Sons Ltd.
Strathclyde Regional Archives (TD 535). NRA 21899.

[109] **JOHN FOSTER & SONS LTD**, worsted, alpaca and mohair spinners and mfrs, Queensbury, Yorks

Partnership papers 1868-84, corresp 1833-c1950, ledgers, cash and bank books 1828-89, intake, weighing-off, cost and price books 1838-73, memoranda, stock and wages books c1820-90, railway, colliery and clay pit records, etc 1828-1923.
Brotherton Library, Leeds University: see Hudson.

[110] **FOX BROTHERS & CO LTD**, woollen mfrs, Wellington, Somerset

Deeds and agreements (1 vol) from c1861, directors' minutes (6 vols, etc) from 1896, directors' attendance books (5) 1940-71, register of directors and shareholders (2 vols) 1909-35, stock books incl partnership accounts, registers of debentures and other share records (12 vols, etc) 1777-1828 and from c1920, annual returns, balance sheets, etc 1734, 1753-91, 1828-1967, letter books (47) 1777-1920, foreign letter books (9) 1781-1827, misc corresp and accounts incl East India trade 1828-37, ledgers (110) 1759-1958 and other accounts (79 vols) c1747-1966, bank ledgers, balances and other financial records 1787-1808, 1884-1970, receipt book c1783, invoice books (6) 1776-1819, 1949-57, order books (2) 1908-17, 1930s, sales summaries 1837-86, 1913-45, sales ledgers and cash books (10 vols) 1906-49, bought and purchase books (16) 1830-c1907, reference book 1879-1922, misc purchase and sales records (5 vols) 1916-43, price lists 1860s-1880s, stock books (c120) 1801-60 and from c1880, calculation books (16) 1842-1920, experiment, analysis, test and trial books (5) 1892-1950, yarn and cloth day books (2) 1837-56, weekly make of goods (2 vols) 1754-63, 1915-30, processing memoranda (1 vol) 1865-1907, tops and warp record books (3) 1892-1930, wool books (4) 1916-47, coating scales (8 vols) 1913-24,

pattern books (6) and cloth samples 1773-20th cent, machine plans 19th-20th cent, misc production records (c22 vols) 19th-20th cent, wages and salaries books (11) 1903-74, account books for gifts, gratuities, etc (4 vols) 1816-76, 1932-43, Coldharbour Mill registers (2) 1830s-1840s, proposals for sick relief fund c1871, misc employment records (8 vols) 1924-63, deeds (3 boxes) 17th-20th cent, rent book 1776-90, valuations (17 vols) 1916, 1920, 1956, annual summaries of buildings and plant expenditure 1872-1980 and other premises records 1948-c1960, legal papers (4 vols) 1892, misc business and family papers 1752-1935, historical notes on the family and firm 20th cent, photographs and press cuttings.
The Company. Not available for research. NRA 30948.

Letters received and sent (60) 1793-1852.
Somerset RO (DD/S/HL, DD/S/MY). NRA 4320.

[111] **E FOX & SONS LTD**, mungo and shoddy merchants, Dewsbury, Yorks

Department ledger 1880-1910, purchase day books (2) 1931-8, order books (4) 1902-19, wages books (7) 1913-37, legal papers 1904-5, misc property records 1883-1930.
West Yorkshire Archive Service, Leeds. NRA 31654.

Sales ledgers and day books 1896-1911, bought ledger 1906-13, wages books 1901-13.
Brotherton Library, Leeds University: see Hudson.

[112] **JAMES FRANCE & CO LTD**, carpet and woollen mfrs and yarn spinners, Dewsbury, Yorks

Directors' and shareholders' minutes (7 vols) 1925-71, share register 1925-70, misc corporate records 1948-71, private ledgers (5) 1902-71, nominal ledgers (7) 1910-69, cash books and other accounting records (7 vols) 1947-71, costing books (2) 1958-71, wages and employment records (8 vols) 1933-71, director's diary 1940-2.
West Yorkshire Archive Service, Kirklees (KC 56). NRA 26792.

Day book 1838-49, account book 1907-13, bill book 1878-1909, order book 1901-6, bought ledger 1895-1902, wages book 1907-12.
Brotherton Library, Leeds University: see Hudson.

[113] **SAMUEL & ROBERT FRYER**, fancy woollen mfrs, Rastrick, Yorks

General account books (2) 1844-71, ledger 1836-53, cash books (2) 1834-53, purchase cash book 1833-5, stock books (2) 1792-1836, stock inventory of shawls c1840, family papers incl executorships 1786-1869.
Durham County RO (D/Wa). NRA 25375.

[114] **EDWARD GARDINER & SONS LTD**, woollen mfrs, Selkirk

Directors' minutes (4 vols) from 1933, register of directors, allotments and mortgages 1910-73, share register 1910-75, ledgers (4) 1938-68, annual abstract and analysis, etc (5 vols) from 1956 and other trading accounts (25 files) from 1954, pattern and sample books (11) c1920-55.
Gardiner of Selkirk Ltd. Enquiries to NRA (Scotland) (NRA(S) 1666). NRA 21886.

[115] **ERNEST GATES & CO LTD**, worsted spinners and mfrs, Bradford, Yorks

Directors' minutes (1 vol) 1926-36, private ledgers (4) 1903-33, account books nd, sales ledger c1928.
West Yorkshire Archive Service, Bradford (25D89).

[116] **ISAAC GAUNT LTD**, worsted spinners, Stanningley, Yorks

Letter book 1899-1905 incl rough accounts 1905-10, ledgers (3) 1907-18, cash books (2) 1908-13, 1923-7, invoice day books (22) 1905-31 and journals (2) 1915-23, sales day book sheets (2 parcels) 1932-48, bought ledgers (2) 1910-18, order books (2) 1905-6, 1909-10, contract book 1920-3, yarn ledgers (7) 1906-18, tops ledgers (3) 1924-32, dyeing samples (1 vol) nd, shade cards (4 boxes) nd.
West Yorkshire Archive Service, Leeds (Acc 1174). NRA 31548.

[117] **REUBEN GAUNT & SONS LTD**, yarn spinners and worsted mfrs, Farsley, Yorks

Records (27 boxes, 1 parcel) mainly rel to wages, welfare, worker-participation and other personnel matters 1909-67, but incl summary particulars (1 folder) of receipts and payments, weft and yarn ordered and sales 1900-14, monthly bank balances, sales figures and graph in triplicate (3 vols) 1906-13, suggestions books 1908-53, letter book of GR Gaunt 1905-19, and papers (1 file) rel to the Textile Institute Committee 1910-16; personal diary (1 vol) of Reuben Gaunt 1841-54.
West Yorkshire Archive Service, Leeds. NRA 31582.

Gaunt family private ledger 1887-99.
West Yorkshire Archive Service, Leeds (John Hainsworth & Sons Ltd Papers). NRA 32031.

[118] **WILLIAM GAWTHORP & CO**, commission wool combers, Bradford, Yorks

Notebooks (2) of yearly balances and accounts 1882-97.
Brotherton Library, Leeds University: see Hudson.

[119] **GIBSON & LUMGAIR LTD**, woollen mfrs, Selkirk

Executive committee minutes 1956-9, corresp 1921-58, progress reports 1953-64, pay sheets and other employment records 1884-1968.
Borders Region Archive (SC/S/9). NRA 32397.

Pattern range books (10) 1938-61.
Scottish College of Textiles, Galashiels. NRA 31124.

[120] **GLOBE WORSTED CO LTD**, worsted spinners, Slaithwaite, Yorks

Memorandum and articles of association 1887, minute book 1886-97, register of directors and annual returns 1910-21, shareholders' register 1926, plans, contracts and tenders 1887-8, deeds and other premises records 1887-1924.
In private possession.

[121] **DANIEL GLOVER & SON**, cloth merchants, Leeds

Wool cash book 1795-1806, invoice book 1797-1805, order book 1789-1806, mill and rack book 1825-7. *Public Record Office, Chancery Lane* (C 114/103).

[122] **GODREMAMOG & DANGRIBYN WOOLLEN MILLS**, Carms

Account books (4) and papers 1899-1936. *Welsh Folk Museum, Cardiff* (MS 1745/2-8). NRA 31986.

[123] **JONATHAN GOMERSAL**, worsted spinners, Cleckheaton, Yorks

Memorandum and articles of association 1925, letter book 1963-8, ledger 1896-1902, journal 1896-1907, daily account books (2) 1950-4, 1962-6, day book 1960-8, work books (3) 1900-5, 1909-12, empty beams book 1949-57, wages book 1896-1901. *West Yorkshire Archive Service, Kirklees* (B/JG). NRA 31068.

[124] **GOODMAN, ABBOTT & WRIGHT LTD**, worsted spinners, Bradford, Yorks

Memorandum and articles of association 1912-52, directors' minutes (1 vol, etc) 1923-50, balance sheets 1913-68, corresp and statistics of yarn deliveries (8 files) 1911-67, private ledger 1913-22, cash books (3) 1912-49, misc accounts (5 vols) 1913-67, purchase book 1912-24, order book 1913-15, blend book 1913, deliveries book 1913-15 and other production and sales records (10 vols, etc) 1931-67, orders and specifications for machinery 1912-13, misc corresp and papers 1911-67. *West Yorkshire Archive Service, Bradford* (81D86). NRA 31947.

[125] **BENJAMIN GOTT & SONS**, woollen cloth mfrs and merchants, Leeds

Corresp, bonds, bills, inventories, etc 1772-1965. *Wakefield Libraries Department of Local Studies* (Goodchild Loan MSS). Formerly in the South Yorkshire Industrial Museum, Cusworth Hall. See Hudson.

Corresp, misc accounts, pattern book, memoranda rel to employees, wages and expenses, and plans 1770-1931. *Brotherton Library, Leeds University*: see Hudson.

Deeds and settlements 19th cent. *West Yorkshire Archive Service, Leeds* (DB 78): see Hudson.

[126] **GRACE & JEPSON**, drysalters and woollen cloth merchants, Leeds

Sales and purchase ledgers, cash, stock, waste, postage, invoice and letter books, etc 1805-61. *West Yorkshire Archive Service, Leeds:* see Hudson.

Letter book 1824. *West Yorkshire Archive Service, Leeds* (Oates Collection).

[127] **THOMAS GREEN & CO**, cloth and wool merchants, London

Corresp, accounts and invoices (c77 bundles) 1809-11. *Public Record Office, Chancery Lane* (J 90/74-7).

[128] **GREENWOOD & CO**, worsted spinners and mfrs, Cullingworth, Yorks

Articles of association 1935, private ledger 1901-18, apprenticeship indentures and title deeds 1853-1935, plan 1904. *The Company.* Access restricted. Enquiries to the Chairman.

[129] **GREENWOOD & WALSH LTD**, woollen mfrs, Morley, Yorks

Memorandum and articles of association 1957, annual returns (5 vols) 1917-64, balance sheets 1936-81, private ledgers (2) 1901-27, ledgers (8) 1914-50, cash books (7) 1935-78, order and purchase records (9 vols, etc) 1953-79, cloth sample books (11) 1907-51, wages books (15) 1920-78, valuations (6) 1941-68. *West Yorkshire Archive Service, Leeds* (Acc 2644). NRA 26080.

[130] **JOHN HAINSWORTH & SONS LTD**, woollen mfrs, Farsley, Yorks

Minute book 1837-70, ledgers (4) 1854-1925, quotation book 1871-82, memoranda book rel to contracts nd, cloth order book 1962-3, blend and account book 1812-56, blend and making books (7) 1882-8, 1912, 1925-6, record book 1916-22, corresp, bills, insurance policies, etc (c25 vols, bundles and items) 1832-1953, spinning account book 1827-51, spinners' day book 1861-8, settled notes for pay days 1841-2, 1849, 1853, valuations of Cape Mills (1 vol, 2 bundles) 1887, 1906-20. *West Yorkshire Archive Service, Leeds.* NRA 32031.

[131] **A HALL & SONS LTD**, wool spinners and carders, Newtown St Boswells, Roxburghshire

Minutes 1924-40, register of members (4 vols), annual reports and accounts (5 files) 1909-61, ledgers (8) 1890-1964, cash books (3) 1935-57, cash balances 1892-5, order and sales books (3) 1916-40, stock books (2) 1932-5, sample book 1929-33, wages books (2) 1912-33, valuations 1886, 1927, 1940-4, engine and machinery plans nd, business diaries (2) 1929-36, Adam Hall's memoirs, trust disposition and settlement 1904-8, nd. *Scottish Record Office* (GD 395). NRA 25423.

[132] **BENJAMIN HALLAS**, blanket mfr, Ossett, Yorks

Account book 1789-1819, deeds and legal and family papers 1797-1894. *Wakefield Libraries Department of Local Studies* (Goodchild Loan MSS). Formerly in the South Yorkshire Industrial Museum, Cusworth Hall. See Hudson.

[133] **HANSON & MILLS**, wool factors, London

Letter books (3) 1795-9, waste book 1795, day books of orders marked 'Yarnton' (2) 1796, order book incl wool samples 1798-9, stock books rel to partnership (3) 1795, pattern sample books (2) 1796-9, summary accounts, papers rel to an American debt, annotated advertisements of wool sales and other misc papers (*c*18 items) 1796-8.
Public Record Office, Chancery Lane (C 113/16-18).

[134] **GEORGE HARRISON & CO (EDINBURGH) LTD**, woollen fabric merchants and mfrs of scarves, rugs, caps and gloves, Edinburgh

Pattern books from 1836.
The Company. Enquiries to NRA (Scotland) (NRA(S) 259). NRA 10789.

[135] **JOHN HARTLEY & SONS LTD** (formerly **GILL ROYD MILLS CO**), woollen mfrs, Morley, Yorks

Memorandum and articles of association 1864, minutes 1902-31, committee book 1835-61, ledgers 1898-1920, account book 1834-6, dyeing ledger 1851-5, deeds, etc 1871-1922.
West Yorkshire Archive Service, Leeds: see Hudson.

[136] **WILLIAM HARTLEY**, woollen mfrs, Sutton-in-Craven, Yorks

Accounts (3 vols) 1911-63, yarn order books (3) 1893-1921.
Yorkshire Archaeological Society, Leeds (MD 433).

[137] **GEORGE HATTERSLEY & SONS**, worsted spinners and mfrs, Haworth and Keighley, Yorks

Letter book, notebooks, accounts, corresp and building and insurance papers 1845-88.
Brotherton Library, Leeds University: see Hudson.

[138] **HAWKER & RICHARDS**, clothiers, Stroud, Glos

Accounts (1 vol, 1 bundle) 1804-46, cash book 1805-46, trade book 1804-[?1817], stock book 1802-33.
Gloucestershire RO (D1181).

[139] **HEALEY OLD MILL CO**, fullers and dyers, Ossett, Yorks

Minutes, subscription and trusteeship papers, deeds and agreements, etc 1785-1892.
Wakefield Libraries Department of Local Studies (Goodchild Loan MSS). Formerly in the South Yorkshire Industrial Museum, Cusworth Hall. See Hudson.

[140] **ROBERT HEATON**, worsted mfr, Keighley, Yorks

Account books (2) 1745-89 and Heaton family papers.
West Yorkshire Archive Service, Bradford. NRA 1090.

[141] **HECKMONDWIKE CARPETS LTD**, carpet mfrs and yarn spinners, Heckmondwike and Liversedge, Yorks

Board minutes (12 vols) 1873-1967, registers of directors and managers (2) 1901-38, weekly reports 1874-86, annual reports and balance sheets *c*1910-1981, share ledgers, registers of transfers and other share records (*c*51 vols) 1873-1982, letter books (3) 1885-1937, private ledgers (4) 1873-1938, bill book 1880-1930, cash books and misc accounting records (19 vols) 1916-81, credit books (2) 1874-1921, purchase and sales analysis books (3) 1896-1936, stock and production records (8 vols) 1925-64, wages records (5 vols) 1922-63, valuations, plans and other premises records 1882, 1933-84, misc papers *c*1873-1960.
West Yorkshire Archive Service, Kirklees (KC 245). NRA 29739.

[142] **HENDERSON & CO LTD**, carpet mfrs, Durham

Private letter book 1878-81, cash book 1832-4, price lists (4 vols, etc) 1871-1913, warehouseman's day books (2) 1849-51, 1860-2, accounts for making dye, test pieces, etc 1842-67, production books (2) 1881-94, dyeing memoranda book *c*1875-80, employees' absences book 1861-71, deeds and papers rel to premises (*c*13 bundles) 1691-1887, schedule of title deeds on purchase of company by Hugh Mackay & Co Ltd 1930, accounts for building weaving sheds and offices (2 vols) 1853-60, plan 1860, scrapbook 1868-*c*1890.
Durham County RO (D/Ma). NRA 18669.

[143] **HENDERSON & EADIE**, woollen mfrs, Lisbellaw, co Fermanagh

Letters received (30 boxes) 1936-62, letter books (38) 1919-50, expenditure books (5) 1860-5, 1869-1934 and other accounting records (5 vols) 1921-44, order books (9) 1911-58, stocktaking book 1879-88, country wool book 1938-42, spinners' and weavers' batch books (10) 1883-*c*1930, piece books (6) 1910-44, yarn mixtures (1 vol) 1902-7, cloth analysis books (4) *c*1882-1910, pattern books (12) 1912-54, dye book with samples 1880s, wages books (9) 1880-1963, weavers' tickets (2 boxes) 1903-9, 1926-7, 1934-9, 1943-4, records of Colooney Mill, co Sligo (1 box) 1929-42 and Enniskillen retail shop (1 box) 1937-49.
Public Record Office of Northern Ireland (D 1938). NRA 31477.

[144] **GEORGE HEY**, woollen mfr, Kirkburton, Yorks

Ledgers (2) 1850-4, schedule of tenants, plant, etc at Linfit Mills 1900, ledger of George Hey 1848-92 and other Hey family account books and papers 1734-1905.
West Yorkshire Archive Service, Kirklees (KC 313). NRA 13680.

[145] **THOMAS HIELD & SONS LTD**, woollen yarn merchants and exporters, Dewsbury, Yorks

Letter book, ledger and order book 1906-16.
Brotherton Library, Leeds University: see Hudson.

[146] **HILL, PAUL & CO**, woollen cloth mfrs, Stroud, Glos

Directors' minute book 1933-8, trading sheets and balance accounts (3 vols) 1902-45, current expenditure, sales and purchase accounts (6 vols) 1920-67, woollen order book 1902-3, register and applications for tailoring trade 1925-46, misc corresp, trade papers, etc 1911-62.
Gloucestershire RO (D3757). NRA 24225.

[147] **STEPHEN HILLMAN**, clothier, Devizes, Wilts

Ledgers (2) 1769-1812.
Wiltshire RO (WRO 1090/52). NRA 5270.

[148] **HIND ROBINSON & SON LTD**, stuff mfrs, Bradford and Norwood Green, Yorks

Pattern and order books (*c*12 vols) 19th cent, 1906, 1913, 1920s, nd.
Bankfield Museum, Halifax. NRA 5855.

[149] **GEORGE H HIRST & CO LTD** (formerly **ALEXANDRA MILL CO**), woollen mfrs, Batley, Yorks

Minute book 1868-91, letter books (2) 1896-1910, nd, cash books (2) 1891-7, bank books (6) 1877-98, misc accounts, stocktaking totals, cloth samples, etc (1 vol, 1 bundle) 1883, *c*1892, corresp rel to orders 1905, blend books (23) 1895-1912, pulling book *c*1894-6, plans, insurance records, papers rel to steam engines, etc (2 bundles, 1 file, etc) *c*1890-1903, 1952, photographs *c*1890-1910, scrapbook 1936-70.
West Yorkshire Archive Service, Kirklees (B/GHH). NRA 32417.

Share registers (4) 1919-28, nominal ledgers (3) 1934-53, sales ledgers (3) 1925-53, order books (6) 1918-35, stock books (2) 1889-94, 1901, pattern books (12) 1912-35, misc estimates, etc (5 items) 1885-96.
West Yorkshire Archive Service, Leeds (Acc 1624). NRA 31767.

[150] **ISAAC HOLDEN & SONS LTD**, wool combers, Bradford, Yorks

Partnership records and accounts for French business 1872-94, technical notes 1833-90, family corresp and papers 1824-97.
Bradford University Library: see Hudson.

Journals and notebooks 1844-88, papers rel to patents, etc *c*1830-*c*1860, political, social and family corresp and papers 1827-*c*1910.
Brotherton Library, Leeds University: see Hudson.

[151] **HOLDSWORTH family**, dyers, scribblers, fullers and woad merchants, Wakefield, Yorks

Agreements, family accounts and papers 1780-1853.
Wakefield Libraries Department of Local Studies (Goodchild Loan MSS). Formerly in the South Yorkshire Industrial Museum, Cusworth Hall. See Hudson.

[152] **HOLLAND & SHERRY LTD**, woollen merchants, London

Partnership agreements 1843, 1869, debtors' ledger 1843, sales dissections (1 bundle) 1891-1917, salaries book 1859-64, private cash book of SG Holland 1869-81.
Westminster City Libraries Archives Section. NRA 13258.

[153] **WILLIAM HOLLINS & CO LTD**, spinners of merino, cotton and knitting yarns, and mfrs of Viyella and other cloths, Nottingham

Memorandum and articles of association from 1890, partnership agreements and share assignments from 1785, directors' and committee minutes (34 vols) 1890-1974, agenda books, etc 1910, 1938-57, register of members (31 vols), annual reports, balance sheets and accounts 1889-1966, share registers, etc *c*1920-60, nd, register of seals 1939-56, corresp (*c*139 files) 1930s-1960s, secretary's files 1882-1953, solicitors' bills and misc head office records 1873-89, 1910-64, private ledgers (10) 1870-1956, ledgers (30) 1870-1980, journals (8) 1825-1934, cash books (66) 1872-1982 and other financial records 1918-1960s, bought ledger 1909-31, sales books (12 vols, etc) 1907-1980s, representatives' and travellers' corresp and accounts 1890-1981, price lists *c*1910-63, stock books (4) 1921-35, production reports, etc 1877-8, 1929-65, trade marks and patents 1890-1959, wages and salaries books (30) 1902-71, registers of employees 1900-*c*1931, apprenticeship indentures 1791-4, profit sharing and other employment records 1918-82, Pleasley Works British School managers' minute book 1903-35, inventories 1901-64, deeds and papers from 1859, visitors' books, press cuttings, photographs, catalogues and advertisements.
Coats Viyella plc. Enquiries to the Company Secretary. NRA 32374.

Directors' minutes (1 vol) 1951-6.
Coats Viyella plc. Enquiries to the Company Secretary. NRA 32377.

Corresp, share books, etc 1960s.
Lancashire RO (DDVc). NRA 30810.

[154] **HOLLY PARK MILL CO LTD**, dyers, scribblers, carders, spinners and fullers, Calverley, Yorks

Articles and capital and shareholders' records 1867-1918, minutes 1868-1957, accounts 1878-1970.
West Yorkshire Archive Service, Leeds: see Hudson.

Ledgers, journals, cash books and other accounts 1827-1941, invoice and wages books 1868-1942, memoranda book 1878-82.
Brotherton Library, Leeds University: see Hudson.

Boiler reports (1 file) 1948-71.
West Yorkshire Archive Service, Leeds (Acc 2836). NRA 31010.

[155] **HORNER & TURNER**, cloth merchants, Leeds

Copies of letters (2 vols) to customers in Italy and the Baltic 1787-90, 1794-1801, cash book 1792-4, bill book 1787-92 with misc accounts 1793-4, order book with samples 1794-5, post book 1792-5.
Public Record Office, Chancery Lane (C 108/101, 312).

[156] **JOSEPH HORSFALL & SONS LTD**, worsted spinners, Halifax, Yorks

Nominal ledgers (2) 1880-4, 1912-35, cash books (2) 1879-91, purchase and sales day books (4) 1879-91, wages books (2) 1882-7, 1919-39.
Brotherton Library, Leeds University. NRA 1099.

[157] **THOMAS HOYLE & SONS LTD**, worsted spinners, Halifax, Yorks

Ledger 1933-50, wages books (12) 1891-1948.
West Yorkshire Archive Service, Calderdale (BM). NRA 26200.

[158] **C HUDSON**, clothier, Halifax, Yorks

Letter and memoranda book 1785-1816.
Liverpool University Library: see *Accessions to repositories 1966*, p56.

[159] **HUDSON, SYKES & BOUSFIELD**, woollen mfrs, Leeds and Morley, Yorks

Partnership deeds and articles 1865-1927, directors' books and share papers 1899-1928, ledgers, cash books and bank books 1865-1932, sales and purchase books *c*1860-1930, wages books 1892-1922, bills, tenders and insurance papers 1894-1929, misc records 1875-1930.
West Yorkshire Archive Service, Leeds: see Hudson.

[160] **HUNT & WINTERBOTHAM LTD**, woollen cloth mfrs, Cam, Glos

Records 1817-1962 incl minutes, share registers, ledgers, cash and day books, purchase and sales books, yarn contract books, analysis, cost and stock books, invoice books, returns book, manufacturing books, weavers', spinners', measuring and wool books, pattern books and samples, wages books, rents ledger, inventories, valuation, and plans.
Gloucestershire RO (D2776). NRA 28631; BAC *Company Archives* no 553.

Minutes from 1914, production costs book *c*1930-70.
The Company. NRA 28631; BAC *Company Archives* no 553.

[161] **THOMAS IBBOTSON**, worsted mfr, Leeds

Costing books (11) *c*1890-*c*1904 incl samples of worsted fabrics.
Leeds University, Department of Textile Industries.

[162] **DANIEL ILLINGWORTH & SONS LTD**, worsted yarn spinners, Bradford, Yorks

Draft agreement 1835, balance sheets and stock accounts 1827-37, Whetley and Soho Mills plans and drawings, etc 1859-1954.
In private possession.

[163] **IRELAND, EDMONDSON & CO**, woollen goods mfrs, Kendal, Westmorland

Letters, papers and vouchers 1845-77, incl corresp with John Wood & Westheads, Manchester 1845.
Cumbria RO, Kendal (WDB/52). NRA 30983.

[164] **RONALD JACK & CO LTD**, carpet mfrs, Paisley, Renfrewshire

Minute book 1909-33, register of members and share ledger 1909-32, balance sheets 1899-1933, private journal and ledger 1909-19, wages book 1890-1908, inventory (2 vols) 1927-8.
Stoddard Carpets Ltd. Enquiries to NRA (Scotland) (NRA(S) 283). NRA 10833.

[165] **JOSEPH JACKSON**, woolstapler, Wakefield, Yorks

Letters received, deeds and agreements 1800-25.
Wakefield Libraries Department of Local Studies (Goodchild Loan MSS). Formerly in the South Yorkshire Industrial Museum, Cusworth Hall. See Hudson.

[166] **JESSOP BROTHERS**, mungo, shoddy, merino and wool extractors, Ossett, Yorks

Nominal ledgers (4) 1900-51, cash books (7) 1900-68, balance books (3) 1900-69, purchase ledgers (3) 1892-1921 and day books (11) 1897-1900, 1905-65, sales ledgers (4) 1892-1969, day books (10) 1902-12, 1923-69 and invoice books (4) 1941-9, order books (2) 1899-1920, stock book 1940-6, test, blend and dyeing books (4) 1933-48, sample book 1925-49, wages books (9) 1897-1944, employee records book 1950-70, mill valuation 1920.
West Yorkshire Archive Service, Leeds. NRA 31654.

[167] **JAMES JOHNSTON & CO**, woollen and tweed mfrs, Elgin, Moray

Letter books (6) 1812-1920, letters received *c*1845-55, ledgers (10) 1799-1914, day books and journals (23) 1798-1914, cash books (12) 1829-47, 1874-1952, purchase ledgers and day books (15) 1800-1952, bought yarns (2 vols) 1905-56, order books (2) 1852-73, parcel and piece books (7) 1817-64, yarn books (2) 1867-1906, dyeing accounts *c*1820-46, worsted and other memoranda books (3) 1807-61, wages books (17) 1872-1923, power loom time and pay book 1884-96, age certificate book 1865-72, inventories 1837-42, notes of local wool trade, letter book 1844-8 rel to Jamaican business unconnected with wool, private and household account books 1800-74.
The Company. Enquiries to NRA (Scotland) (NRA(S) 592, 597). NRA 14947, 14948.

[168] **JOHN D JOHNSTONE LTD**, woollen mfrs, Leeds

Cash books 1909-38, sales, purchase and production books 1883-1951, wages books 1912-48, misc papers 1898-*c*1960.
West Yorkshire Archive Service, Leeds: see Hudson.

[169] **JACOB JONES & SON**, tweed and cloth mfrs, Tan-y-Grisiau and Blaenau Ffestiniog, Merioneth

Account books (8) 1886-1911.
University College of North Wales, Bangor (MSS 1899-1904, 2338-9).

Account books (4), diaries (9), certificates and misc papers 1886-1939.
Welsh Folk Museum, Cardiff (MS 2394). NRA 31986.

[170] **JOHN JONES**, Bargod Woollen Mills, Drefach-Velindre, Carms

Corresp (1 bundle) 1881-1920, vouchers (46 bundles) c1875-1924, misc papers (15 bundles and items) 1886-1921 incl bank orders, price lists, and publicity leaflets.
Dyfed Archive Service, Carmarthen (DB/58). NRA 29913.

[171] **ROBERT JOWITT & SONS LTD**, wool merchants, combers, scourers and carbonizers, Bradford, Yorks

Corresp 1775-1909, ledgers 1775-1941, journals 1896-1901, cash books 1805-71 and other accounting records 1914-55, sales and purchase records 1831-1949, costing books 1927-52, stock and production records 1896-1949, mill and branch books 1904-52.
Brotherton Library, Leeds University: see Hudson.

[172] **JULIUS, COHEN & JOSEPHY** (afterwards **HIRSCH & SON LTD**), wool and yarn export merchants, Bradford, Yorks

Records 1870-20th cent incl deeds of partnership, articles, etc 1901-58, balance sheets 1907-14, letter books (4) 1870-1925, corresp (4 files) 1907-45, account books (5) 1874-1958, private ledgers (8) 1907-52, ledgers (5) 1882-1930, private journals and other accounting records 1908-c1961, insurance papers 1909-39, and Hirsch family and business papers 19th-20th cent.
West Yorkshire Archive Service, Bradford (85D80). NRA 31080.

[173] **JAMES KAY**, clothier, Almondbury, Yorks

Business corresp (67 items) 1799-1811, nd, account books (2) 1780, 1803-6, bills and receipts (55 items) 1780-1815, lists (5) of expenses, debts, materials, etc 1803-5, 1809, nd, inventory by Kay of his estate 1780, notebooks (3) on accounting methods 1780, nd, misc family papers 1784-1815.
West Yorkshire Archive Service, Kirklees (KC 5). NRA 26730.

[174] **KELLETT, BROWN & CO LTD**, spinners, scribblers, scourers, fullers and tenterers, Calverley, Yorks

Committee minutes 1845-1917, letter books 1874-1916, ledgers and cash books 1833-1930, mill ledgers, day books and account books 1835-1922, wages and employment records 1853-1921.
Brotherton Library, Leeds University: see Hudson.

[175] **JOHN KELLY**, woollen mfr, Norwich, Norfolk

Pattern books with prices (2 vols) 1763, 1767.
Victoria & Albert Museum, Department of Textile Furnishings & Dress (T. 67-1885, T. 68-1885). NRA 30151.

[176] **JF & C KENWORTHY LTD**, woollen mfrs, Uppermill, Yorks

Account books (2) 1909-26, account and wages books (2) 1892-1902, bank books (2) 1883-9, stock records (5 vols and some loose items) 1885-1940, pattern books (5) 1928-39, wages books (4) 1904-10, 1917-36.
Oldham Local Interest Centre (MISC/15). NRA 29988.

[177] **JAMES KENYON & SON LTD**, woollen weavers, Bury and Heywood, Lancs

Letter books (6) 1866-1906, monthly financial summaries (3 vols) 1873-92, general ledger 1830-58, cash book 1882-7 and cash receipts (2 vols) 1829-55, ledger of cloth sent for milling 1842 with stocktaking 1843-60, journals (2) of wool bought 1834-70, notebook of orders for weaving 1902, price lists (9) 1867-1905, sample costings of felt and jacket making (1 vol) 1864-74, weaving prices 1869, production journals (7) 1820-79, ledger of blanket weavers' production for Thomas Timble 1830-45, blanket samples (1 vol) late 19th cent, schedules of piece work rates late 19th cent, cuttings book rel to Factory Acts 1867-95, deeds of Crimble Mill 1714-1826.
Lancashire RO (DDX 823). NRA 16491.

[178] **HUGH KERSHAW & SONS LTD**, woollen mfrs, Mossley, Lancs

Articles of association 1907, registers of directors, etc (2 vols) 1907-48, accounts and balance sheets (1 vol, 4 bundles) 1917-76, misc share records (2 vols, etc) 1907-54, letter books (76) 1930-59, British and foreign business corresp (98 bundles) 1913-57, nd, private corresp (11 bundles) 1881-1915, 1928-47, 1958, card cloth corresp (1 bundle) nd, general ledgers (18) 1889-1974, private ledgers (2) 1901-56, day books (31) 1903-73, cash and expenditure books (8) 1926-77, bank books, statements, etc (8 vols, 6 bundles) 1920-66, purchase books and ledgers (7) 1914-79, trade exports ledgers and papers (3 vols, 11 bundles) 1901-77, order, contract and invoice records (23 vols, 12 bundles) 1897-1901, 1906-76, stock and stocktaking records (46 vols, 6 bundles) 1897-1977, milling book 1874-6, census of production (1 bundle) 1907-39, survey of scouring and milling in the woollen industry (1 vol) nd, patent records (2 bundles) 1938-66, wages books, registers of employees and other personnel records (c50 vols, bundles and items) 1882-1970, property and insurance records (c50 vols, bundles and items) 1852, 1896-1971.
Tameside Local Studies Library (DDKM). NRA 31003.

[179] **KIRK & STEEL LTD**, woollen mfrs, Morley, Yorks

Articles of association 1915, directors' and general meeting minutes (2 vols) 1915-61, share register 1915-50, ledger and day book 1895-8, day books (5) 1896-1913, private ledgers (3) 1915-49, cash books (3)

1952-67, petty cash and bank books from 1895, invoices for goods bought (2 vols) 1907-14, sales, purchase and order books 1944-68, summaries and analysis books (19) 1927-79, commission accounts 1953-77, stock books 1921-74, blend books from 1895, wages books (12) 1912-65, salaries book 1949-57, tax and insurance papers 1914-50, rent books 1933-47, factory inspection reports 1939-77, misc papers.
West Yorkshire Archive Service, Leeds (Acc 2306). NRA 24682.

[180] **JH KNOWLES & CO LTD**, worsted spinners, Bradford, Yorks

Letter books 1921-60, ledgers 1908-61, cash books 1893-1958, sales books 1893-1962, bought ledgers 1893-1955, stocktaking books 1893-1923.
West Yorkshire Archive Service, Bradford: see Hudson.

[181] **LAIDLAW & FAIRGRIEVE LTD**, woollen yarn spinners, Galashiels, Selkirkshire

Balance sheets (1 vol) 1912-16, summary of capital assets, etc (1 vol) 1912-16, abstracts of output and expenditure c1900, 1917-55, stock books (2) 1865-7, 1917, costings and tests, wages analysis, etc (1 folder) 1910-53, census of production 1933-7, misc business corresp 1880-1927, machinery estimates and specifications (1 bundle) 1883-6, drawings and plans 1874, 1883, c1900, nd, building and maintenance accounts 1866-85, 1912, 1917, inventories and valuations 1874-1924, fire certificates and other premises records 1895-1940, balance sheets and share certificates of other firms 1879-1931, list of investments of William Laidlaw's Trust 1887 and minutes of trustees 1897.
The Company. Enquiries to NRA (Scotland) (NRA(S) 1665). NRA 21885.

[182] Number not used.

[183] **LANCASHIRE FELT CO LTD** (afterwards **LANCASTER CARPETS LTD**), hat body mfrs and dealers in hatters' materials, Denton, Lancs

Memorandum and articles of association 1865, directors' minutes (8 vols) 1866-1949, share ledger 1890-1920, memoranda books (2) 1889-1902, photographs 1932-3.
Tameside Local Studies Library (DD234/10). NRA 26457.

Minute books c1940s.
Coats Viyella plc. Enquiries to the Company Secretary. NRA 32377.

[184] **A LAVERTON & CO LTD**, worsted mfrs, Westbury, Wilts

General ledgers (2) 1849-75, private ledgers (5) 1872-8, 1888-1913, 1922-34, cash books (2) 1859-72, 1895-1903, petty cash book 1877-88, order books (9) 1882-1918, stock book 1872-81, pattern books (3) 1900-12, pattern or range reference books (50) 1805, 1869-1968, shade book 1923-4, making books (2) 1958-9, 1966, notebook rel to machinery acquisition

and buildings repair 1886-1919, valuation of Bitham and Angel Mills 1962, private ledger and cash book of Abraham Laverton 1872-84.
Wiltshire RO (WRO 954, WRO 1445). NRA 22078.

[185] **JOSEPH LAWTON & CO**, woollen merchants, Saddleworth, Yorks

Records c1825-55 incl articles of partnership, partnership accounts and statements c1825-55, letter books (2) England and United States 1825-6, 1854, notebook recording letters received and answered 1834-9, business and personal corresp (2 parcels, 12 bundles) 1848-53, account balances 1839-42, accounts 1844-8, ledger 1850-4, cash book 1843-4, bill books (2) 1849-55, receipts 1840-52, personal accounts 1820s-1850s, notebook of orders, costs and samples of cloth 1850-2, papers rel to estates of Charles and Ralph Lawton 1831-55, and history of partnership nd.
Greater Manchester RO. NRA 28631 (no 114).

[186] **FRANCIS & JOHN LEA**, carpet mfrs, Kidderminster, Worcs

Articles of partnership 1819, stock book 1781-97 incl accounts of TS Lea 1844, corresp of Thomas Lea, George Butcher and others c1810-40, memoranda rel to appointment of spinning mill managers nd, indentures 1821.
Kidderminster Art Gallery & Museum. NRA 30806.

Sample book of Bombazeen patterns with note by TS Lea 1843, John Lea's private ledger 1789 and household accounts 1818-31, misc corresp, patent specification rel to Venetian carpeting 1811.
Patrick Lea Esq. LD Smith, 'The carpet weavers of Kidderminster 1800-1850' (University of Birmingham PhD thesis, 1982).

[187] **LEAR, BROWNE & DUNSFORD LTD**, woollen merchants, Exeter, Devon

Day books (2) 1895-8, private cash book 1896-8, printed buyer's order book 1895.
In private possession. NRA 3506 (68/22).

[188] **LEAROYD BROS & CO**, worsted mfrs, Huddersfield, Yorks

Minutes, ledgers, journals, day books, corresp, pattern books, samples, order cards and staff records (c120 boxes) c1900-78.
West Yorkshire Archive Service, Kirklees.

[189] **JAMES LEES**, clothier and merchant, Saddleworth, Yorks

Letter book 1838-52, ledgers (2) 1818-20, accounts for building and machinery 1832-53, agreement 1792.
Saddleworth Central Library. NRA 11135.

[190] **JOHN & RICHARD LEES**, woollen mfrs, Galashiels, Selkirkshire

Account book 1788-1817, cash book 1796-1824, pocket ledger 1826.
The Old Gala Club, Galashiels. Enquiries to NRA (Scotland) (NRA(S) 2176). NRA 19459.

[191] **ROBERT LEGGET & SONS LTD**, wool merchants, skinners and tanners, Edinburgh

Letter books (8) 1936-53, corresp from c1950, private ledgers (3) 1922-45, bank books (2) 1844-9, trading ledgers (8) 1896-1951, purchase, sales, invoice and stock books (22 vols) 1925-66, wages books (16) 1908-67 and other staff records (7 vols) 1915-61.
Scottish Record Office (GD 286). NRA 17688.

[192] **LERRY MILLS**, flannel and tweed mfrs, Tal-y-bont, Cards

Account book 1840-55.
National Library of Wales: see *Annual report 1969-70*, p56.

Account books and papers (c30 boxes) 1929-79.
SJS Hughes Esq.

[193] **LEWIS family**, flannel mfrs, Drefach-Velindre, Carms

Account books (2) 1878-1903.
Welsh Folk Museum, Cardiff (MS 2432). NRA 31986.

[194] **LISTER BROS & CO LTD,** worsted spinners, Leeds and Horsforth, Yorks

Letter books 1888-1913, ledgers 1852-1924, day books 1869-1928, cash and bill books 1857-90, order and invoice books 1871-1938, memoranda and quotation books 1876-1942, stock books 1873-1916, wool, yarn, weaving and dyeing books 1866-1944, plans and drawings, etc 1866-1922.
West Yorkshire Archive Service, Leeds: see Hudson.

[195] **LISTER & CO LTD**, wool combers, silk spinners and knitting wool mfrs, Bradford, Yorks

Records 1857-1983 incl share papers, ledgers, cash books, trade mark and production records, employees' register, wages, salaries, property and plant books, rent accounts, plans, photographs, and notes on company history; misc corporate and premises records of S Bottomley & Bros Ltd, Walter Sykes Ltd and other subsidiaries 1898-1982.
Lister & Co plc. NRA 28631; BAC *Company Archives* no 661.

Memorandum, reports and statements 1889-1952.
Brotherton Library, Leeds University: see Hudson.

Attleborough Works, Nuneaton, wages book 1914-16.
Warwick County RO: see *Accessions to repositories 1984*, p40.

[196] **JOHN LOCKWOOD & SONS LTD**, woollen mfrs, Milnsbridge, Yorks

Ledgers (9)1878-99, 1907-60, cash books (11) 1896-1963, sundries day book 1931-56, bought day books (4) 1881-98, 1903-4, sold day books (45) 1885-1924, 1938-65, invoice books (10) 1909-60, order books (130) 1910-15, 1930-70, delivery books (14) 1956-70, lot books (36) 1904-71, production and misc records (38 vols) 1909-70, nd, pattern weaving plans, specifications, etc (18 bundles and items) 1912-54, wages books (73) 1903-69, time books (3) 1921-37.
West Yorkshire Archive Service, Kirklees (B/JL). NRA 31069.

[197] **LOWENTHAL BROTHERS**, wool merchants, Huddersfield, Yorks

Statistics of wool purchases (1 vol) 1830-82 incl at the colonial wool sales in London 1853-79.
Tolson Memorial Museum, Huddersfield: see Hudson.

[198] **JOSEPH LUMB & SONS LTD**, worsted yarn spinners, Huddersfield, Yorks

Ledger 1862-8, corresp, orders, specifications, etc 1871-6.
West Yorkshire Archive Service, Kirklees (B/L). NRA 26729.

[199] **WILLIAM LUPTON & CO LTD**, woollen and worsted mfrs and traders, Leeds

Letter books 1760-1851, ledgers 1748-1919, cash and day books 1801-51, stock and trading accounts 1812-1921, family papers, etc c1694-c1860.
Brotherton Library, Leeds University: see Hudson.

Account book and stock inventory 1819-67.
West Yorkshire Archive Service, Leeds (GA/2/65): see Hudson.

[200] **GEORGE LYLES & SONS LTD**, carpet yarn spinners, Mirfield, Yorks

Annual reports 1914-33, private ledgers 1906-50, other ledgers and accounts 1873-1980, day books 1882-1967, cash books 1906-80, purchase and sales ledgers, delivery books and invoices 1884-1980, stock books 1895-1980, production books 1892-1981, blend books 1874-1979, samples c1930-80, wages books, registers of young employees and other personnel records 1881-1980, plant, premises and machinery records 1891-1943, printed papers, blocks, etc c1920-1974.
West Yorkshire Archive Service, Wakefield Headquarters (C486).

[201] **A & J MACNAUGHTON LTD**, woollen mfrs, Pitlochry, Perthshire

Cash book as grocers and warehousemen 1878-97, order book 1918-21, specification book incl army blankets 1914-18, wages book 1881-90, price list nd; lecture notes (8 vols) of FG and Arthur Macnaughton, Leeds University Department of Textile Industries 1904-5.
The Company. Enquiries to NRA (Scotland) (NRA(S) 2034). NRA 23018.

[202] **JOHN MAGEE & CO**, clothiers, Belfast

Out-letter books 1854-91.
Public Record Office of Northern Ireland (D 2015).
Deputy Keeper's Report 1966-72, p86.

[203] **D & H MALLALIEU LTD**, woollen mfrs, Delph, Yorks

Records 19th-20th cent.
Greater Manchester RO (1328 B30).

[204] **GEORGE MALLINSON & SONS LTD**, woollen and worsted mfrs, Linthwaite, Yorks

Stock book 1911-20, cost books (8) 1911-41, range books (2) 1915-26, wages books (5) 1940-61, income tax returns 1941-4, history of firm nd.
West Yorkshire Archive Service, Kirklees (B/GM). NRA 32418.

[205] **MARLING & CO**, woollen and worsted mfrs, Stonehouse and Stroud, Glos

Partnership deeds 1825-66, stock balance books (3) 1842-85, ledger 1881-6, misc corresp, memoranda and accounts 1856-1900, contracts and specifications for building work at Ebley Mills 1862-6, Marling family papers 16th-20th cent.
Gloucestershire RO (D873). NRA 10646.

Account of wool purchased 1880-1909, dyeing book 1794-1804.
Gloucestershire RO (D948).

[206] **RV MARRINER LTD**, worsted spinners and mfrs, Keighley, Yorks

Letter book 1930-42, ledgers 1841-87, cash and bank books 1793-1911, balance sheets and other accounts *c*1816-53, order books 1869-*c*1887, price books 1838-*c*1870, weavers' account books 1804-45, production books 1868-77, nd, brass band papers 1844-*c*1870, corresp and papers 19th-20th cent, family papers incl diaries 18th-20th cent; Watson, Blakey, Smith & Greenwood proposal and articles for building factory 1784, sales and purchase account book 1786-91, bills, private accounts, corresp and misc papers rel to partnership with William and Benjamin Marriner 1784-*c*1820.
Brotherton Library, Leeds University: see Hudson.

[207] **MARSHALL, KAYE & MARSHALL LTD**, fancy woollen mfrs, Ravensthorpe, Yorks

Ledgers 1880-1947, cash books 1880-1966, purchase and sales books 1880-1965, production records *c*1890-1954, misc papers incl bills and receipts *c*1880-1968.
Dewsbury Central Library: see Hudson.

[208] **JAMES MATHERS & SONS**, union, melton, tweed and fancy coating cloth mfrs, Leeds

Ledgers (3) 1876-1903, petty cash book 1902-36.
West Yorkshire Archive Service, Leeds (Acc 1273): see Hudson.

[209] **HENRY MELLOR & SON**, woollen merchants, Huddersfield, Yorks

Account book 1885-8, cash books, delivery notes and misc accounting records 1907-68.
West Yorkshire Archive Service, Kirklees (B/L). NRA 26729.

[210] **MIDDLEMOST BROS**, woollen mfrs, Huddersfield, Yorks

Letter book from 1894, boiler house and engine records 1889-95.
West Yorkshire Archive Service, Leeds (Acc 1624): see Hudson.

Agreements (1 file) 1895-1914, papers (1 file) rel to strike 1930.
West Yorkshire Archive Service, Kirklees (B/GHH). NRA 32417.

[211] **THOMAS MILLER**, woollen mfr, Dundee area

Day books (2) 1829-39.
Scottish Record Office (CS 96/101-2). *Court of Session Productions*, List & Index Society, special series vol 23, 1987, p447.

[212] **WILLIAM MILROY**, woollen mfr, Kirkcowan, Wigtownshire

Pattern, piece and order books (8) 1891-1945.
Dumfries Archive Centre (GD 1). NRA 31757.

[213] **ROWLAND MITCHELL & CO LTD**, woollen mfrs, Lepton, Yorks

Cash books 1917-56, invoices and receipts 1911-65, sales and purchase books and ledgers 1894-1965, order books 1923-71, production and wages books 1893-1946, corresp 1924-67, certificates of shipment, etc 1964-7.
West Yorkshire Archive Service, Kirklees (B/RM): see Hudson.

[214] **CHARLES MOON'S SUCCESSORS LTD**, woollen yarn spinners, Huddersfield, Yorks

Memorandum and articles of association 1925, corresp (60 files) 1937-73, ledgers (3) 1926-57, cash books (9) 1913-70, bank books (8) 1907-30, balance books (2) 1926-57, purchase and sales books (21) 1911-68, order books (4) 1929-72, wages books (12) 1907-44, valuations 1918-71, catalogues, invoices, etc 1903-76.
West Yorkshire Archive Service, Kirklees (B/CMS). NRA 32419.

[215] **MOORHOUSE & BROOK LTD**, woollen mfrs, Huddersfield, Yorks

Minute books and corporate records from 1915, cash book 1900-*c*1913, personal cash book 1903-12 incl balance sheets and profit and loss accounts; corporate records of subsidiaries.
The Company. Enquiries to the Chairman.

[216] **WILLIAM MORRIS & SONS LTD**, worsted mfrs, Sowerby Bridge, Yorks

Accounting and production records (*c*150 vols) *c*1846-*c*1950, order books 1933-45, delivery books 1922-37, registers and certificates of young employees 1844-1937, wages books 1926-47.
West Yorkshire Archive Service, Wakefield Headquarters (C240).

[217] **MORTON & SONS**, carpet mfrs, Kidderminster, Worcs

Stock books and sheets (20 vols, etc) 1893-1916.
Kidderminster Library. NRA 28020.

[218] **JAMES MOWAT JUNIOR**, woollen goods mfr, Denny, Stirlingshire

Day book 1823-6, cash book 1822-5.
Scottish Record Office (CS 96/3915-16). *Court of Session Productions*, List & Index Society, special series vol 23, 1987, p353.

[219] **JOHN MURGATROYD & SON LTD**, worsted mfrs, Luddenden, Yorks

Articles of partnership 1876, letter books (32) 1860-1911, corresp files 1851-1969, ledgers (19) 1844-1917, day books (40) 1844-1904, cash books (20) 1869-1976 and other accounts 1846-88, 1921-54, account book of pieces sold to Staffordshire and Manchester 1833-4, order books (26) incl samples 1865-1973, purchase day books, ledgers, etc (23 vols) 1860-1963, sales accounts, etc (33 vols) 1848-71, 1904-63, invoices (64 vols, etc) 1897-1981, misc order and sales books (12) 1850-68, 1898, stock books (27) 1834-1933, wool, warp, coating, costing and other production books (c65 vols) 1848-1967, shade and pattern books nd, samples 1862-1949, nd, wages books, etc (167 vols, etc) 1842-1969, registers, etc of young employees (35 vols, etc) 1849-1904, nd, age certificate books (42) 1859-1907, accounts of loans, etc to employees (5 vols) 1907-38, employees' leave book nd, apprenticeship agreements 1850-89, Oats Royd Mills Brass Band financial papers, etc 1864-91, machinery stock accounts 1897-1930, valuations, property specifications, etc 1823-1966, plans (131) 1863-1967, Murgatroyd family papers and estate records 1845-1951.
West Yorkshire Archive Service, Calderdale (JM). NRA 25837.

Spindle band book 1875-6, weaving record book 1865-73, pattern and sample books (44) incl details of orders and payments 1840-1911, samples with associated corresp and papers 1860-1942, railway despatch books (2) 1863-4, weaving diagrams c1820-20th cent, payment books (6) 1850-64, 1874-83, millwright's receipt book 1848-51 and work book 1850-2.
Bankfield Museum, Halifax. NRA 5855.

[220] **TM NEWMAN & SONS**, wool brokers, Nailsworth, Glos

Articles of partnership 1854, notices (14) of changes of partnerships in various firms 1858-68, forms ledger 1932-64, journals, cash books, accounts and invoices (6 vols, 4 bundles) 1953-64, wool books (10) 1855-6, 1859-73, 1894-7, 1920-4, 1933-46, 1960-3, prices of colonial wools sold in London 1865-99, sales books (3) 1905-35, 1950-63, import and purchase books (8) 1936-60, samples book from 1935, misc corresp and papers rel to wool sales, prices, etc 1836-1972 incl wool market reports 1873, 1875, notes by RM Newman on history of firm 20th cent.
Gloucestershire RO (D2794). NRA 17634.

[221] **NILLION, DOCKRAY & CO**, worsted spinners, Rawtenstall, Lancs

Accounts and work books 1820-40, wages book 1831-3 incl medical certificates 1836-44, account book rel to building of mill 1798, insurance policy 1843.
Rawtenstall District Library (Rc 677 CLO). NRA 30888.

[222] **GH NORTON & CO LTD**, fancy cloth mfrs, Scisset, Yorks

Records (15 boxes) 1867-1968, mainly calculations books and pattern books, but incl ledgers and rent books (5) 1923-55, raw wool purchase book 1889-94, spinning books (3) 1889-93, time books (2) 1896-1913, 1928-35, ideas book 1900-13, and wages books (2) c1914, 1918-19.
West Yorkshire Archive Service, Kirklees (B/N, KC 60, KC 234). NRA 31070.

[223] **NOTTIDGE family**, baymakers, Bocking, Essex

Volume containing ledger 1772-92, day book 1772-1810 and cash accounts 1810-22.
Essex RO, Chelmsford (D/DO/B1). NRA 9821.

[224] **JOSIAH OATES & SON**, woollen cloth merchants, Leeds

Account book 1786-1828 incl details of bills of exchange and prices for dressing and dyeing.
West Yorkshire Archive Service, Leeds (Oates Collection): see Hudson.

[225] **MARK OLDROYD & SONS**, blanket and woollen mfrs, Leeds and Dewsbury, Yorks

Prospectus, dividend warrants, annual reports and balance sheets 1874-80.
Wakefield Libraries Department of Local Studies (Goodchild Loan MSS). Formerly in the South Yorkshire Industrial Museum, Cusworth Hall. See Hudson.

Complaints book 1861-88.
Dewsbury Central Library. NRA 8067 (item 361).

[226] **OVENDEN WORSTED CO LTD**, worsted mfrs, Ovenden, Yorks

Memorandum and articles of association 1871, minute book 1871-1906, share transfer ledger 1874-1906, general, invoice, agents' and manufacturing letter books 1890s-early 1900s, vouchers and receipts (c20 boxes) c1880-c1906, Holmfield and Shay Mill accounts c1866-90, sales ledgers nd, piece and yarn order books c1880-c1900, time books nd, wages books c1873-c1901, schedule of deeds 1914.
West Yorkshire Archive Service, Wakefield Headquarters (C300).

[227] **DANIEL PACKER**, clothier, Painswick, Glos

Letter books (2) 1760-1, 1768-9, misc Packer family deeds and papers 1719-93.
Gloucestershire RO (D149/F86-114). NRA 10491.

[228] **PANDY WOOLLEN MILL**, Caerphilly, Glam

Cloth accounts (2 vols) 1856-61, 1872-3, spinning accounts (1 vol) 1859-89.
Glamorgan Archive Service (D/D Xfc 1, 3-4). NRA 5196.

[229] **PARKWOOD MILLS CO LTD**, commission weavers, Longwood, Yorks

Directors' and general meeting minutes (3 vols) 1896-1956, registers of directors and annual returns 1923-9, 1946-66, directors' corresp file 1962, share corresp file 1895-1927, share certificate register 1887-1911, ledgers (10) 1896-1953, cash books (8) 1908-66, expenditure analysis books (3) 1958-66, weekly wages analysis books (with Longwood Finishing Co Ltd) (9) 1940-60, mill rent books (2) 1873-1930, inventories and valuations (4) 1916-68, insurance register 1924-6.
West Yorkshire Archive Service, Kirklees (KC 17). NRA 31065.

[230] **JOHN PATON, SON & CO LTD** (afterwards **PATONS & BALDWINS LTD**), spinners of woollen yarns for hosiery, hand knitting and rug making, Alloa, Clackmannanshire

Contract of copartnery 1879, 1888, minute of agreement 1893, file rel to liquidation of John Paton, Son & Co Ltd 1920, corresp rel to amalgamation of Patons and J & J Baldwin 1920, minutes (2 vols, 1 file) 1906-25, 1946-59, seal book 1877, private letter book 1881-90, balance books (2) 1874-1906 and sheets 1903-19, partners' accounts 1898-1905, private ledgers (8) 1861-1906, price lists 1836-96, stock sheets, etc 1874-1924, private salaries book 1875-95, insurance file 1867-98, specification for Clackmannan Mill 1875, inventory and valuation 1919, nd, closing accounts and receipts rel to Keilanbrue Spinning Co (1 bundle) 1873, misc files rel to overseas trade 1924-59, Clackmannan Mill school registers 1876-8, papers of the trustees of AP Forrester-Paton 1921.
The Company. Enquiries to NRA (Scotland) (NRA(S) 751). NRA 17531.

Darlington works records incl stock accounts 1807-42, 1893-1902; Leicester branch balance sheets 1844-1900.
The Company. Enquiries to the Company Secretary. NRA 1099.

[231] **HENRY PEASE & CO LTD**, worsted spinners, Darlington, co Durham

Memorandum and articles of association and related papers 1902-3, out-letter book 1884-94, account book 1845-59, private ledgers (2) 1838-67, other ledgers and accounts (4 vols) 1930-77, private journals (2) 1882-1900, cash books (4) 1833-40, bill book 1903-7, memoranda book 1846-8, office diaries (17) 1833-54, purchase and sales day books (5) 1957-78, suppliers' quotations 1851-7, invoices for yarn, tools and spindles *c*1833-5, 1844, 1896-7, stock accounts (4 vols) 1835, 1841, 1851-61, 1944-72, lists of stock, workers, etc 1891-1919, records of trials 1836-46, 1853-4, cash books (2) of the Women and Children's Association 1814-30, Recreation Fund minutes 1936-51, plans 1933-62, rent receipts book 1892-6, misc letters, calculations, statistics, etc from 1831.
Durham County RO (D/HP). NRA 25374.

Records 1833-1982 incl minutes, annual reports, share records, private ledgers and other accounts, quotation and stock books, plant ledgers, inventory, plans, and notebooks.
Lister & Co plc. NRA 28631; BAC *Company Archives* no 661.

Woolcombers' wages (1 vol) 1829, Pease family papers 1785-1919.
Durham County RO (D/Ho). NRA 12281.

Corresp rel to wool business and other family papers 1808-1911.
Durham County RO (D/Pe). NRA 25741.

[232] **PEPPER, LEE & CO LTD**, worsted mfrs, Bradford, Yorks

Memorandum and articles of association 1950, registers of directors, members and shares 1866-1920, share certificates and returns *c*1908-32, corresp *c*1950s, balance sheets *c*1928-64, private ledgers (5) 1909-66, misc accounts 1922-69, sales book 1928, summary of stock 1927-57, plant book 1932-48, inventories 1950, salaries and wages books (4) 1934-57.
West Yorkshire Archive Service, Bradford (25D89).

[233] **PETERSON family**, woollen cloth merchants and dressers, Wakefield, Yorks

Accounts, corresp, property and family papers, etc *c*1750-1874.
Wakefield Libraries Department of Local Studies (Goodchild Loan MSS). Formerly in the South Yorkshire Industrial Museum, Cusworth Hall. See Hudson.

[234] **JE PICKARD & SONS LTD**, wool spinners, Leicester

Account and memoranda book 1854-9, private ledgers (7) pre-1879-1936, class ledger 1924-42, day books (2) 1919–26, cash books (3) 1875-8, 1895-1903, bank ledgers (3) 1891-6, *c*1902, nd, purchase corresp (19 boxes) 1911-34, 1937, 1944-5, sales corresp (7 boxes) 1940, bought day book 1861-7, bought ledgers (6) 1875-81, 1885-1922, 1931-41, sold ledgers (10) 1875-1910, 1917-31, invoices (2 boxes) 1913-22, order books (5) 1868-1906, 1937-46, contract books (2) 1912-15, 1936-46, job books and other sales and order records (14 vols) 1907-26, 1940-60, stocktaking book 1910, wool, yarn and spinners' books (16 vols) 1918-47, time records (3 vols, 2 bundles) 1939-44, 1957-9, wages books (2) 1873-6, 1899-1904, staff Christmas gifts record 1879-1957, papers (5 envelopes, 1 folder) rel to war damage and reconstruction 1940-53, title deeds and related papers (263 items) 1705-1920.
Leicestershire RO (26 D 60, DE 1418, DE 3044). NRA 31382.

[235] **T PICKLES & SONS**, worsted spinners, Halifax, Yorks

Letter book 1890-6, private ledgers (2) 1901-9, cash book 1886-94, wages books (4) 1886-1912.
Bankfield Museum, Halifax. NRA 5855.

[236] **WILLIAM PLAYNE & CO LTD**, woollen mfrs, Minchinhampton, Glos

Register of shareholders 1939-49, letter book 1841-56, corresp (15 files) incl related papers and patterns 1900-58, private ledgers (3) 1895-1943, cash books (27) 1834-44, 1895-1974, ledgers, vouchers, etc (3 vols,

1 file) 1911-42, bill books (2) 1828-49, purchase ledger and day books (15 vols) 1897-1973, sales journals and ledgers (8) 1863-1967, day books of orders despatched (11) 1905-15, abstract of purchases (2 vols) 1907-20, travellers' sales (1 vol) 1910-27, bought and sold credits and returns (7 vols) 1895-1969, order books (2) 1836-49, 1897-1902, invoice books (5) 1829-1930, stock and price books, etc (4 vols, 2 bundles) 1895-1935, sorted wools and scoured wools (8 vols) 1826-1918, manufacturing books (21) 1897-1943, overlooking books (2) 1856-1912, wool pickers' book 1887-90, spinning books (7) 1897-1910, warpers', weavers' and burlers' books (3) 1863-91, millman's sort book 1899, milling book 1899-1902, shearmen's books (2) 1848-69, load books (3) 1855-74, length books (6) 1864-1908, 'cost make' book 1897-1903, pattern and sample books (4) c1897-1911, time and wages books (12) 1861-1948, history of the firm and advertisements c1959, executors' accounts (1 bundle) 1935-46.
Gloucestershire RO (D4644). NRA 26394.

[237] **POLLARD & HOLDEN LTD**, worsted coating mfrs, Bradford, Yorks

General meeting minutes 1910-58, share ledger, etc 1910-44, balance sheets, reports and accounts 1910-57.
Courtaulds plc, Coventry. Enquiries to the Head of Archives. NRA 29343.

[238] **RICHARD POPPLETON**, worsted spinner, Horbury, Yorks

Stock books, inventories, balance sheets, etc 1810-65.
Wakefield Libraries Department of Local Studies (Goodchild Loan MSS). Formerly in the South Yorkshire Industrial Museum, Cusworth Hall. See Hudson.

[239] **E POSSELT & CO LTD**, woollen yarn exporters, Bradford, Yorks

Ledgers 1863-1950, order books 1927-65, wages books 1879-1965, list of employees 1872-1903, misc papers 1886-97.
West Yorkshire Archive Service, Bradford: see Hudson.

[240] **PRICE BROS & CO LTD**, woollen and bedding mfrs, Wellington, Somerset

Directors' minute book 1897-1936, reports on restructuring the firm (1 folder) 1951, register of members 1898-1919, accounts (1 vol) 1867-74, calculations books (2) 1901, c1905, price list with engravings of factories c1905, register of employees 1899-1930 incl prices and rules for piece work 1899.
Somerset RO (DD/PRC). NRA 28397.

[241] **JOHN & WALKER PRIESTLEY**, woollen mfrs, Halifax, Yorks

Letter book 1805-14, ledger and cash book 1810-22, stock account book 1805-22, drawing for packing press 1825, plan 1824.
In private possession. Enquiries to West Yorkshire Archive Service, Leeds. NRA 9568.

[242] **RACEVIEW WOOLLEN MILLS LTD**, Broughshane, co Antrim

Memorandum and articles of association 1896, corresp (over 1,000 items) c1898-1912, letter books (2) c1898, 1900-2, balance sheets c1897-c1908, balance book 1890-9, private ledgers (5) 1897-1951, nominal ledger 1938-53, cash books (11) 1893-1965, day books (3) 1905-8, 1953-62, bill books 1901-12, current account book 1920-30, analysis books (c11) c1895-1905, 1913-31, reference books (2) c1906-1923, purchase ledgers (3) 1893-1924 and journals (2) 1893-1907, 1929-38, sales ledgers (9) 1893-1911, 1919-62, journals (23) 1893-1962 and return books (4) c1920-1938, invoice books (4) 1924-9, receipts 1918-33, pattern order book 1904-5, memoranda books rel to yarn prices, contracts, etc 1898-9, 1904-6, notes rel to South African agency 1914, stock books (3) 1906-19, pattern books (2) nd, wages books (9) 1907-45.
Public Record Office of Northern Ireland (D 1933/1-12). NRA 31476.

[243] **JOHN RAISTRICK & SONS**, woollen mfrs, Idle, Yorks

Order book, corresp and papers 1864-90.
Brotherton Library, Leeds University: see Hudson.

[244] **THOMAS RATCLIFFE & CO LTD**, blanket mfrs, Mytholmroyd, Yorks

Accounts, cash books and other financial records (12 vols) 1914-57, contract and purchase books (4) 1934-8, wages books (10) 1887-1935, display book nd.
West Yorkshire Archive Service, Calderdale (RA). NRA 23841.

[245] **RAWDON LOW MILL CO** (afterwards **SAMUEL GRAY & CO**), woollen mfrs, Rawdon, Yorks

Draft of copartnership 1841, articles of partnership 1847, minute book 1843-52, share register 1861, assignments and transfers of shares (c24 items) 1848-75.
West Yorkshire Archive Service, Leeds (William Gray's Trust Papers). NRA 31586.

[246] **ISAAC RECKITT**, wool merchant and flour miller, Boston, Lincs, Nottingham, and Hull, Yorks

Ledgers (2) 1830-5, cash books (6) 1818-39, account books (3) 1830-55, sack account book 1833-9.
Brynmor Jones Library, Hull University (DRA 617-29). NRA 10731.

[247] **JOHN REDDIHOUGH LTD** (formerly **REDDIHOUGH & MURGATROYD**, woolstaplers), wool merchants, top makers and wool combers, Bradford, Yorks

Letter book 1889-1922, private ledgers 1893-1919, notebook 1875-1922, wages book 1883-1906.
Brotherton Library, Leeds University: see Hudson.

[248] **JB REED & CO**, wool merchants and farmers, Great Torrington, Devon

General ledgers (7) 1885-1925, 1943-54, day books (9) 1876-1926, account and analysis books (11) 1879-1979, bank books, etc (30) 1865-1972, account books for wool (9) 1870-1956 and for lime, manure, coal, meat and grain (37) 1878-1954, farm books (6) 1851-98, 1950-70, mill ledger and general account book 1912-13, general bought ledger 1882-1904, account and delivery book 1898-1909, sales day book 1945-9, invoice book 1943-56, stock book 1903-22, wages book 1921-4, rent books (3) 1892-1976, corresp, insurance policies and receipts (3 vols, 21 bundles) 1897-1955, family diaries, bank books, etc 1912-80.
Devon RO (3579B). NRA 25372.

[249] **WM RENNIE & CO LTD**, worsted spinners, Leeds

Records c1900-62 incl register of members, balance sheets, ledgers and other accounts, sales returns, and inventories.
West Yorkshire Archive Service, Bradford (25D89).

[250] **ALBERT RHODES & CO LTD**, woollen merchants and woollen and worsted spinners, Heckmondwike, Yorks

Letter books 1864-1925, ledgers, day books and cash books 1863-1937, purchase books 1862-1924, order books 1893-1926, despatch and delivery records 1875-1915, blend, production and stock books 1862-1925, plans, etc 1859-1936.
West Yorkshire Archive Service, Leeds: see Hudson.

[251] **RHODES & BROADBENT**, wool scourers, scribblers and slubbers, Diggle, Yorks

Balance sheets 1840-58, account books (6) 1826-67, debtors' personal ledgers (4) 1821-65, lists of debts 1840-58, payment and receipt vouchers 1843-68, mill production books (3) 1822-52, rent book 1850-7, valuation of machinery 1867, misc financial papers 1814-71, nd.
Saddleworth Museum (M/RB). NRA 11134.

[252] **J & S RHODES LTD**, woollen mfrs, Morley, Yorks

Minute book 1904-57, register of members and share ledger 1904-41, nominal ledger 1932-62, pattern books (19) 19th cent-c1980, misc corresp, plans and other records 1857-1977.
West Yorkshire Archive Service, Kirklees (KC 197). NRA 29742.

[253] **WILLIAM RHODES LTD**, flock mfrs, Leeds and Birkenshaw, Yorks

Ledgers (2) 1845-69, 1895-6; Morley Cloth Finishing Co contracts and papers 1902-19.
Brotherton Library, Leeds University: see Hudson.

[254] **RHYDYGWYSTL WOOLLEN FACTORY**, Abererch, Caerns

Accounts (3 vols) 1835-51.
University College of North Wales, Bangor (MSS 454-6).

[255] **JF & H ROBERTS LTD**, mfrs of woollens, calicoes, trimmings and linings, Manchester

Minutes, directors' reports and accounts, customers' account books, and reports and corresp from Australian and New Zealand branches 1877-1966.
CV Home Furnishings Ltd. NRA 28631; BAC *Company Archives* no 261.

[256] **RONALD & RODGER**, wool brokers, Liverpool

Financial records, etc from 1822.
Liverpool RO: see *Accessions to repositories 1980*, p33.

[257] **ROYAL TAPESTRY WORKS**, Windsor, Berks

Papers 1881-1905 mainly rel to liquidation, incl memorandum and articles of association 1881, and catalogues of tapestries 1888, 1892.
Berkshire RO (D/EX 788).

[258] **SAMUEL SALTER & CO LTD**, woollen cloth mfrs, Trowbridge, Wilts

Records (c220 vols, c1,300 files, bundles, etc) 1700-1982 incl articles of partnership 1860, petty ledger 1863-5, cash book 1898-1900, credit enquiry book 1868-88, reports on Australian cloth firms (1 vol) 1879-93, address book late 19th cent, production statistics, etc (7 vols) 1886-1915, pattern books (2) 1769-82, cloth pattern plan book 1906, factory inspectorate registers (10) 1907-72, inventory and valuation of Home Mills and Duke Street Mills 1885, and deeds and related papers 1700-1966.
Wiltshire RO (WRO 926, 1387). NRA 18828.

[259] **SALTS (SALTAIRE) LTD**, worsted and worsted yarn spinners, Saltaire, Yorks

Agreements (1 file, etc), directors' minutes (6 vols) 1895-1977, general meeting minutes (2 vols) 1923-77, private minutes (1 vol) 1934-59, list of members 1881, register of directors 1923-77, seal books (3) 1881-1919, 1948-63, annual reports and financial statements, private ledgers (5) 1895-1939, ledger 1918-23, cash books (12) 1962-74, private journal 1924-38, account book 1924-30 and other misc accounts 1960-74, nd, purchase and sales books (15) 1934-74, order books (6) 1941-71, address book 1937, stock books (2) 1938-60, wool tops and noils ledger 1960-6, drawing record book 1932, overlooker's notebook 1958, sample room book 1965, plush department references 1890, wages and salaries books (31) 1918-84, machine books (2) 1924-62, plant register (2 vols) 1948-9, 1956, inventories (3 vols) 1923, nd, boiler reports, insurance notes, etc (15 files) 1960s-1970s, nd, schedule of deeds 1960, Salts' Schools deed of endowment, visitors' book 1895-1966, press cuttings (4 vols, etc) 1899-1982; John Wright (Ingrow) Ltd account book, private ledgers (2) 1914-26, misc papers c1912-25.
West Yorkshire Archive Service, Bradford (25D89).

Salts' Schools and Saltaire Institute records with misc Salt family papers c1871-1968.
West Yorkshire Archive Service, Bradford: see *West Yorkshire Archive Service Report 1987-8*, p42.

Day book of Titus Salt 1834-7.
Bradford University Library.

[260] **SANDERSON & MURRAY LTD**, wool merchants and fellmongers, Galashiels, Selkirkshire

Private letter books (9) 1855-82, letter books (5) 1878-1915, foreign letter books (2) 1881-98, private ledger 1895-1921, private journal 1882-95, balance books (2) 1872-1908, legal papers and agreements 1789-1915, misc corresp and papers, mainly rel to property, valuations, etc 1852-1915, engine and boiler house weekly record ledgers (4) 1925-45.
Borders Region Archive (SC/S/6). NRA 32398.

[261] **R & A SANDERSON & CO LTD**, woollen mfrs, Galashiels, Selkirkshire

Day books (5) 1928-54, order books (5) 1933-52, stock books (7 bundles) 1886, 1935-52, yarn ledgers (16) 1888-1953, measuring ledgers (8) 1908-18, 1930-7, twisting ledgers (4) 1942-53, yarn compilation books (11) 1934-55, batch books (13) 1913-53, pattern books (158) 1853-9, 1867-1956, nd, pattern notebooks (6 bundles) nd, time and wages books (40) 1862-1956.
Scottish College of Textiles, Galashiels. NRA 31124.

[262] **WILLIAM C SCOTT**, wool merchants and skinners, Dundee

Ledgers and cash books (4) 1845-65, 1913-45, purchase and sales books (19) 1895-1973, order books (5) 1903-39.
Dundee University Library. NRA 20246.

[263] **JOHN SHAW & SONS**, woollen mfrs, Stainland, Yorks

Account book incl samples 1806-18, 1830-6, production book 1831-6.
Bankfield Museum, Halifax. NRA 5855.

[264] **R SIM & CO** (afterwards **HEATHER MILLS CO LTD**), woollen mfrs, Selkirk

Directors' minute book 1932-72, private ledgers (5) 1899-1931, ledger 1919-31, journals (2) 1896-1910, invoice book 1945-51, wholesale cost book 1940-6, wages books (3) 1909-11, corresp, quotations and specifications rel to machinery, etc (1 bundle) 1916-60, catalogues, photographs, Scottish wool sample book, company history, misc papers.
The Company. Enquiries to NRA (Scotland) (NRA(S) 1667). NRA 21734.

[265] **RICHARD SMITH & SONS**, carpet mfrs, Kidderminster, Worcs

Deed of partnership 1875, private ledgers (3) from 1890, stock sheets 1905-10, price list 1893, patents nd, salaries book from 1912.
Kidderminster Library. NRA 28020.

[266] **H & M SOUTHWELL LTD**, carpet mfrs, Kidderminster, Worcs

Share ledger nd, private ledgers (5) from 1890, nominal ledgers (2) from 1927, journal from 1944, deeds 1713-57, 1817-73.
Kidderminster Library. NRA 28020.

[267] **SPARROW, BROWN, HANBURY, SAVILL & CO**, weavers and clothiers, Bocking, Essex

Bank book 1818-32, bank receipts (9) 1816-21, trade receipts and expenditure book 1813-20, wool purchase account book 1743-1817, stock books (2) 1762-1817, Bulford Mill stock book 1799-1806, history of firm 1960, Savill family deeds, accounts and papers 17th-19th cent.
Essex RO, Chelmsford (D/DCd). NRA 8158.

Accounts and receipts (1 file) rel to the bay trade 1740s-1750s, Savill family deeds, etc.
Essex RO, Chelmsford (D/DSv). NRA 8158.

[268] **JOHN SPENCER & SONS**, woolstaplers, Keighley, Yorks

Business account books and memoranda books (c11 vols) of David and John Spencer 1795-1804, 1810-32, stock accounts 1800, 1816-18, David Spencer's diary 1804, misc business corresp early 19th cent, Spencer family papers and corresp 18th-19th cent.
Brotherton Library, Leeds University: see Hudson.

[269] **STANSFELD family**, woollen mfrs, merchants and mill owners, Sowerby, Yorks

Letter book 1722-40, financial papers incl bankruptcy 1725-1885, account books (3) 1801-7, 1809-10, 1815-27, waste books (3) 1789, 1815-17, 1821, bill book for Stansfeld Mill 1815-18, trade ledgers (2) 1782-1808, sales journal 1815-17, wool sales books (3) 1783-1805, c1809, wool tables 18th cent, lists of bales (1 vol) 1810-11, wages books 1815-26, time books (3) and sheets 1819-26, rules, etc of Stansfeld Mill 1831, 1833, leases, etc 1811-46 incl to J Wilks & Co, flax spinners c1815-20, and to Joseph Mallalieu, cotton spinners c1837-40; goods book, flax, etc 1815-19, hecklers' book 1825, account book of John Hargreaves, Kidderminster 1815-26, record of yarn delivered to Kidderminster 1823-5.
West Yorkshire Archive Service, Calderdale. NRA 7834.

[270] **AF STODDARD & CO LTD**, carpet mfrs, Elderslie, Renfrewshire

Memorandum and articles of association 1894, directors' and general meeting minutes (3 vols) 1894-1959, register of mortgages, bonds and charges 1887-1947, reports and accounts (1 vol) 1894-1951, list of dividends, sales and profits, etc from 1894, ledgers (2) 1918-45, private journals (2) 1894-1930, journal 1940-5, cash books (9) 1933-51, purchase and order books (3) 1932-48, shipping book 1920-36, price and quotation books (3) 1906-42, wages and insurance books (8) 1882-1948, provident society and sick club minutes 1853-68, 1924-59, corresp rel to amalgamation with Ronald Jack & Co Ltd and Caledonian Carpet Co Ltd 1918, press cuttings, advertisements and photographs from 1870.
Stoddard Carpets Ltd. Enquiries to NRA (Scotland) (NRA(S) 283). NRA 10833.

Designs.
In private possession. Not available for research.

[271] **MP STONEHOUSE LTD**, worsted spinners, Wakefield, Yorks

Letter book 1917-19, cash books 1853-1914, sales and purchase books 1850-1923, stock book and balance sheets 1880-1915, wages and employment records 1855-1921.
Wakefield Libraries Department of Local Studies (Goodchild Loan MSS). Formerly in the South Yorkshire Industrial Museum, Cusworth Hall. See Hudson.

[272] **STOTT & INGHAM**, worsted spinners, Halifax, Yorks

Cash book 1886-91, bill book 1894-1929, sales, order and purchase records 1886-1963, stock book 1898-1918, production records 1932-47, wages books 1886-1965, records of engines, etc 1888-1944.
West Yorkshire Archive Service, Calderdale (STO): see Hudson.

[273] **G & J STUBLEY LTD**, woollen mfrs, Batley, Yorks

Receiving and bought day books (6) 1864-80, rough ledgers (2) of customers' and suppliers' accounts 1868-81, blend books (14) 1869-82, nd, registers (6) of young employees 1867-1912, doctors' certificates (1 vol) 1870-9.
West Yorkshire Archive Service, Kirklees (KC 74, KC 192). NRA 27915.

Masons' wages book 1871-83.
West Yorkshire Archive Service, Kirklees (KC 80). NRA 26729.

Blend book 1903-5.
Brotherton Library, Leeds University: see Hudson.

[274] **JOHN SUTCLIFFE**, worsted mfr, Holdsworth, Yorks

Memoranda book 1768-77, day book 1791-3, money order 1791, family papers 1751-1863.
West Yorkshire Archive Service, Calderdale (HAS 418-51). NRA 6546.

[275] **JOHN SUTCLIFFE & SONS LTD**, mungo and shoddy mfrs, noil and waste merchants, Huddersfield, Yorks

Certificate of incorporation 1900, balance sheet 1901, nominal ledgers (2) 1900-20, cash books (2) 1904-66, bank books (13) 1887-1930, purchase day book 1919-31, lot books *c*1949-76, wages books (4) 1914-68, deeds and other premises records 1855-1907; Joseph Beaumont & Sons bank book 1867-74.
West Yorkshire Archive Service, Kirklees (B/JS). NRA 31951.

[276] **JAMES SUTTON**, clothier, Salisbury, Wilts

Account books (3) 1788-1837, day book 1809-36, cash books (2) 1795-1843.
Wiltshire RO (WRO 1900/238, 1902/81-5).

[277] **GODFREY SYKES & SONS**, plush, astrakhan and pile fabric mfrs, Kirkheaton, Yorks

Taking-in books (18) 1888, 1901-62, pattern books (13) 1922-38, design book *c*1900, make book 1895, piece and make book 1908-16, day book 1935, shed foremen's books (9) 1900-38, weaving scales 1883, *c*1930, copies of letters (1 vol) to New York agent from 1890.
Tolson Memorial Museum, Huddersfield (GS). NRA 13680.

Birkhouse Mill wages book 1916-18.
West Yorkshire Archive Service, Kirklees (KC 10). NRA 26729.

[278] **JAMES SYKES & SON LTD**, worsted mfrs, Milnsbridge, Yorks

Delivery books (9) 1900-29, lot books (8) 1929-71, raw materials stock books (2) 1932-71.
West Yorkshire Archive Service, Kirklees (B/S). NRA 31071.

[279] **JOSEPH SYKES & CO**, worsted mfrs, Brockholes, Yorks

Pattern books (9) 1895-1935.
West Yorkshire Archive Service, Leeds.

List of menders, burlers, etc at Rock Mills 1904-60.
Tolson Memorial Museum, Huddersfield. NRA 13680.

Records *c*1930-50.
West Yorkshire Archive Service, Kirklees.

[280] **G & H TALBOT & SONS**, carpet mfrs, Kidderminster, Worcs

Stock books (4) 1822-47, private accounts 1821-47.
Charles Talbot Esq. LD Smith, 'The carpet weavers of Kidderminster 1800-1850' (University of Birmingham PhD thesis, 1982).

Misc corresp, deeds and indentures.
G Talbot-Griffiths Esq. LD Smith, ibid.

[281] **JAMES TANKARD LTD**, worsted yarn spinners, Bradford, Yorks

Memorandum and articles of association 1895, 1924-5, directors' minutes (1 vol) 1950-60, registers of directors and members and share records 1895-1951, letter book 1891-9, corresp files (44) 1924-48, letters incl financial memoranda 1904-48, annual accounts, etc (1 vol, etc) 1874-1904, 1943-50, private ledger 1888-1921, ledgers (16) 1869-1945, cash books (18) 1872-1974, bill books (2) 1882-93, 1915-39, bank books (9) 1896-1922, receipt books (2) 1906-7, 1916-24, orders and contracts (56 vols, 55 files) 1921-60, stocktaking accounts (181 vols, etc) 1909-57, production book 1917-19, wages books (2) 1954-72 and other employment records 1894-1950, inventories, valuations and insurance papers 1858-68, 1886-1972.
West Yorkshire Archive Service, Wakefield Headquarters (C357). NRA 24885.

Bill book 1893-1983, misc financial and employment records *c*1954-1980s.
West Yorkshire Archive Service, Bradford (25D89).

[282] **CHARLES TAYLOR**, woollen mfr and clothier, Almondbury, Yorks

Letters and orders received c1830-60, pattern books (2) 19th cent, list of yarn issued to outworkers nd.
Tolson Memorial Museum, Huddersfield. NRA 13680.

[283] **JE TAYLOR BROS** (formerly **NOWELL BROS**), woollen mfrs, Almondbury, Yorks

Account book 1814-1900, spinners' book 1854-1904.
West Yorkshire Archive Service, Kirklees (KC 164). NRA 31072.

Samples c1840, pattern, sample and sales book 1866 incl details of building work, etc 1880-2.
Tolson Memorial Museum, Huddersfield. NRA 13680.

[284] **J, T & J TAYLOR**, woollen mfrs, Batley, Yorks

Partnership papers, articles of incorporation, etc 1842-1958, minutes (3 vols) 1897-1953, registers of members and share ledgers (8 vols) c1904-1948, profit sharing trust reports, accounts, etc (45 vols, etc) 1899-1967, balance sheets (22 bundles) 1902-67, letter books (3) 1898-1918, corresp (12 bundles, etc) 1862-87, 1908-54, general account book 1834-51, ledgers (27) 1834-1968, day books (35) 1848-1969, cash books (41) 1836-1968, bill books (5) 1873-88, bank books (2) 1852-62, other accounting records (39 bundles, etc) 1895-1957, purchase ledgers and day books (35) 1902-68, sales day books, notes and invoices (16 vols, 17 bundles) 1863-1966, order books (10) 1860-4, despatch books (12) 1835-45, shipping books (2) c1936-1964, agents' notebooks, etc 19th cent-1909 incl Europe and Philadelphia, stock books (41) 1849-1965, blend books (85) 1843-1962, production, manufacturing and making books (55) 1866-1945, spinners' day book 1827-31, weavers' books (19) 1852-88, finishing book 1839-58, various production and costing books (30) 1839-1965, wages books, etc (172) 1838-1968 and other employment records (13 vols) 1912-66, plans of mills (6) 19th cent, 1950-61, valuations, etc 20th cent, property receipts 1851-73 and rents 1921-38.
West Yorkshire Archive Service, Wakefield Headquarters (C149). NRA 24385.

Bank corresp and statements 1873.
West Yorkshire Archive Service, Kirklees: see *West Yorkshire Archive Service Report 1987-8*, p53.

[285] **TAYLOR & LITTLEWOOD LTD**, woollen mfrs, Huddersfield, Yorks

Account books (7) 1873-1926, ledgers (10) 1876-88, 1895-1965, private ledgers (6) 1895-1959, day books (3) 1890, 1944-77, cash books (10) 1903-73 and other accounting records (5 vols) 1914-75, purchase and sales books (14) 1930-78, order and pattern books (101) 1917-c1980, stock books 1962-81, make book 1914-15, departmental books (2) 1944-72, wages books (31) 1873-1956, rent roll 1914-65, new building account book late 19th cent.
West Yorkshire Archive Service, Kirklees (KC 51). NRA 27963.

[286] **JOHN TAYLORS LTD**, woollen mfrs, Huddersfield, Yorks

General account book 1888-1923, bill book 1846-62, purchase and sales ledgers 1843-1908, costing books 1870-c1891, production notebook incl patterns 1896.
West Yorkshire Archive Service, Kirklees (B/JT): see Hudson.

[287] **TAYSIDE FLOORCLOTH CO LTD**, floorcloth and carpet mfrs, Newburgh, Fife

Minute book 1891-1917, pattern and design books (4) 1893-c1935, time book 1927-32.
In private possession. Enquiries to NRA (Scotland) NRA(S) 1266). NRA 19896.

[288] **JAMES TEMPLETON & CO**, worsted spinners, Stirling

Analysis book 1936-61, wages and production figures, historical notes, etc (1 file) 1908-25, plans (8) 1898-1952, charts of East India yarn prices 1926-40.
Central Regional Archives Department (PD5). NRA 24511.

[289] **JAMES TEMPLETON & CO LTD**, carpet mfrs, Glasgow

Copartnery papers 1907-10, notes for partners (2 files) 1930-41, private letter book 1909-29, memoranda books (2) 1879-1907, 1932-6, journals (2) incl stock records, etc 1876-1913, private ledgers (5) 1888-1932, income tax ledger 1909-30, loans ledger 1922-9, sales analysis book 1910-16, production and export book 1892-1910, price list 1913, design number book 1931-68, photograph albums (71) of carpet and rug designs, wages books (8) 1887-1935, employment statistics, etc 1902-58, minute books, accounts and notes (7 vols) rel to Templeton trusts c1874-1970, plans (79) 19th-20th cent, inventories and valuations 1925, publicity catalogues, photographs and notes, JS Templeton's ledgers (4) 1884-1934 and cash book 1885-1918, Templeton family genealogical notes.
Stoddard Holdings plc. Enquiries to NRA (Scotland) NRA(S) 2189). NRA 10834.

Sales analysis book, London and Glasgow 1879-1910.
Glasgow University Archives (UGD/90). NRA 10834.

[290] **TEXTILE MANUFACTURING CO LTD**, curtain, carpet and rug mfrs, Stourport, Worcs

Annual lists and summaries 1894-1926, share register nd, private ledgers (3) from 1892, journal 1895-1903, day book from 1917, purchase ledger nd, sales journal from 1924, stock sheets 1911-16.
Kidderminster Library. NRA 28020.

[291] **THOMAS family**, clothiers, Nailsworth, Glos

Business and family accounts and papers (17 bundles) 1787-1840.
Gloucestershire RO (D1406).

[292] **WILLIAM THOMSON & SONS LTD**, woollen mfrs, Huddersfield, Yorks

Deed of dissolution of partnership 1875, agreement 1887, balance sheets 1879-85, annual returns 1918-20, statement of accounts 1887-90, 1894, share certificates, bills and misc financial records 1875-1961, list of weavers and pay 1899, 1909, c1915-19, plans, drawings and related papers 1881-1961, Thomson family financial and executorship papers 1856-1909.
In private possession.

George Thomson papers and corresp c1870s-1921 rel to profit-sharing and copartnership.
West Yorkshire Archive Service, Kirklees (GT/C). NRA 27952.

[293] **JAMES TOLSON & SONS**, woollen mfrs and merchants, Huddersfield, Yorks

Pattern book and list of goods sent to the Great Exhibition 1851.
Tolson Memorial Museum, Huddersfield. NRA 13680.

[294] **TOMKINSONS CARPETS LTD**, carpet mfrs, Kidderminster, Worcs

Partnership agreements, memorandum and articles of association, etc 1885-1951, minutes (3 vols) and register of directors from 1928, corresp files 19th-20th cent, ledgers, account books, invoices, etc 1922-70, cash book 1912-23, bill book 1879-80, trade ledger c1884-9, summary of trading (1 vol) 1902-20, goods issued (1 vol) 1938-45, stock book 1929-61, price lists and catalogues 19th-20th cent, costings and production schedules (1 vol, 3 rolls, etc) 1926-50, design record books (30) 19th-20th cent, designs (several thousand) incl Edouard Glorget, Marianne Pepler and CFA Voysey, drawings, patents and design and trade mark registration certificates 1877-c1940, wages accounts (2 vols) 1872-5 and other employment records 1914-18, 1928-31, workmen's sick and benefit society minutes, etc (3 vols) 1894-1906, 1924-65, property records (1 vol, etc) 1934-c1950, plans of works 1903, 1942, photographs, history of company, notes, press cuttings and other printed material.
The Company. Not normally available for research. Enquiries to the Managing Director. NRA 30872.

[295] **ELI TOWNEND**, mungo mfrs, Ossett, Yorks

Nominal ledger 1915-27, cash books (5) 1900-32, purchase ledgers (4) 1900-32 and day books (5) 1903-34, sales ledgers (4) 1905-33 and day books (4) 1905-38, order book 1914-18, wages books (7) 1901-32.
West Yorkshire Archive Service, Leeds. NRA 31654.

[296] **AH TUCKER LTD**, woollen mfrs, Frome, Somerset

Dye pattern books (3) 1750-c1850.
Bath Reference Library. NRA 25737.

[297] **ULSTER WOOLLEN CO LTD**, woollen mfrs, Crumlin, co Antrim

Letter books (6) 1887-1909, corresp (97 boxes) 1909-61, private ledger 1907-17, ledgers (3) 1927-c1956, cash account books (8) 1886-1928, general cash book 1894-1907, letter press account books (5)

1931-48, journals (10) 1887-1932, day book sheets 1910-19, petty cash books (5) 1892-8, 1910-13, 1918-26, 1944-66, order books (77) 1894-1900, 1908-17, 1932-64, invoices and invoice books (33 boxes and vols) 1887-1964, sales day books, ledgers and cash books (30) 1887-1933, bought ledger 1888-1907, purchase ledger 1907-16 and sheets 1928-40, notebooks (2) rel to wool purchase 1926-31, commission account books (34) 1922-65, supply, despatch and consignment records (c30 boxes, vols, etc) 1908-65, status reports (1 vol) on various firms 1900-52, range books (4) c1920, Utility Control Board returns 1941-9, wages books (18) 1886-1924, 1930-7, 1949-65, weavers' ticket books (2) 1904-5, 1908-9, time books (28) 1924-61, insurance records (1 parcel, 1 vol) 1912-24, ration coupon records (3 vols) 1941-9, mill, farm and rental accounts (2 vols) 1926-48.
Public Record Office of Northern Ireland (D 1941, D 2423). NRA 31478.

[298] **JOHN WALKER**, worsted mfr, Norwood Green, Yorks

Account books 1892-1911, pattern, sample and order books c1830-c1950, patent records 1895-1909, memoranda and technical notebooks c1880-c1940.
West Yorkshire Archive Service, Calderdale (WAL): see Hudson.

[298A] **JOHN & EDWARD WALLINGTON**, clothiers, Dursley, Glos

Corresp rel to Spanish wool, etc (93 items) 1789, 1791, 1801-2, 1808.
Gloucestershire RO (D149/F188-90). NRA 10491.

[299] **ROBERT WALTON & CO**, worsted and woollen yarn mfrs, Alston, Cumberland

Monthly account book 1841-53, wages book 1853-9.
Cumbria RO, Carlisle (DX/688). NRA 21925.

[300] **WANSEY & CO**, clothiers and dyers, Warminster, Wilts

Account books (3) 1683-1714 incl samples, personal account book of William Wansey 1746-1805, stock inventories (1 vol) 1755-61, draft letters of George Wansey (2 vols) 1772-94 mainly rel to wool trade and letters to him (1 vol) 1772-84, misc papers and corresp 17th-19th cent.
Wiltshire RO (WRO 314:1). NRA 5630.

[301] **JAMES WATKINSON & SONS LTD**, woollen mfrs, Holmfirth, Yorks

Records 1881-1980 incl accounts 1902-71, summaries of sales 1888-1980, group prices 1921-56, contracts and tenders 1927-59, pattern books 1930-78, and peg plan books 1881-1933.
West Yorkshire Archive Service, Kirklees.

[302] **WILLIAM WATSON & SONS**, tweed and woollen mfrs, Hawick, Roxburghshire

Records 1847-1950 incl account books 1888-1915, ledger 1920-40, inventory 1923, and schedule of machinery 1950.
Edinburgh University Library (Gen 921-1209). NRA 29821.

[303] **CHRISTOPHER WAUD & CO LTD**, mohair and alpaca worsted spinners, Bradford, Yorks

Debtors' and creditors' ledgers and invoices 1885-1919.
Brotherton Library, Leeds University: see Hudson.

[304] **ROBERT WAYLEN**, clothier, Devizes, Wilts

Pattern book c1814.
Wiltshire RO (WRO 1553/55). NRA 1335.

[305] **WELSH FLANNEL MANUFACTURING CO LTD** (afterwards **HOLYWELL TEXTILE MILLS LTD**), woollen cloth mfrs, Holywell, Flints

Records 1877-1980 incl board and committee minutes, share papers, annual reports, balance sheets and accounts, trade mark papers, valuation, inventory, deeds, and corresp.
The Company. NRA 28631; BAC *Company Archives* no 195.

[306] **RR WHITEHEAD & BROS LTD**, felt mfrs, Greenfield, Yorks

Records 1728-1980 incl minutes, registers, share records, takeover papers, annual reports and accounts, out-letter books, general files, ledgers, bank books, order book, stock book, costing papers, machine book, patents, trade marks, salaries and wages books, deeds, inventories, valuations, plans, photographs, JD Whitehead's diary, and notes on company history.
Greater Manchester RO. NRA 28631; BAC *Company Archives* no 114.

Directors' and general meeting minutes from 1870, register of directors and secretaries from 1932, share certificates from 1902.
Bury Cooper Whitehead Ltd. NRA 28631; BAC *Company Archives* no 114.

Reports of meetings 1914-32, annual reports and accounts 1914-32, bills and vouchers c1840-60.
Saddleworth Museum. NRA 11134.

[307] **WHITWELL & CO LTD**, carpet and rug mfrs, Kendal, Westmorland

Memorandum and articles of association 1908, directors' minute book 1892-1918, register of members and share ledger 1893-6, letter book 1912-17, misc administrative corresp and papers (5 folders) 1879-1918, ledgers (5) 1861-1918, day books (2) 1910-18, bank books (3) 1893-1918, salaries ledger and bank account 1872-1911, pattern book for L'Allègre, Paris 1911-12, valuation and account book 1861-92, mill valuations 1880-1903, inventory of plant 1893-1903.
Cumbria RO, Kendal (WD/AG, boxes 8-10A). NRA 30979.

[308] **WHITWORTH & CO LTD**, worsted mfrs, Ovenden, Yorks

Records 1799-1920 incl accounts, sales, plans, bankruptcy and probate documents, deeds, and agreements.
West Yorkshire Archive Service, Calderdale (FW 93). NRA 21715.

[309] **HENRY WIDNELL & STEWART LTD**, carpet mfrs, Eskbank, Midlothian

Copartnery records 1871-95, minutes 1895-1966, shareholding records 1895-1960, price lists 1883-1940, production and costing records c1873-1959, patterns nd, wages and salaries books 1856-1962, misc accounts, corresp and papers from 1828, plant inventories, valuations, etc 1861-1969, leases, rents and details of properties 1867-1954, history of firm from 1830, photographs 20th cent.
Scottish Record Office (GD 405). NRA 10794.

[310] **WILLIAM WILLANS**, wool merchant, Huddersfield, Yorks

Cash books, ledger, invoices, corresp, etc 1825-36.
Brotherton Library, Leeds University: see Hudson.

[311] **ISAAC WILLIAMS & SON**, woollen mfrs, Llanwrtyd, Brecon

Account books and receipts (4 vols) 1891-1933.
Welsh Folk Museum, Cardiff (MS 2524). NRA 31986.

[312] **BENJAMIN WILSON**, clothier, Blyth [?Notts]

Business letters (49) mainly from Jonathan Dickinson of Sheffield 1760-3, accounts (10 items) 1755-61.
London University Library (MS 698). *Catalogue of additional manuscripts (MS 555-MS 884)*.

[313] **C WILSON & SON**, woolstaplers, Kettering, Northants

Accounts and corresp (2 vols, c60 items) 1786-1829.
Northamptonshire RO (ZB310). NRA 4039.

[314] **ISAAC WILSON & SON**, woollen mfrs, Kendal, Westmorland

Letter book 1774-6.
Cumbria RO, Kendal. NRA 4843.

[315] **JAMES WILSON & SON LTD**, worsted spinners, Lothersdale, Yorks

Draft agreement for building mill, partnership deeds and related corresp 1792-1897, sales ledgers (6) 1808-1943, wages book 1919-61.
In private possession. NRA 13472.

[316] **JOHN WILSON (GILDERSOME) LTD**, woollen and clothing mfrs, Gildersome and Morley, Yorks

Ledger 1856-77, day book 1870-3, copies of letters and commission accounts (1 vol) 1883-1913.
West Yorkshire Archive Service, Leeds. NRA 31032.

[317] **JOHN K WILSON & CO LTD**, woollen mfrs, Belfast

Memorandum and articles of association 1898, papers (1 bundle), rel to flotation of company 1898, balance sheets, trading accounts, profit and loss accounts, etc (2 boxes) 1862-89, 1893-1905, 1912, list of

shareholders and dividends 1902, private ledger
1862-5, private ledger and day book 1866-75 incl
ledger balances 1862-94, statement book 1896-c1903.
Public Record Office of Northern Ireland (D 1933/
12-13). NRA 31476.

[318] **WILLIAM WILSON & SON**, tartan mfrs,
Bannockburn, Stirlingshire

Incoming letters, orders and receipts, with some draft
replies (350 vols, etc) 1778-1873, letter book 1778-83,
1791, ledger 1770-87, day book 1771-80, misc accounts
1783-1878, order book 1772-5, notes of sales (1 vol)
1783-4, commercial travellers' accounts (1 vol)
1812-22, agreements with workers 1809-22, legal
papers 1782-1879, history of company 20th cent.
National Library of Scotland (MSS 1863, 5319,
6660-7000, 9662-77, 9803).

Corresp with the Army and other customers, tartan
samples late 18th-early 19th cent.
Royal Museum of Scotland, Queen Street, Edinburgh.

Letters to and from the company 1783-1867, shipping
documents 1797-1900, pattern book compiled by
William Wilson 1819.
Scottish Tartans Museum, Comrie.

Corresp and accounts (5 boxes) rel to uniforms
supplied to Scottish regiments 1793-1873.
Scottish United Services Museum, Edinburgh. NRA
30070.

[319] **WILSONS (DUNBLANE) LTD**, worsted
spinners, Dunblane, Perthshire

Ledgers (9) 1853-1956, day books (10) 1853-1960,
balance sheets 1854-75, copy specifications and corresp
rel to building operations at Springbank Mill 1863-7.
Central Regional Archives Department (PD59). NRA
21894. Further records are believed to have been
destroyed c1983.

[320] **WILTON ROYAL CARPET FACTORY
LTD**, Wilton, Wilts

Memorandum and articles of association 1889, 1905,
minute books (4) 1905-77, papers (2 files) rel to merger
with Solent Carpet Co 1944-5, capital and trading
accounts 1905-22, misc corresp, accounts, etc (1 file
and loose items) c1900-1946, ledgers, cash books and
account books (7) c1920-1971, order books (5) 1902-12,
1922-40, estimate book c1908-35, misc sales records
(several files) 1955-74, price lists and catalogues
1902-37, stocktaking book 1946-64, costing books (3)
1927-46, descriptions and sketches of designs (1 vol)
c1892, Axminster patterns and sketches sent to
London (2 vols) 1912-40, Jacquard pattern record
book c1925, designs (over 120 items) mainly 1930s,
wages books 20th cent, factory administration book
1922-3, list of plant and machinery c1902-54, deeds
(42) rel to factory premises 1818-98; Wilton Weavers
Guild minutes 1947-71 and misc papers 1865-1908,
nd.
The Company. Enquiries to the Curator, Wilton Royal
Carpet Factory Museum. NRA 31063.

[321] **THOMAS WOOD**, scribbling and fulling
miller, Alverthorpe, Yorks

Papers rel to wool dealings c1825, deeds and
inventories 1787-1893.
Wakefield Libraries Department of Local Studies
(Goodchild Loan MSS). Formerly in the South
Yorkshire Industrial Museum, Cusworth Hall. See
Hudson.

[322] **WOODWARD, GROSVENOR & CO LTD**,
carpet mfrs, Kidderminster, Worcs

Directors' minutes (2 vols) from 1935, annual returns
c1918-47, stockholders' interest (1 vol) 1928-49,
private ledgers (5) 1899-1951, nominal ledger 1905-13,
private journal 1890-1942, designs, point papers, etc
(over 300 parcels) from c1790, Brussels and Axminster
colour books and pattern enumerators (18 vols)
19th-20th cent, stamping duplicate book 1963-7, New
Zealand designs (1 vol) c1967, patents and related
papers (83 items) 1879-1946, valuations of mills and
machinery (7 vols) 1925, 1937, 1963, corresp rel to
electrification (1 file) 1912-13, photographs (1 file, 2
packets) 20th cent, Carpet Manufacturers Association
minutes, etc 1936-41, typescript notes and misc
papers.
The Company. Not normally available for research.
Enquiries to the Company Secretary. NRA 31034.

[323] **WOOLCOMBERS LTD**, Bradford, Yorks

Corresp with subsidiary companies (13 files) 1905-23.
West Yorkshire Archive Service, Wakefield Headquarters
(C234).

[324] **WORMALDS & WALKER LTD** (formerly
HAGUE & COOK), blanket mfrs, Dewsbury, Yorks

Letter books 1823-64, ledgers 1810-70, purchase and
sales ledgers 1880-1900, order books 1862-1913, cost
books 1876-87.
Brotherton Library, Leeds University: see Hudson.

[325] **YOUNG & ANDERSON LTD**, wholesale
woollen merchants and warehousemen, Belfast

Annual reports and accounts 1931-61, prospectus
1907, balance sheets (45 items) 1811-1920, abstract of
accounts 1888-1913, sales day books and journals (4)
1886-7, 1913-51, hosiery and fancy department stock
book 1885, lists of drapery businesses c1895, draft
article and related corresp about firm's history 1890-1.
Public Record Office of Northern Ireland (D 3641).
NRA 31468.

COTTON

[326] **ACME SPINNING CO LTD**, cotton spinners,
Pendlebury, Lancs

Minute book 1904-20.
Salford Archives Centre (U 280/AM 1).

[327] **THOMAS AITKEN & SON LTD**, cotton
goods mfrs, Edenfield, Lancs

Quotation books (2) 1899-1906.
Rossendale Museum, Rawtenstall. NRA 30829.

[328] **RF & J ALEXANDER & CO LTD**, cotton thread mfrs, Manchester and Neilston, Renfrewshire

Ledger 1892-1900, capital and depreciation ledger 1893-1947, private ledger nd.
Tootal Group plc. NRA 28631; BAC *Company Archives* no 592.

[329] **AMERICAN THREAD CO LTD**, thread mfrs, London

Private ledger 1907-30, private journal 1915-30.
Tootal Group plc. NRA 28631; BAC *Company Archives* no 592.

[330] **DAVID & JOHN ANDERSON LTD**, pullicate and gingham mfrs, Glasgow

Memorandum and articles of association 1911, directors' attendance book 1911-40, letter book 1897-1915, balance sheets 1880-1907, income tax books (2) 1862-1908, private ledgers (2) 1892-1909, cash and costs book 1872-7, weekly orders (2 vols) 1908-45, sales records 1923–43, wages books (3) 1914-24, inventory, etc of Atlantic Mill 1910.
Glasgow University Archives (UGD/22). NRA 10854.

Journal 1826-9, cash books (5) 1827-47, sales book 1833-41, cash sales book 1846-51.
Strathclyde Regional Archives (TD 187). NRA 10854.

[331] **SIR RICHARD ARKWRIGHT & CO LTD**, cotton mfrs, Cromford and Matlock Bath, Derbys and Manchester

Wages books, flesh books, apprenticeship agreements, truck tickets, etc (*c*700 items) of Sir Richard Arkwright, his son Richard and Samuel Oldknow 1782-1815.
Rare Book & Manuscript Library, Columbia University, New York (ERA Seligman Collection).

Wages books (4) 1786-8, 1793-6, 1804-11.
Chesterfield Public Library (Accs 805-6, 1735-6).

Private ledger 1929-49.
Tootal Group plc. NRA 28631; BAC *Company Archives* no 592.

Misc deeds and papers of Sir Richard Arkwright and his son Richard *c*1782-1825, incl Sir Richard's plan of improvement in cotton spinning.
British Library (Add MSS 6668-97 *passim*).

[332] **ARMITAGE & RIGBY LTD**, cotton mfrs, Warrington, Lancs

General meeting minute book 1888-1939, board minute book 1919-41, costings book 1898-1962.
The Company. Enquiries to the Company Secretary.

Cockhedge Mills inventories 1891, 1896.
Warrington Library (MSS 2277-8).

[333] **THOMAS ASHTON & SONS**, cloth merchants, Manchester

Letter book 1850-1.
John Rylands University Library of Manchester (Eng MS 870). *Supplementary hand-list of Western manuscripts . . . 1937*, p22.

[334] **H & E ASHWORTH** (afterwards **HENRY ASHWORTH & SONS**, New Eagley, and **EDMUND ASHWORTH & SONS LTD**, Egerton), cotton spinners, New Eagley and Egerton, Lancs

Corresp 1831-75 incl Atkinson, Tootal & Co, reviews of management of H & E Ashworth and Atkinson, Tootal & Co, order book 1846-50, stock book 1847-8, stock account 1877, samples of cotton (1 envelope) nd, registers of young employees at New Eagley Mill (4 vols) 1886-1904, valuations (2 vols) 1834, 1836 and plans (2) 1889, nd of New Eagley Mill, misc accounts 1817-80 incl contracts for steam engine, building specifications and valuation of New Eagley Mill, papers rel to water power 1822-70 incl letters and plans from William Fairbairn, papers rel to New Eagley village and school 1839-41, nd, Ashworth family papers and corresp *c*1800-94 incl Henry Ashworth's personal and business accounts and his notes on cotton production and manufacture, etc.
Lancashire RO (DDAs). NRA 30812.

Registers of children and young persons at New Eagley Mill (2 vols) 1879-87, valuations (2) of New Eagley Mill and related corresp 1863-6, Henry Ashworth's personal accounts 1823-74 and letters to him (17 items) 1856-67 mainly from correspondents in the United States, diary of George Binns Ashworth 1849.
Bolton Metropolitan Borough Archives (ZWL 50, 69, ZZ/31). NRA 27224.

Business and personal diaries of Henry Ashworth 1849-53, Ashworth family papers and corresp 1841-1975.
Staffordshire RO (D 3016). NRA 21616.

Letters to Henry Ashworth (*c*50 items) *c*1841-65 rel to cotton manufacture, etc, with samples of cotton (24 items).
Blackburn Museum & Art Gallery.

Notebooks of Henry Ashworth, diaries of George Binns Ashworth 1845-8, family corresp, etc.
Sir Rhodes Boyson, MP.

Stock book 1831-79 and stock accounts 1832-52.
John Rylands University Library of Manchester (Eng MS 1201).

[335] **JOSHUA BARBER & CO LTD**, cotton and cotton waste merchants, Bolton, Lancs

Articles of association 1886, balance sheets 1898-1933, 1954-70, private ledgers 1917, 1933, salaries and wages books 1908-55.
Lancashire RO (DDBx). NRA 30355.

[336] **BARLOW & JONES LTD**, cotton spinners, Manchester and Bolton, Lancs

Account books (2) 1900-11.
Manchester Central Library (MISC 611/1-2).

Directors' minutes (1 vol, etc) 1926-63.
Manchester Central Library (M127).

[337] **BARNARD & HUGHES**, cotton merchants, Manchester

Out-letter book 1802-6.
Baker Library, Harvard University, Cambridge, Massachusetts: see *Manuscripts in the Baker Library*, 1978, p285.

[338] **JOHN BARNES & SONS**, cotton mfrs, Accrington, Lancs

Memorandum and articles of association 1907, company registration papers (1 vol) 1908-20, summaries of share capital and shares 1912-22, financial records (3 files, etc) 1912–25 incl trading accounts and profit and loss accounts.
Lancashire RO (DDX 1307). NRA 3510.

[339] **BARRON & CO OF BELFAST LTD**, cotton and jute bag mfrs, Belfast

Records (15 vols and items) comprising cash books 1899-1911, sales book 1897-1904, purchase book 1920-9, costing books 1896-1910, salaries books 1898-1936, and corresp 1908-9.
Public Record Office of Northern Ireland (D 3582).

[340] **WILLIAM BASHALL & CO**, cotton spinners, Farington, Lancs

Ledger 1834-87, private ledger 1900-3, receipt and payment book incl Farington Sunday School fund and mill wages 1897-1908, sales book 1887-1903, yarn production book 1893-1903 with sales ledger 1911-18, cotton mix book 1898-1900.
Lancashire RO (DDX 819). NRA 16485.

[341] **BAXTER, STEEDMAN, & COATS**, thread mfrs, Liverpool

Ledgers (5) 1869-75, day book 1872-5, balances book 1888-9.
Coats Patons plc. Enquiries to NRA (Scotland) (NRA(S) 2461). NRA 20914.

[342] **BIRLEY & CO**, cotton spinners and mfrs, Manchester

Letter book 1841-6, annual statements (1 vol) 1837-57, account adjustments (1 vol) 1832-89, ledger of Henry Birley 1842-77, book of costs 1849-70, inventory of stock (1 vol) 1810-20, inventory and valuation of land, premises, stock and machinery (1 vol) 1821-44.
University of Florida Libraries, Gainsville (Accounting Collection Group 8). NRA 31376.

[343] **BIRTWISTLE & FIELDING LTD**, cotton spinners and mfrs, Blackburn, Lancs

Papers (25) rel to building and equipping Grange Mill 1905-6, design book of JA Birtwistle 1907, list of weavers' wages 1937.
Lancashire RO (DDX 1198). NRA 21922.

[344] **WILLIAM BIRTWISTLE**, cotton spinners and mfrs, Blackburn, Lancs

Annual returns 1933-52, quarterly accounts 1907, private ledger 1901-47, nominal ledgers (2) 1901-57, cash books (2) 1949-63, expenditure analysis books (2) 1953-62, purchase, order and sales books (5) 1929-71, stock book 1928-51, wages book 1964, insurance ledgers and schedules, etc (2 vols, 2 files) 1919-48, machinery catalogues and contracts 1936-c1960.
Lancashire RO (DDX 868). NRA 18080.

[345] **BLACK LANE MILLS CO LTD**, cotton spinners, Radcliffe, Lancs

Minutes 1907-39, balance sheets 1909-41, 1946-70, private ledgers 1907-53.
Lancashire RO (DDBx). NRA 30355.

[346] **WALTER BLACKMORE & CO**, bolting-cloth mfrs, London

Memoranda book 1783-5 with additions to 1831, misc letters and bills early 19th cent, plan of works 1869.
London University Library (MS 462). *Catalogue of additional manuscripts (MS 244-MS 554).*

[347] **THOMAS BOLD**, cotton goods mfr, Swinton, Lancs

Pattern books (3) of coloured wovens and order sheets (2) with point paper designs late 19th-early 20th cent.
Salford Museums & Art Galleries (H100-1986/1-3). NRA 30500.

[348] **JOHN BOWMER & SONS**, tape mfrs, Wirksworth, Derbys

Memorandum and articles of association 1957, letter books (18) 1934-51, day books (16) 1896-1965, cash book 1933-55, order books (3) 1908-59 incl price lists, invoice book 1942-4, costs ledger 1911-17, sales ledgers (2) 1914-45, wages book 1950-8, plans 1957, misc corresp and papers incl the Midland Tape Manufacturers Association copy minutes and circulars 1942-58.
Derbyshire RO (396/B). NRA 11080.

Ledgers (3) 1910-46, ledger summary 1928-53, plan of Gorsey Bank Mill c1880.
Bowmer-Bond Narrow Fabrics Ltd. NRA 11080.

[349] **JOHN BRIGHT & BROS LTD**, cotton spinners and mfrs, Rochdale, Lancs

Half-yearly and yearly reports and statements of account 1920-64, trust deeds 1923, share transfers 1922-50 and certificate book, ledger 1888-1905, index register.
Rochdale Local Studies Department (C/IND/COT/BRI/1). NRA 31024.

[350] **MARY BROADBENT & SON**, cotton spinners, Oldham, Lancs

Partnership agreement 1857, private account book 1854-82, private ledger 1857-67, bank book 1868-81, receipts 1865-73, stock book 1856-65, deeds of Hopwood and Wellington Mills 1823-72, valuation (1 vol) 1867.
Manchester Central Library (M177/18).

[351] **JONAS BROOK & BROS LTD**, thread mfrs, Huddersfield, Yorks

Memorandum and articles of association 1896, minutes (5 vols) 1896-1962, register of directors, members and shares (5 vols) 1896-1964, annual lists and summaries 1937-44, letter book 1837-40, corresp with architect

1841 and misc corresp 1860-90, pensions list 1897, historical notes and extracts.
Coats Patons plc. Enquiries to NRA (Scotland) (NRA(S) 3088). NRA 20914.

Private ledger 1896-8, cash books (8) 1862-78, capital renewals and revenue expenditure 1920-34, order book 1885-90, contract ledgers (2) 1856-95.
Glasgow University Archives (UGD/199). NRA 20914.

[352] **BRYCE, SMITH & CO**, cotton goods merchants, Manchester

Account books (5) 1844-99, pattern books incl estimates of costs and specifications (10 vols) 1801-94, nd, laboratory trials 1884, bill of quantities for erection of warehouse 1873.
Lancashire RO (DDX 2/32-55 *passim*). NRA 3510.

[353] **BURY BROS LTD**, cotton mfrs, Accrington, Lancs

Private ledger 1866-1923, stock book 1901-23.
Lancashire RO (DDX 812). NRA 16481.

[354] **CANNON BROS LTD**, cotton spinners, Bolton, Lancs

Minute book 1920-38, papers rel to winding-up 1937-9, general register 1899-1938, private ledgers (3) 1899-1938, accounts 1929-37, extension papers, contracts and machinery schedules 1917-24.
Lancashire RO (DDBx). NRA 30355.

[355] **PAUL CATTERALL SON & CO (1920) LTD**, cotton spinners and mfrs, Preston, Lancs

Minute books (7) *c*1913-1972, registers (2) of directors, managers and members, misc share records (3 vols, etc), profit and loss accounts 1850-1912, annual reports and balance sheets from 1885, annual summary 1896-1915, annual returns 1944-8, letter book *c*1920, bank books (2) 1911-19, interest book 1865-1910, stock book 1890-1914, wages books (3) 1933-45, mill inventory 1912, insurance register 1958-61 and inventory nd.
Courtaulds Spinning. Enquiries to the Company Secretary. NRA 30126.

[356] **CENTRAL AGENCY LTD** (formerly **SEWING COTTON AGENCY**), thread mfrs' agents, Glasgow

Memorandum and articles of association nd, minutes (7 vols) 1889-1962, registers of directors, members and seals (13 vols) 1897-1962, corresp 1884-9, letter books (4) 1906-9, 1925-30, private letter book 1892-6, ledgers (14) 1871-1959, cash books (5) 1927-58, private journal 1937-54, price lists 1890-1904, 1941, misc records 1924-41.
Coats Patons plc. Enquiries to NRA (Scotland) (NRA(S) 3088). NRA 20914.

Ledgers (18) 1890-1949, journals (19) 1892-1937.
Glasgow University Archives (UGD/199). NRA 20914.

Central Agency (Australia) Ltd corresp 1892-1906, 1931-42, reports 1937-8, accounts 1921-42, samples 1933-9.
Melbourne University Archives: see *Guide to collections*, 1983, p104.

[357] **JAMES CHADWICK & BROTHER LTD**, cotton spinners and thread mfrs, Eagley, Lancs

Memorandum and articles of association, agreement and prospectus 1891, minutes (6 vols) 1891-1963, agenda book 1891-5, registers of directors and shareholders (2 vols) 1893-1964, share indexes and applications (10 vols) 1891-6, annual returns 1944-8, report and balance sheet 1892, private ledger 1898-*c*1938, private journal 1898-1945, inventories and valuations of Eagley Mills 1891, 1913, historical notes.
Coats Patons plc. Enquiries to NRA (Scotland) (NRA(S) 3088). NRA 20914.

Private ledger 1893-7, American capital ledger 1893-8.
Glasgow University Archives (UGD/199). NRA 20914.

Diary 1830, notes on applicants for jobs 1843-50.
Manchester Central Library (M97). NRA 24109.

[358] **WM CHRISTY & SONS LTD**, towel mfrs, Droylsden, Lancs

Balance sheets 1857, 1874-91, 1905-8, bank books (4) 1884-1914, ledger balances and misc accounts (1 box, etc) 1910-16, 1927-8, sales book 1857-1948, stock book 1833-54, foremen's pocket books (5) *c*1860-99, production figures 1888-9, patents (29) 1851-92, registered fabric designs, patterns and trade marks (1 box, etc) mainly 19th cent, corresp 1853-1939 incl with London agents, papers rel to building and equipping Fairfield Mill 1838, legal and other records mainly rel to property 1839-1939, insurance records, rateable value 1849-59, inventory and valuation (2 vols) 1913, misc corresp and papers (1 box) 19th-20th cent.
John Rylands University Library of Manchester. NRA 25970.

[359] **CLARK & CO LTD**, thread mfrs, Paisley, Renfrewshire

Memorandum and articles of association 1880, 1896, minutes (4 vols) 1896-1963, register of directors, members and shares (5 vols) 1896-1964, letter books (4) 1880-1931, corresp 1869, private ledgers (2) 1880-1928, journal 1880-96, receipt books (2) 1896-1908, cheque books (2) 1900-1, registers of titles, sasines, etc (2 vols) 1897-1913, nd, historical notes and extracts.
Coats Patons plc. Enquiries to NRA (Scotland) (NRA(S) 2461). NRA 20914.

Ledger 1883-5, private journal 1897-1928.
Glasgow University Archives (UGD/199). NRA 20914.

[360] **GEORGE A CLARK & BROTHERS** (afterwards **CLARK THREAD CO**), thread mfrs, Paisley, Renfrewshire

Minutes (2 vols) 1897-1940 incl certificate of incorporation, inventory of records 1823-73.
Coats Patons plc. Enquiries to NRA (Scotland) (NRA(S) 3088). NRA 20914.

[361] **JOHN CLARK JUNIOR & CO**, cotton spinners and thread mfrs, Glasgow

Misc papers (1 box) 19th cent.
Strathclyde Regional Archives. NRA 15348.

Notes rel to Mile End Works 1891-1950.
Coats Patons plc. Enquiries to NRA (Scotland)
(NRA(S) 3088). NRA 20914.

[362] **J & J CLARK & CO**, thread mfrs, Paisley, Renfrewshire

Letter books (4) 1821-42, 1880-9, cash books (2)
1821-38, purchase ledger 1813-21, sales and wages
ledgers (2) 1813-39, historical notes 19th-20th cent
incl extracts from ledgers 1860-96, price lists 1864,
1868.
Coats Patons plc. Enquiries to NRA (Scotland)
(NRA(S) 3088). NRA 20914.

[363] **IP CLARKE & CO LTD**, thread mfrs' agents, Leicester

Memorandum and articles of association 1907, minutes
(3 vols) 1907-62, register of directors 1939-60, register
of members and share ledger 1907-46, annual returns
1907-48, private ledger 1907-32, ledger 1938-48,
journal 1938-48.
Coats Patons plc. Enquiries to NRA (Scotland)
(NRA(S) 3088). NRA 20914.

Private journal 1907-32.
Glasgow University Archives (UGD/199). NRA 20914.

[364] **E CLEGG & SON LTD**, cotton spinners and mfrs, Littleborough, Lancs

Certificate of incorporation 1947, minute books (2)
1883-1915, c1950-70, share transfer papers
(1 envelope) c1960-70, ledger 1866-78, private ledgers
(4) 1883-93, 1904-42, nominal ledgers (2) 1955-65,
purchase and sales returns, etc (1 vol, 7 files)
1955-c1970, stock book 1931-66, staff book c1960-70,
superannuation certificates (1 file) c1950-70, insurance
wages book c1950-60, particulars of property and
assets c1883.
Lancashire RO (DDVc). NRA 30810.

[365] **CLIFF SPINNING CO LTD**, cotton spinners, Preston, Lancs

Directors' minutes (2 vols) 1939-62, balance sheets
1924-41, accounts 1904-40.
Coats Viyella plc. Enquiries to the Company Secretary.
NRA 32376.

Private ledger and cash books 1933-53.
Lancashire RO (DDHs). NRA 19214.

[366] **J & P COATS LTD**, thread mfrs, Paisley, Renfrewshire

Memorandum and articles of association 1890,
directors' and committee minutes (121 vols)
1884-1979, register of members and share ledgers, etc
(327 vols) 1885-1965, letter books (7) 1881-1911,
corresp (11 boxes) 1848-1973, Nevsky corresp and

papers (16 vols, 19 bundles) 1889-1917, ledgers (8)
1838-43, 1873-96, private ledgers (11) 1871-84,
1890-1961, private journals (2) 1897-1915, private cash
book 1943-67, receipt book of James Coats 1808-24,
capital expenditure analysis 1898-1947, balances book
1890-1, purchase ledger 1887-90, invoice books and
misc expenses, etc c1800-1931, trade marks and
infringements (5 boxes, 52 vols, etc) 1891-1975,
patents (2 boxes, 11 parcels, 18 vols, etc) 1893-1981,
register of powers of attorney (15 vols) 1902-79, pay
book 1833-6. employment registers (56) 1843-1951,
pension fund registers, etc (13 vols) 1893-1972 and
other employment records 1887-1940, property
register 1949-71, dyehouse specifications 1900,
photographs of Conant Thread Co, USA and Ferguslie
Mill 1878-1950, misc records 1872-1954 incl
chairman's speeches, overseas operations and historical
notes and extracts.
Coats Patons plc. Enquiries to NRA (Scotland)
(NRA(S) 2461, 3088). NRA 20914.

Ledgers (32) 1830-57, 1870-1970, general journals (15)
1888-1970, private journals (7) 1848-1961, cash books
(64) 1857-1949, bank and cash letter books (7) 1913-32,
capital expenditure and investment ledgers, etc (16
vols) 1888-1944, bill books (3) 1888-1937, bought
ledgers (20) 1891-1935, salaries books (11) 1901-42,
valuations, etc 1890-1934, misc papers 1845-1939.
Glasgow University Archives (UGD/199). NRA 20914.

Tender applications 1932-65, technical drawings
1888-1959, photographs and catalogues of machinery
1908-54, misc leaflets, etc 1910-56.
Strathclyde Regional Archives (TD 406). NRA 20914.

[367] **ABRAHAM COCKCROFT**, fustian mfrs, Hebden Bridge, Yorks

Ledgers and business papers (1 bundle) 1853-92.
West Yorkshire Archive Service, Calderdale (SU 376).
NRA 11488.

[368] **COLOURED COTTON SPINNING CO LTD**, Mirfield, Yorks

Minutes 1936-54, balance sheets and profit and loss
accounts 1920-70, tax reconstruction papers 1952-3,
private ledgers (2) 1911-32, valuation of plant and
schedules 1897-1923.
Lancashire RO (DDBx). NRA 30355.

[369] **CROAL SPINNING CO LTD**, cotton spinners, Bolton, Lancs

Directors' and general meeting minutes (8 vols)
1907-55, balance sheets 1955-70, scrapbooks (2).
Lancashire RO (DDBx). NRA 30355.

[370] **A & A CROMPTON & CO LTD**, cotton spinners, Crompton, Lancs

Ledgers (6) 1805-60, account book 1822-40, day books
(6) 1833-60, private journal 1874-7, cash books (3)
1848-75, bill book 1807-73, bank books (3) 1835-75,
misc financial corresp, receipts and accounts incl prices
for machinery (2 boxes, etc) 19th cent, sales ledgers
(2) 1834-59, order books (2) 1835-58, particulars of

yarn sales and summary of cotton purchases (1 bundle) 1881, stock books (2) 1848-81, stocktaking accounts (1 bundle) c1860-70, samples of sewing cotton (1 envelope) 1848, reelers' book 1843-6, time book 1851-66, wages books (4) 1837-53, weekly wages lists (1 bundle) 1845-6, misc factory inspection papers 1845-6 incl numbers of children and young persons 1846, rent book 1840-72, rent lists (13 items) 1842, schedules of deeds late 19th cent, copies of fire insurance policies (1 folder) 1871-4, executors' accounts (2 vols) 1884-98 and other Crompton family financial papers and account books (6 boxes) 1794-1900.
Lancashire RO (DDCp). NRA 30811.

Family, estate and misc business papers (7 boxes) 1724-1957 incl letter book 1874-8, ledger 1857-67, account books (5) 1864-1915, nd, order book 1868-73, wages book 1884-1901, and valuation of premises and machinery 1878.
Oldham Local Interest Centre (MISC/35). NRA 29987.

Minute books (5) 1882-1956, registers of directors 1901-48, private ledger (incl H Travis Milne Ltd) 1945-c1966, private balance book 1947-62.
Courtaulds plc, Coventry (CRO). Enquiries to the Head of Archives. NRA 29343.

Minute book 1898-1966, preference share register and ledger from 1890, register of transfers.
Courtaulds Spinning. Enquiries to the Company Secretary. NRA 30126.

[371] **SAMUEL CROMPTON**, muslin mfr and bleacher, Bolton, Longworth and Darwen, Lancs

Business and family papers 1672-1862 incl cash and account books (19) 1786-1813, corresp rel to orders and sales of muslin 1798-1820, consignment book 1800, payments to weavers 1822, spindle enquiry papers 1811, and corresp and papers rel to the spinning mule 1802-12; Samuel Crompton & Co accounts and corresp 1813-23, inventories 1813-14, valuations 1814, 1822, diagrams 1814, c1819; Wylde & Crompton accounts 1815-23.
Bolton Metropolitan Borough Archives (ZCR). NRA 27114.

Corresp and papers 1801-26 mainly rel to his claim for a reward from the government.
British Library (Eg MS 2409).

[372] **PETER CROOK LTD**, cotton spinners, Bolton, Lancs

Records 1884-1977 incl minutes, registers of members, directors and shares, balance sheets, loan ledger, stock and balance book, private wages books, and valuation of Drake Mill.
Courtaulds plc, Coventry. Enquiries to the Head of Archives. NRA 28631; BAC *Company Archives* no 474.

[373] **CROSSLEE COTTON SPINNING CO**, Houston, Renfrewshire

Ledger 1793-8, state of accounts (2 vols) 1793-1804.
Scottish Record Office (CS 96/257, 3746-7). *Court of Session Productions*, List & Index Society, special series vol 23, 1987, p144.

[374] **DANIEL JONES CROSSLEY**, cotton spinner, Hebden Bridge, Yorks

Staff wages books, papers, etc 1872-1917.
West Yorkshire Archive Service, Calderdale: see *West Yorkshire Archive Service Report 1987-8*, p49.

[375] **DAISY BANK MILL CO LTD**, cotton goods mfrs, Culcheth, Lancs

Records incl minute books, share registers, ledgers, account books, etc c1870-1950.
Rossendale Museum, Rawtenstall. NRA 30829.

[376] **GEO & R DEWHURST LTD**, cotton spinners, mfrs and shippers, Preston and Farington, Lancs

Letter book 1875-89, ledger 1904-14, stock and other accounts (8 items) 1837-1900, sales ledgers (2) 1854-67, 1911-18, twist, weft, etc prices 1892, 1907, 1910, 1928-40, cotton memoranda and mill instructions 1899-1915, stores book 1911-12, tapers book 1914-19, weavers' wages book 1926-7, plans c1890, orders for furniture 1915, photographs c1950, 1964; Daniel Arkwright Ltd minutes 1900-8.
Lancashire RO (DDX 819). NRA 16485.

[377] **DOUGLAS, DALE & McCALL** (afterwards **MATTHEW HOPE**), cotton mfrs, Newton Stewart, Wigtownshire

Ledger and index 1808-10, cash book 1808-11, mechanics' and carders' wages book 1796-1810, spinners' and reelers' wages book 1800-10.
Scottish Record Office (CS 96/1303-4, 1960, 2263, 4909). *Court of Session Productions*, List & Index Society, special series vol 23, 1987, p129.

[378] **DOWRY SPINNING CO LTD**, cotton spinners, Oldham, Lancs

Nominal ledger 1884-1928, share ledger 1882-1935.
Courtaulds plc, Coventry (DRY). Enquiries to the Head of Archives. NRA 29343.

[379] **NATHANIEL DUGDALE & BROS**, cotton mfrs, Padiham, Lancs

Lists, valuations and inventories of machinery and premises (6 vols) 1807-51.
John Rylands University Library of Manchester (Eng MS 1200). *Hand-list of additions to the collection of English manuscripts . . . 1952-1970*, p20.

[380] **THOMAS & RICHARD ECCLES LTD**, cotton goods mfrs, Lower Darwen, Lancs

Directors' minute book 1897-1937, annual returns 1930-66, private ledger 1897-1953, personal ledger balances 1944-73, order books (3) 1906-25, stock books (2) 1931-55, design books (2) 1932-72, jacquard pattern books (23) 1906-70 incl two from George Burton Ltd, dobby pattern and peg books (4) c1898, c1950-65, inventories 1901, 1912, scrapbooks (2) from 1912, photographs and misc papers 1914-57.
Lancashire RO (DDX 868). NRA 18080.

[381] **ECKERSLEYS LTD**, cotton spinners and cloth mfrs, Wigan, Lancs

Share registers and annual lists and summaries (6 vols) 1874-1918, register of mortgage debentures 1884-1905, cotton statistics book 1906-38, trade mark registration papers (12 bundles, 4 items) 1887-1962, factory plans (10) 1872-88, nd, machinery measurements (5 bundles) 1830-1956.
Wigan RO (D/DY Eck). NRA 30988.

[382] **WILLIAM ECROYD & SONS LTD**, cotton goods mfrs, Nelson, Lancs

Memorandum and articles of association 1886, articles of partnership and related papers 1880-1908, draft minutes (1 bundle) 1896, deeds and plans (7 boxes) 19th-20th cent, personal account book of Edward Ecroyd 1888-92.
Lancashire RO (DDBd). Closed to research.

[383] **ELLENROAD SPINNING CO LTD**, cotton spinners, Rochdale, Lancs

Engineers' log books (8) 1872-1918, 1955-73 incl sketches and dimensions of steam engines, fuel consumption books c1963-83, nd, engine drawings from 1891, misc records mainly 1970s incl corresp, cotton order books, and stocktaking and yarn returns.
Ellenroad Trust Ltd, Rochdale. NRA 32394.

Weekly report books (7) 1927-60 incl cotton stocks, yarn sales and cash statements.
Saddleworth Museum (M/GX/T/BA/11-17). NRA 11134.

[384] **ENGLISH SEWING COTTON CO LTD**, sewing cotton mfrs, Manchester

Memorandum and articles of association and related papers 1948, 1958-66; minutes of executive committee (111 vols) 1909-47, board (13 vols) 1900-68, directors and shareholders (2 vols) 1897-1900, board and committees (5 vols) 1900-2, finance committee (1 vol) 1900, pension fund (1 vol) 1918-62, Pension Trust Ltd (1 vol) 1924-60; annual reports, etc 1898-1967, share ledgers (120 vols) 1897-c1913, Arkwright House register of tenants incl plans 1928-c1949.
Manchester Central Library (M127).

Records (44 vols) 1897-1966 incl private ledgers, journals, cash books, works ledgers, and property, plant and machinery ledger; private ledgers of various branches incl RF & J Alexander & Co Ltd, Sir Richard Arkwright & Co Ltd, Edmund Ashworth & Sons Ltd, William Clapperton & Co Ltd, John Dewhurst & Sons Ltd, Ermen & Roby Ltd, Portwood Spinning Co Ltd, WG & J Strutt Ltd, J & E Waters & Co Ltd, and George Wigley & Co Ltd.
Tootal Group plc. NRA 28631; BAC *Company Archives* no 592.

Sales journal 1896-9.
Coats Patons plc. Enquiries to NRA (Scotland) (NRA(S) 2461). NRA 20914.

[385] **ERA RING MILL LTD**, cotton spinners, Rochdale, Lancs

Registers of directors 1918-39 and directors' holdings 1948-66, share and loan ledgers (4) 1897-1972, dividend books (3) 1948-75, annual summary 1921-8, cash and account books (17 vols) 1915-73, misc corporate and financial papers 1898-1975, allocation of orders (15 vols) 1903-70, particulars of orders (1 vol) 1953-6, trade ledgers, journals, etc (11 vols) 1929-74, stock records (16 vols) 1898-1975, production records (9 vols) 1939-67, cotton futures book 1898-1954, cotton statistics book 1932-56, wages records, time books, factory registers and accident books (50 vols) 1897-1972, coal book 1944-54, visitors' book 1899-1910, misc papers rel to premises and machinery 1897-1925, nd.
Rochdale Local Studies Department (C/IND/COT/ERA). NRA 31082.

[386] **ERMEN & ROBY (ARMENTIERES) LTD**, sewing cotton mfrs, Manchester

Trading accounts 1897-1902, private ledgers (2) 1899-1949.
Tootal Group plc. NRA 28631; BAC *Company Archives* no 592.

[387] **WALTER EVANS & CO LTD**, sewing cotton mfrs, Darley Abbey, Derbys

Corresp (1 vol) 1787-1809, ledgers (2) 1795-1810, cash books (3) 1830-3, 1856-62, 1897-1908, bank book 1832-42, stock book 1815-26, wages books (5) 1876-9, 1914-23.
Derby Central Library (DL 119). NRA 27877.

Memorandum and articles of association 1905, minutes (2 vols) 1905-62, register of members and share ledger (2 vols) 1905-63 incl annual returns 1905-12, annual returns 1918-48, inventories and valuations of Boar's Head Mills and machinery 1888, 1903, 1920, historical notes.
Coats Patons plc. Enquiries to NRA (Scotland) (NRA(S) 3088). NRA 20914.

[388] **FACIT MILL CO LTD**, cotton mfrs, Whitworth, Lancs

Directors' minutes (6 vols) 1904-26, 1941-62, cotton purchase and stock book 1956-67, inventory of plant 1920.
Lancashire RO (DDX 639). NRA 16896.

[389] **FERGUSON BROS LTD**, cotton spinners and mfrs, Carlisle, Cumberland

Memorandum and articles of association and partnership deeds 1862-98, minutes (4 vols) 1866-75, 1900-75, general administrative papers 1839-1969, registers of directors and managers 1900-71, share registers 1913-71, balance sheets and accounts 1865-1963, letter books (4) 1846-99, private ledgers (3) 1827-1964, account books (2) 1861-7, 1897, account of debts due 1830-61, commission books incl samples 1956-77, records of dye experiments 1846-57, shade book incl dye recipes and samples nd, photographs of

dress patterns 1926-9, wages books 1839-1977, pension books 1934-51, canteen committee minute book 1947-62, rent book 1898-1927, valuations of works, stock and machinery 1833-40, 1863, 1880-95, estimates for spinning machinery 1855, maps and plans 1809-52, nd, legal and misc papers 1839-1900.
Cumbria RO, Carlisle (DB/13). NRA 17337; *Report of the County Archivist* May 1977 p3, April 1985 p3.

Account books (5) 1807-27.
London University Library (MS 616). *Catalogue of additional manuscripts (MS 555-MS 884).*

[390] **FIELDEN BROS LTD**, cotton mfrs, Todmorden, Yorks

Memorandum and articles of association, resolutions, etc 1889-1966, annual returns, accounts and balance sheets 1845-1965, letter books (34) 1844-90, 1895-1949, secretary's papers (49 vols, files, etc) 1844-1959 incl analysis and financial records, ledgers (7) 1846-90, 1959-66, journals (3) 1867-80, cash books (28) 1860-1962, invoice books (37 vols, 79 files) 1847-1964, stock, order, sales, purchase and production books (c100 vols, etc) 1844-1962 incl some from Manchester sales office, wages books (c100) for various mills 1842-1957, accident, personnel and time books (15 vols, etc) 1865-1964, machinery specifications, tests and registers (9 vols, etc) 1825-1965, misc papers 1803-1948 incl Todmorden Valley Millowners Committee papers.
West Yorkshire Archive Service, Wakefield Headquarters (C353). NRA 24883.

Directors' minutes (6 vols) from 1890, general meeting minutes (1 vol) 1957-66, registers of directors and shareholders 1900-52, letter books (4) 1890-5, 1910-14, 1922-5, 1932-5, ledgers and journals (6 vols) 1890-1965, cash books (4) 1888-98, 1949-53, wages books (17) 1855-65, 1872-90, 1900-9, 1912-24, deeds, plans and inventories (28 parcels, etc) from 1727.
Waterside Plastics Ltd. NRA 24883.

Corresp (1 folder, 8 bundles) 1814-50, bills (3 boxes) c1840-90, sales and production figures, inventories of stock, estimates of costs, mill plans and other financial and legal papers (3 bundles) 1811-1905.
John Rylands University Library of Manchester.

[391] **FINE SPINNERS & DOUBLERS LTD**, cotton spinners and doublers, Bolton, Lancs

Minutes of executive directors (36 vols) 1898-1954, board (9 vols) 1898-1962, general committees (1 vol) 1898-1961, shareholders (1 vol) 1898-1961, finance committee (2 vols) 1908-62, chairman (1 vol) 1946-70, board of management (3 vols) 1954-62, export department (1 vol) 1926-33, and American, French and productivity panels (3 vols) 1951-4; directors' attendance book 1899-1949, registers of directors (2 vols), registers of seals (5 vols) 1899-1956, summary of capital expenditure 1898-1928, deeds rel to debenture stocks 1898-1960, first mortgage debenture stockholders 1917-37, balance sheets and chairman's reports 1919-54, statements of bonuses, etc 1898-1948, accounts and schedules 1949-59, profit and loss

accounts 1962-5, abstracts of purchases, Romanian debts 1936-7, foreign department 1935-50, trusts 1940-62, pension schemes, insurance schedules, etc 1943-59, circulated papers nd.
Courtaulds Spinning. Enquiries to the Company Secretary. NRA 30126.

Misc records incl private cash book 1960-7.
Courtaulds plc, Coventry (FSD). Enquiries to the Head of Archives. NRA 29343.

[392] **JAMES FINLAY & CO LTD**, cotton mfrs, merchants and managing agents, Glasgow

Deeds and agreements 1787-1938, minute book 1845-83, partners' minutes (1 vol) c1900, agenda 1873-1914, annual statements 1859-71, letter books (10) 1835-c1920, corresp 1848-1940, general accounts (1 vol) 1857-65, private ledger 1874-1942, ledgers (13) 1792, 1853-1936, private journals (4) 1825-1934, journals (3) 1880-8, balance books (6) 1789-1935, bill books (4) 1813-58, 1943-62, doubtful debts ledger 1804-56, cash and other accounts (16 vols, etc) 1844-1969, agreement books (5) 1880-1931, overseas consignment book 1818-54, foreign departments' orders, accounts and corresp 1882-1972, charges on merchandise (1 vol) 1814-27, wages books (22) 1907-53, staff memoranda (4 vols) c1880-1921, nd, legal papers 1870-1942 incl title deeds, plans of mills and machinery 19th-20th cent, trust and executry records 1846-1956, misc papers 1829-1969 incl personal cash books and notebooks of James Finlay; Catrine Bleaching Works annual statements (1 vol) 1857-64, balance book 1823-67, ledgers, journals and cash book (6 vols) 1893-1943; Catrine Cotton Works ledgers and journals (6 vols) 1896-1917, 1929-66, employees' registers (10) 1879-1959, enquiry into employment of children nd, labour indenture between Claude Alexander & Co and young employees 1791-2, weather reports for Catrine area (2 vols) 1898-1939, Catrine village register 1863 and Penny Savings Bank minutes 1872; Deanston Cotton Works letter book 1840-4, day book 1792-3, journals (5) 1829-36, 1908-45, ledger 1931-45, river gauge book 1831-70, letters received, details of stock and sales, etc (18 bundles) 1809-1915, misc accounts and papers 1896-1930 incl for building new school; Ballindalloch, Catrine and Deanston Works statements and accounts (20 vols, etc) 1835-56, 1915-68, list of workers at Catrine 1813-33, inventory of Catrine and Deanston Mills 1904; accounting records and general papers 1862-1972 of Finlay Clark & Co, Finlay Muir & Co, Webster, Steel & Co and other related and subsidiary companies.
Glasgow University Archives (UGD/91). NRA 23054.

[393] **JOHN FISH LTD**, cotton spinners and mfrs, Livesey, Lancs

Memorandum and articles of association c1900, 1919, directors' minutes (5 vols) 1874-1947, share ledgers (2) 1897-1947, transfer ledger 1875-1948, register of shareholders 1874-97, lists of shares, etc 1876-1948, annual returns 1953-66, out-letter book 1902-7, ledger 1889-90, private ledgers (3) 1881-1964, nominal ledgers (4) 1922-64, balance book 1908-30, cash books (6) 1914-21, 1931-58, expenditure analysis books (4)

1941-56, sales books (2) 1926-55, stocktaking book 1932-48, loom patent declaration and diagram 1852-3, private wages book 1915-37, inventories of Bank and Waterfall Mills.
Lancashire RO (DDX 659/2, DDX 868). NRA 18080.

[394] **JOHN FLETCHER & SONS**, cotton spinners, Ashton-under-Lyne, Lancs

Letter books (2 vols, 2 bundles) 1891-1902, 1914-29, payments ledgers (2) 1849-53, ledgers (6) 1882-1925, account books (2 bundles) 1831-56, cash books (5) 1883-1925, receipts and vouchers (5 vols, c24 bundles) 1869-c1925, order books (3) 1888-1907, delivery books (2) 1902-25, stock books (2) 1904-28, report books (3) 1908-12, 1917-27, production record book 1897-1907, hours worked book 1907-30, wages books (2) 1890-1904, 1918-29, rent ledgers (4 vols, 1 bundle) 1869-1910.
Tameside Local Studies Library (DDFM). NRA 31002.

[395] **FYLDE MANUFACTURING CO LTD**, cotton spinners and mfrs, Kirkham, Lancs

Minute book 1875-82.
Lancashire RO (DDS). NRA 488.

[396] **GARDNER & BAZLEY**, cotton mfrs, Barrow Bridge, Lancs

Returns of employees 1838, 1844, black book 1842-51, rules for sick list 1832, Dean Mills visitors' book 1851-2, notes on running of workers' shop nd, photographs and misc papers 1833-91, nd.
Bolton Metropolitan Borough Archives (ZHB). NRA 19836.

[397] **GRAPE MILL CO LTD**, cotton spinners, Royton, Lancs

Directors' minutes (3 vols) 1905-49.
Shiloh plc. Enquiries to the Chairman and Managing Director. NRA 31773.

[398] **WILLIAM GRAY & SON**, cotton spinners and mfrs, Darcy Lever, Lancs

Ledgers (2) 1795-1801, day books (2) 1795-1802, register of bank transactions and letters of credit 1800-12, account and stock book 1801-18, memoranda book 1804-32, skip book 1820-9.
Bolton Metropolitan Borough Archives (ZGR). NRA 27109.

[399] **GREAT LEVER SPINNING CO LTD**, cotton spinners, Great Lever, Lancs

General register from 1904.
Courtaulds Spinning. Enquiries to the Company Secretary. NRA 30126.

[400] **GREAT WESTERN COTTON FACTORY**, cotton mfrs, Bristol

Letter book 1843-76, accounts 1844-5, cash book 1878, memoranda book 1860-3, cloth sample book 1843-4, trade cards, lists, reports and misc papers rel to equipment and production 1842-58, deeds of

properties, partnerships and trusts 1709-1859, papers rel to company's financial difficulties 1866-77, press cuttings.
Bristol RO (Acc 13423). NRA 7563.

[401] **THOMAS GREENWOOD**, cotton spinner and mfr, Stansfield, Yorks

Day books (2) 1856-74, accounts (1 vol) 1857-73, cash book 1857-74, wages book 1857-74, employment certificates 1853-66.
West Yorkshire Archive Service, Calderdale (SU 362-5, 377). NRA 11488.

[402] **R GREG & CO LTD**, cotton spinners and doublers, Styal, Cheshire and Reddish, Lancs

Minutes and mill memoranda (2 vols) 1784-1924, corresp (c500 items) c1850-1968, ledgers (13) 1867-1963, day books (3) 1934-6, cash books (11) 1910-64, bank book 1907-12, order books (2) 1868-93, 1936-58, invoices and receipts (3 vols) 1894, 1945-62, stock books (6) 1859-1955, stock and production sheets 1919-38, cotton statement (1 vol) 1855-70, cotton ledger 1852-68, cloth construction books (2) 1879, nd, sizing books (3) 1885-94, trial balances (1 vol) 1876-82, trial accounts (1 vol) 1890-6, weaving accounts (1 vol) 1879-94, production ledgers (4) 1869-1921, weft weight book 1931, weaving samples (1 vol) from G Brochgert & Sohn 1909, mechanics' ledger 1868-71, weavers' wages ledgers (3) 1873-6, labourers' and workers' wages (6 vols) 1924-64, list of apprentices 1837, doctor's prescription book c1820, lists of tenants 1845-53, rent book 1869-90, maps and plans (c250) 1835-1975, nd, inventories 1790, 1910, Styal Oak British School accounts 1900-13, insurance and misc legal and financial papers 20th cent, Greg family account books and estate records 1823-1950; R & N Hyde pattern book 1796.
Quarry Bank Mill, Styal. NRA 29998.

Partnership accounts incl Quarry Bank, Ancoats, Bury, Caton, Lancaster and Reddish mills (8 vols) 1805-1912, transfer book 1857-90, weekly accounts, etc (5 vols) 1834-1918, ledgers (5) 1815-91, day book 1803-6, cash books (4 vols) 1787-1920, contingent expenses ledger 1853-6, consignment book 1847-1945, invoices and receipts (2 vols, etc) 1784-8, 1842-1905, stock books and valuations (5 vols) 1794-1923, accounts of twist and spun (1 vol) 1803-5, 1814-22, cloth construction book 1848-96, weaving production book 1909-14, prices paid for mule spinning (1 vol) 1851-1937, wages books (12) 1789-1929, stoppage ledgers (2) 1815-47, register of workers 1843-9, age certificate books (9) 1844-55, agreements with workers and apprenticeship indentures (2 vols, 292 items) 1784-1866, record of doctor's visits and treatments (2 vols) 1804-45, reports of inspectors of the Association for Prevention of Steam Boiler Explosions (1 vol) 1855-74, mill and estate memoranda (1 vol) 1804-37, Greg family estate accounts, etc (8 vols, etc) 1809-1927, misc papers and corresp 1788-1906.
Manchester Central Library (C5). NRA 30132.

Minute books (6) 1902-44, minutes of overlookers and management meetings (2 vols) 1919-78, balance sheets, annual reports, private accounts, etc c1930-68, ledgers (2) 1852-6, 1860-1908, impersonal ledger 1889-95,

stock books (6) 1908-70 and stock papers 1931-56, memoranda books (4) incl orders and prices c1890-1910, fancy yarns books (9) 1933-74, nd, double yarn journal 1910-12, yarn quotations books (2) 1920-31, yarn sample books (2) 1893-7, 1927-31, production notebooks (20) 1852-c1964, weekly summaries of production and wages costs 1930-51, employment agreements 1943-68 and misc employment records 1951-70, nd, general notes on mill management incl fire prevention 1942-9, machinery estimates, etc 1937-46, plans and drawings of Reddish estate, mill premises and machinery (c150 items) c1850-1979, details of rents and tenancies (2 vols, etc) c1920-60, visitors' book 1926-37, misc pamphlets, notes on company history.
Stockport Central Library (DDGr). NRA 30858.

Cressbrook Mill, Derbys, letter book 19th cent.
W Salt Esq. Mary B Rose, *The Gregs of Quarry Bank Mill*, Cambridge 1986.

Memoranda of Greg concerns 1750-1867 by RH Greg, journal of RH Greg, misc corresp.
Mr and Mrs SBL Jacks. Mary B Rose, ibid.

[403] **GRIMSHAWS & BRACEWELL**, cotton spinners and mfrs, Barrowford, Lancs

Accounts incl carding cotton wool and warp sizing 1785-6, 1819, 1833-70, misc bills and receipts 1813-39, wages books (2) 1835-9, 1846-60, draft specification for new factory 1824, and other Grimshaw family business and estate papers 1642-c1870.
Manchester Central Library (L1/16/3). NRA 17338.

[404] **THOMAS HAIGH**, cotton importer, Liverpool

Letter books, warehouse order books, invoice and work books, sample and delivery orders and records of cotton and dock weights 1855-9.
Public Record Office, Chancery Lane (J 90/994-8).

[405] **JOHN HALL LTD**, quiltings, vestings and cotton dress goods mfrs, Manchester and Bury, Lancs

Sample books (4) 1837, 1839-40, nd.
Bury Art Gallery & Museum. NRA 31020.

Display pattern book 1912.
Manchester Polytechnic Library (F 677 2164 JOH).

[406] **WILLIAM HANSON & CO LTD**, cotton spinners and doublers, Halifax, Yorks

Minutes (4 vols) 1889-1932, registers of shares, members and debentures (2 vols) 1889-1962, annual returns 1928-48, ledger 1867-86, private ledgers (3) 1887-1906, 1930-51, deposit ledger 1898-1930, account book 1904-5, cash book 1898-1930, inventories and valuations late 19th cent-1921.
West Yorkshire Archive Service, Calderdale (MISC 189). NRA 26817.

Records (112 vols) 1924-54 incl ledgers, invoices, production books, and wages books.
Brotherton Library, Leeds University. NRA 26802.

[407] **JAMES HARRISON**, cotton spinner, Manchester

Bank book 1811-27, papers rel to the administration of his estate and other Harrison and Mottram family papers 1824-1970 incl notes on hat proof and dye mixtures 1860-70.
Stockport Central Library (DD/MO).

[408] **JOHN HAWKINS & SONS LTD**, cotton spinners and mfrs, Preston, Lancs

Memorandum and articles of association 1899, directors' and general meeting minutes (3 vols) 1899-1946, registers of shares and shareholders 1899-1943, ledger 1939-54, journal 1962-5, order and pattern book 1895-1900.
Lancashire RO (DDX 659, DDX 868). NRA 18080.

[409] **J & J HAYES LTD**, cotton spinners, Leigh, Lancs

Records 1818-1960 incl ledgers, day and cash books, order, costing and stock books, wages book, schedule of deeds, photographs, and Hayes family papers.
Wigan RO (D/Dy Ha). NRA 28631; BAC *Company Archives* no 366.

Minute books (2) 1927-86, register of members.
Courtaulds Spinning. Enquiries to the Company Secretary. NRA 30126.

[410] **HEALEY WOOD MILL CO LTD**, cotton spinners and mfrs, Burnley, Lancs

Records c1870-c1950 incl minute books, share registers, ledgers, and account books.
Rossendale Museum, Rawtenstall. NRA 30829.

[411] **HOLLAS & CO** (afterwards **JOSEPH JOHNSON LTD**), cotton mfrs, Bolton, Lancs

Sample books (c200) and record book 1880s-1968.
Bolton Museum (BY.56.1973). NRA 29093.

[412] **HOLLY MILL CO LTD**, cotton spinners, Royton, Lancs

Directors' minutes (7 vols) 1890-1949, shareholders' minutes (1 vol) 1930-49.
Shiloh plc. Enquiries to the Chairman and Managing Director. NRA 31773.

[413] **GEORGE HOLT & CO**, cotton brokers, Liverpool

Articles of partnership 1812, profit and loss accounts, etc 1823-64, ledgers and day books (6 vols) 1812-71, private ledgers (2) of George Holt 1837-71, account book of William Durning 1818-30, receipts 1837-56, daily cotton purchases and sales books (5) 1814-66, statements of quotations of cotton wool in Liverpool 1846, 1859, 1861-4, 1868, 1870-1, papers rel to George Holt's interest in cotton, etc in New South Wales 1838-41, Liverpool Cotton Brokers Association circulars and reports 1867-1929, autobiography of George Holt and other Holt and Durning family business corresp and papers 18th-20th cent.
Liverpool RO. NRA 8155.

Papers and corresp of George Holt 19th cent. *In private possession.* NRA 8155.

[414] **WH HORNBY & CO** (formerly **CARDWELL, BIRLEY & HORNBY**), cotton mfrs, Blackburn, Lancs

Private ledgers (2) 1793-1810, stock books (4) 1768-1858.
John Rylands University Library of Manchester (Eng MS 1199). *Hand-list of additions to the collection of English manuscripts . . . 1952-1970,* pp19-20.

[415] **HORROCKSES, CREWDSON & CO LTD**, cotton mfrs, Preston, Lancs

Partnership and amalgamation papers (3 boxes) 19th cent, directors' attendance book 1896-1904, balance sheets, etc incl subsidiaries (2 boxes, etc) 1836-1958, stock transfer books and files 1887-1960, managing director's corresp files 1947-9, ledgers (25) 1799-1945, journals (19) 1818-1947, cash books (28) 1823-1961, day books (2) 1933-60, bill books (3) 1795-6, 1811-17, 1833-6, misc accounts (8 vols, etc) 1810-1945, cloth sales and price lists 1844-80, foreign trade corresp incl tea and spice trade (3 boxes, etc) 1818-60, Thomas Miller's letter book 1836-48, stock books (4) 1839-1960, power loom notes (2 vols) 1842-50, pattern books (120) 1900-62, trade mark papers (1 box) nd, yarn books and misc production records (6 vols) 1959-62, machinists' accounts 1800-5, pay book 1859-62, salaries, wages and pension books (6) 1881-*c*1944, wages and time sheets *c*1940-60, index of child employees 1852-82, sick fund books (3) 1882-1946, strike papers 1853, deeds 1743-1953, plans (12 boxes) *c*1810-*c*1950, mill valuation 1845, rent book 1938-46, photographs 19th-20th cent, press cuttings (3 vols) *c*1930-60, misc papers and pamphlets 19th-20th cent.
Lancashire RO (DDHs, DDX 103). NRA 19214.

Partnership agreements, etc 1885-1950, directors' minutes (2 vols) 1887-1902, 1937-43, finance committee minutes 1887-1916, management committee minutes and reports 1923-4, 1949-51, registers of directors, members and shares 1887-1960s, debenture stock notices and meetings 1901-56, annual accounts, balance sheets, etc from 1887 incl those of subsidiaries, managing director's corresp (4 boxes) 1944-53, nd, secretarial and executive corresp, reports and working papers (4 boxes) 1940s-1950s, letter books (4) 1894-1922, private ledger 1906-11, cash books (2) 1886-90, 1953-71, memorandum of sales (1 vol) 1870-85, sales receipt books (1 box) nd, sales accounts 1941-1950s, spinning and weaving production book 1882-1918, apprenticeship articles (1 vol) 1837-1914, service agreements (1 box) *c*1903-24, salaries and other employment records from *c*1920, deeds (15 bundles, etc) from 1738, list of boilers (1 vol) early 20th cent, visitors' books (4) 1845-1960, advertisements (1 vol) 1902-4, press cuttings (2 vols) 1947-60; financial papers 1910-32 of Sir Arthur Hollins, etc.
Coats Viyella plc. Enquiries to the Company Secretary. NRA 32376.

[416] **A & J HOYLE LTD**, shirting and gingham mfrs, Radcliffe, Lancs

Ledger 1941-69, invoice books (2) 1858-61, returns books (2) 1941-68, notebook rel to prices 1900, stock book 1937-68, notebook of John Hoyle 1886, sample books, leaflets, price lists and other advertising material *c*1895-*c*1975.
Bury Art Gallery & Museum. NRA 31020.

[417] **JOSHUA HOYLE & SONS LTD**, cotton spinners and mfrs, Bacup, Lancs

Plans, specifications and corresp (284 items) 1874-1969, mainly rel to Brooksbottom Mill.
Bury Archive Service. NRA 30197.

Pattern books (8) 1890-1913 (probably Hoyles), samples and misc papers 1927-78.
Bury Art Gallery & Museum. NRA 31020.

Minute book 1912-23, registers of members and share ledgers.
West Yorkshire Archive Service, Bradford (25D89).

Fuel book for Brooksbottom Mill 1957-60.
Greater Manchester RO (1279 Q124).

[418] **WILLIAM JOHNSTON**, cotton spinner, Glasgow

Cash book 1801-4, buying and sales book 1801-4.
Scottish Record Office (CS 96/3339-40). *Court of Session Productions,* List & Index Society, special series vol 23, 1987, p114.

[419] **HENRY KAY & CO**, smallware and silk mfrs, Middleton, Lancs

Receipt books with patterns (4 vols) 1888, 1902-3, nd.
Manchester Central Library (M75).

[420] **KERR & CO LTD**, thread mfrs, Paisley, Renfrewshire

Memorandum and articles of association 1888, minutes (3 vols) 1888-1962, registers of directors, members and mortgages (3 vols) 1886-1962, annual summary 1912-47, corresp *c*1953, journal 1897-1901, purchase ledger 1889-98, historical notes.
Coats Patons plc. Enquiries to NRA (Scotland) (NRA(S) 2461). NRA 20914.

Private ledger 1890-7, ledger 1888-90, general and department ledger 1898-1901, general cash book 1898-1909.
Glasgow University Archives (UGD/199). NRA 20914.

Kerr, Pollock & Co incidents book 1751-61, journal 1757-61, ledger index nd, sales books (2) 1756-61, and memoranda book of James Kerr 1750-2.
Scottish Record Office (CS 96/2009, 2020-2, 3033, 3173). *Court of Session Productions,* List & Index Society, special series vol 23, 1987, pp33, 36.

[421] **LANARK TWIST CO** (afterwards **WALKER & CO**; **LANARK SPINNING CO**), cotton mfrs, New Lanark

Letter books 1815-16, 1881, general ledger 1804-8, account book 1873-81, order books (3) 1811-20, sales book 1814-15, produce book 1803-5, report and wages books (4) 1801-8, 1855-70, 1879-1904, wages tickets

c1820, statement of wages paid 1885, visitors' books
(3) 1795-1832, insurance premium of Robert Owen
1825, valuation book 1903, rent roll 1901-27, school
certificate book 1852, New Lanark population statistics
incl numbers employed at the mills 1806-61, registers
of births, marriages and deaths (3 vols) 1818-53,
corresp rel to New Lanark Village, etc 1876-1914.
Glasgow University Archives (UGD/42). NRA 10832.

Corresp and misc papers (c3,000 items) of Robert
Owen 1821-58, incl letters rel to cotton trade and
yearly statements of wages and produce for New
Lanark Mills.
Co-operative Union Library, Manchester. NRA 16003.

Journal 1814-16.
Allen & Hanburys Ltd. NRA 384. Microfilm copies
are in the Brynmor Jones Library, Hull University,
and in Glasgow University Archives.

New Lanark Institution cash book 1816-25.
Edinburgh University Library (DC.6.110).

Diary of Robert Owen 1813-22.
Gourock Ropework Co Ltd. Photocopies are in Glasgow
University Archives (UGD/42/31/17).

[422] **JOHN LEAN & SONS LTD**, muslin mfrs,
Glasgow

Letter books (118) 1852-1951, ledger 1837-99, private
ledgers (10) 1854-1932, account books (2) 1853-65,
1906-39, cash books, day books and journals (10 vols)
1881-1955, indent books (12) 1893-1926, bill book
1893-1941, shipping ledgers (4) 1916-24, 1954-7,
delivery receipt book 1863-1958, wages book 1919-41,
inventories and valuations 1875, 1881, 1930.
Glasgow University Archives (UGD/2). NRA 21576.

[423] **JAMES LEES, SON & CO**, cotton spinners,
Oldham, Lancs

Deed of partnership 1823, profit and loss accounts
1844-51, ledgers (3) 1804-8, 1827-52, 1896-1906,
journal 1844-59, cash books (5) 1822-38, memoranda
books (2) 1841-6, stock accounts 1808-20, 1844,
trading accounts 1896-1920, power looms patent and
related papers 1834-7, purchasing account of
machinery and equipment 1822-6, improvements
accounts 1844-51, inventories (6) 1843-4, 1882-3,
corresp and accounts rel to bankruptcy of Holroyd's
Bower Mill 1889-90.
Lancashire RO (DDRe). NRA 15328.

[424] **JAMES LONGSDON**, fustian mfr, Great
Longstone, Derbys

Deeds of partnership and related papers 1783-1813,
nd, corresp 1781-6, account book 1786-1811,
memoranda book incl sales and prices c1783, details
of stock, debts, etc and misc accounts 1777-98, list of
looms 1828, Longsdon family deeds and papers.
Derbyshire RO. NRA 23053.

[425] **S LONGWORTH & SONS LTD**, cotton
mfrs, Whalley, Lancs

Memorandum and articles of association 1922, minutes
of briefing meeting in New York 1949, letter book
1874-6, general ledgers (3) 1875-1912, private ledger
1913-21, day book 1935-50, stock book 1912-20,

pattern books (7) 1917-c1940 incl orders and order
sheets, wages book 1938-47, valuation and inventory
(2 vols) 1906, 1914, deeds (3 boxes), schedule and
plan (1 vol) 1871, plans (1 parcel, etc) 1908, 1946;
trustees of S Longworth minute book 1895-1910,
ledgers (4) 1895-1922, nd, and cash book 1895-1926.
Lancashire RO (DDG).

[426] **LOSTOCK HALL SPINNING CO**, cotton
spinners, Walton-le-Dale, Lancs

Memorandum and articles of association c1874,
directors' and shareholders' minutes (2 vols) 1876-8.
Lancashire RO (DDX 938). NRA 3510.

[427] **GEORGE LUMB LTD**, cotton spinners and
doublers, Elland, Yorks

Memorandum of association 1891, minute books from
1901, list of shareholdings 1891, private ledgers and
other financial records from late 19th cent, stock list
c1923, plans 1935, 1946, inventory 1938, photographs
20th cent, misc papers and corresp 1891-1953.
The Company. Enquiries to N Harrison Esq.

[428] **McCONNEL & CO LTD** (formerly
McCONNEL & KENNEDY) cotton spinners,
Manchester

Letter books (23) 1795-1869, letter entry book
1816-21, letters received (31 boxes) 1795-1826, account
book 1795, ledgers (8) 1795-1840, day books (6)
1795-1831, cash books (3) 1796-1841, bill books (7)
1795-1831, bank books (6) 1795-1823, purchase books
(4) 1795-1843, orders and receipts (2 boxes) 1805-9,
yarn deliveries, output, stock and account books (7)
1804-63, Nottingham, Glasgow, Belfast, etc sales (13
vols) 1795-1874, consignments book 1809-29, postage
book 1826-7, warehouse journals (2) 1841-54, cotton
pickers' journal 1795-6, carding and roving journal
1795-6, wages book 1822-31, rent book 1815-c1840,
inventories (2 vols) 1797-1827.
John Rylands University Library of Manchester. NRA
25974.

Records of production, sales, values and wages (4 vols)
1852-97.
Courtaulds plc, Coventry (MCC). Enquiries to the Head
of Archives. NRA 29343.

Register of members, deeds.
Courtaulds Spinning. Enquiries to the Company
Secretary. NRA 30126.

Wages book 1876-9.
Manchester Central Library (MISC 743).

[429] **WILLIAM McCORMICK**, cotton mfr,
Kirkintilloch, Dunbarton

Waste book, journal and ledger 1789, ledger 1789-92,
day book 1789-92, spinning books (2) 1789-91,
spinning cash books (2) 1789-92, mill cash books (2)
1789-92, mill wages book 1789-90, account book with
Sir John Stirling of Glorat 1792-3.
Scottish Record Office (CS 96/1361-71). *Court of Session
Productions*, List & Index Society, special series vol
23, 1987, p99.

[430] **T & W McGUFFOG**, cotton spinners, Preston, Lancs

Letter book 1874-86, bill book 1871-86.
Lancashire RO (DDX 842). NRA 3510.

Stock book 1881-5, spinners' wages book 1884-5, valuation (1 vol) 1876.
Lancashire RO (DP 445). NRA 3510.

[431] **MACHINE COTTONS LTD**, Glasgow

Memorandum and articles of association nd, minute book 1930-62, registers of directors, members and sealed documents (5 vols) 1901-60, share ledger and annual summaries 1900-60, private ledger 1948-59.
Coats Patons plc. Enquiries to NRA (Scotland) (NRA(S) 3088). NRA 20914.

Cash book 1934-8.
Glasgow University Archives (UGD/199). NRA 20914.

[432] **MAPLE MILL LTD**, cotton spinners and doublers, Oldham, Lancs

Minute books (7) 1903-71, share ledger.
Courtaulds Spinning. Enquiries to the Company Secretary. NRA 30126.

[433] **THOMAS MELLODEW & CO LTD**, cotton spinners and doublers, Oldham, Lancs

Records 18th-20th cent incl letter book, receipt books, pattern books, patent specifications, and deeds; John Jackson Shiers & Sons Ltd pattern books (3) nd.
Oldham Local Interest Centre.

Minutes 1896-1971.
Coats Viyella plc. Enquiries to the Company Secretary. NRA 32377.

[434] **MILNROW SPINNING CO LTD**, cotton spinners, Rochdale, Lancs

Letter books (3) nd, account books (4) 1910-12, 1940-51, 1969-74, day books (6) 1907-8, 1911-38, cash books (4) 1907-46, bank book 1913-14, purchase and sales records (17 vols) 1907-71, yarn order book 1907-15, order books (23) 1949-53, delivery records (42 vols) 1915-52, manifold books (21) 1927-49, wrapping books (13) 1962-75, stock book 1908-71, particulars of sundries received (9 vols) 1923-62, misc sales and production records (12 vols) 1907-74, telegram books, notebooks, etc (11 vols) 1925-75, staff and wages records (19 vols) 1907-76.
Greater Manchester RO. NRA 29448.

[435] **MOORFIELD SPINNING CO LTD**, cotton spinners, Shaw, Lancs

Memorandum and articles of association 1875, directors' and general meeting minutes (6 vols) 1877-1949, balance book 1891-1902, annual accounts 1965-74.
Courtaulds plc, Coventry (MOO). Enquiries to the Head of Archives. NRA 29343.

Minute book 1957-79, register of members.
Courtaulds Spinning. Enquiries to the Company Secretary. NRA 30126.

[436] **MUSGRAVE SPINNING CO LTD**, cotton spinners, Bolton, Lancs

Wages books (2) 1863-6.
Courtaulds plc, Coventry (MVE). Enquiries to the Head of Archives. NRA 29343.

Deeds 19th cent.
Courtaulds Spinning. Enquiries to the Company Secretary. NRA 30126.

Plans and drawings 1878-1906.
Greater Manchester Museum of Science & Industry. NRA 29510.

[437] **JAMES NEILSON**, cotton mfr, Paisley, Renfrewshire

Letter book 1806-11, ledgers (2) 1798-1811 and index 1798-1807, journal 1808-11, cash books (2) 1806-10, incidents book 1808-10, sales book 1806-8, weaving book 1807-10, spinning books (2) 1807-10, executor's cash book 1810-13, roup of household and business stock 1810-11.
Scottish Record Office (CS 96/629-37, 1234-7). *Court of Session Productions*, List & Index Society, special series vol 23, 1987, p136.

[438] **JAMES NUTTER & SONS LTD**, cotton mfrs, Barnoldswick, Yorks

Memorandum and articles of association 1907-50, share certificates 1907-47, misc accounting records 1907-57, order, sales and production books (30) 1919-62, wages books (15) 1937-61, stock and insurance inventories 1918-50.
Lancashire RO (DDX 1232). NRA 22567.

[439] **ROBERT & THOMAS OGDEN**, cotton spinners, Manchester

Articles of partnership, etc 1815-51, title deeds (57) 1789-1960, insurance papers 1893-1920.
Manchester Central Library. NRA 20935.

[440] **SAMUEL OLDKNOW & CO**, cotton spinners and weavers, Mellor, Lancs

Account books, ledgers, invoices, etc (5 vols, etc) 1782-1820, sales day books (4) 1782-90, notebooks of debts, sales, etc (11) 1795-1807, order book 1790-1, prices books (3) c1770, 1788, 1792, stock books and sheets (13 vols, etc) 1788-1808, cotton receipt book 1803-4, pickers' books and bills (2 vols, etc) 1790-3, shop notes 1793-4, spinning, winding and reeling accounts (6 vols, etc) 1786-95, reed-making books, etc (2) 1787-9, cutting frames book 1787, warp output book 1810, manufacture to spinning account books (2) 1791-4, warping books (14) 1787-94, 1804-7, weavers' ledgers, taking-in and stock account books (5 vols) 1784-93, finishing book 1788, stretchers' work book 1805, sizing accounts (1 vol) 1788-9, costing books (2) c1788, c1791, weight book 1788, output records (3 vols, etc) 1793, 1797, 1806-13, delivery books (2) 1789-93, carriers' book 1799-1800, wages book, ledger, etc (2 vols, 67 items) 1789-1811, pay tickets (3,153) 1789, 1794, time books (8) 1791-1809,

index of workers nd, disgrace account 1787, inventories of furnishings and tools c1787, nd, calicoes, etc for sale at East India House 1789, letters (334) to Samuel Oldknow and estate accounts 1783-1812.
John Rylands University Library of Manchester (Eng MSS 751-840). *Hand-list of additions to the collection of English manuscripts . . . 1928-35*, pp49-61.

Wages books, flesh books, apprenticeship agreements, truck tickets, etc (c700 items) of Samuel Oldknow, Sir Richard Arkwright and his son Richard 1782-1815.
Rare Book & Manuscript Library, Columbia University, New York (ERA Seligman Collection).

Corresp with London Friendly Hospital rel to apprentices 1797-c1843.
Marple Antiquarian Society. A microfilm is in Manchester Central Library.

Orders for payments to weavers 1789-93.
Lancashire RO (DDX 199). NRA 3510.

Weavers' pay slips 1791-4.
Stockport Central Library (B/JJ/6/26). NRA 27964.

[441] **ORCHARD MANUFACTURING CO**, cotton mfrs, Croston, Lancs

Corresp, bills, receipts and memoranda c1900-6.
Lancashire RO (DDX 1288).

[442] **ORMROD, HARDCASTLE & CO LTD**, cotton spinners and mfrs, Bolton, Lancs

Register of members, deeds.
Courtaulds Spinning. Enquiries to the Company Secretary. NRA 30126.

Sample book c1820.
Bolton Museum (T.1.1968). NRA 29093.

[443] **JAMES ORR & SONS LTD**, cotton spinners and mfrs, Castleton, Lancs

Certificate of incorporation 1948, transfer deeds, etc (2 envelopes) 1938-56, minute book 1907-47, balance sheets, annual returns and other corporate and share records (11 vols, envelopes, etc) 1907-53, private ledgers (2) 1907-48, nominal ledger 1927-44, valuation of Empire House (1 envelope) 1938-41, Bluepit Mills sale particulars (1 bundle) 1935.
Lancashire RO (DDVc). NRA 30810.

[444] **ROBERT ORR & WILLIAM GLEN**, cotton and linen goods mfrs, Paisley, Renfrewshire

Account book 1760-2; ledgers (2) 1750-68 and waste or day book 1750-8 of a stocking factory in which Orr was a partner.
Scottish Record Office (CS 96/2262, 4444-7). *Court of Session Productions*, List & Index Society, special series vol 23, 1987, pp33-4, 46.

[445] **OSBORNE MILL CO LTD**, cotton spinners, Oldham, Lancs

Memorandum and articles of association 1906, 1908, general meeting minutes 1915-53, directors' minutes 1922-57, loans ledger 1889-1900, share deposit book 1889-1905 and other share records 1907-57, profit and loss accounts 1889-1939, impersonal ledger 1889-1913, cash books (2) 1941-64 and misc accounts 1947-69, ledger and journals (2) for outward trade 1918-64, cotton stock and yarn books (6) 1918-67, cotton mixing books (3) 1951-65, wages books (5) 1891-c1960, operatives' holiday account books (5) 1939-58, plans, tenders, specifications, etc rel to buildings and plant 1887-1948, misc Cotton Association records and price lists 1912-61; Gresham Mill Co memorandum and articles of association, with amendments 1903-53, minutes (incl Gresham Mill Co (Holdings) Ltd) 1948-57, register of directors 1903-62.
Lancashire RO (DDX 869). NRA 18057.

[446] **OWEN OWENS & SON**, cotton mfrs and shippers, Manchester

Corresp (14 packets) 1821-46 incl from overseas agents, ledgers (4) nd, cash books (2) 1816-43, summary accounts 1831-48, petty cash book 1821-52, bill book 1825-53, bank books 1808-46, cheque book stubs (19) 1831-46, sales day books (5) 1819-46, bills of purchase (2 files) 1840-6, accounts of sales overseas (3 vols) 1831-46, sales of produce book from 1838, particulars of cloth purchase (1 vol) 1838-46, memoranda book 1840-5, packing and length books (8) nd, bleachers' book 1829-44, wages and petty cash book 1815, 1820-9; ledger of Messrs Cunliffe, debtors, 1813.
John Rylands University Library of Manchester. NRA 25953.

[447] **PARK MILL (ROYTON) LTD**, cotton spinners, Royton, Lancs

Directors' minutes (6 vols) 1904-53, shareholders' minutes (2 vols) 1938-53, contract ledger 1912-43, wages books (9) 1927-68.
Shiloh plc. Enquiries to the Chairman and Managing Director. NRA 31773.

[448] **PARK & SANDY LANE MILLS CO LTD**, cotton spinners, Royton, Lancs

Directors' minutes (6 vols) 1885-1949, wages books (10) 1931-70.
Shiloh plc. Enquiries to the Chairman and Managing Director. NRA 31773.

[449] **ROBERT PARKER & NEPHEWS**, cotton merchants, Manchester

Corresp, patterns, etc (3 boxes) 19th cent.
Cumbria RO, Kendal (WD/Pkr).

[450] **WILLIAM PATON LTD**, mfrs of thread, braids and shoe laces, Johnstone, Renfrewshire

Contract of copartnery 1879, minute books (3) from 1897, balance sheets 1897-1904, cash books from 1841, private ledger 1895-7, private journal 1897-1903.
The Company. Enquiries to NRA (Scotland) (NRA(S) 633). NRA 15639.

[451] **PEAR NEW MILL CO LTD**, cotton spinners, Stockport, Cheshire

Directors' minutes (4 vols) 1912-26, register of bonds and mortgages 1919, balance sheets (2 vols) 1913-52, general register for factories 1943-9, bills receivable 1937-57, stocktaking records 1913-34, 1949-60, papers

rel to wages and taxation 1907-59, tenders, plans, etc 1912-13, memoranda, estimates, etc rel to mill and plant 1912-13, valuation 1915, misc papers incl some rel to the cotton industry reorganisation scheme 1959-65.
Stockport Archive Service (B/NN/3,4). NRA 20423.

[452] **ISAAC PEARSON LTD**, cotton spinners, Stockport, Cheshire

Ledger, test books, misc corresp and plans 1897-1980.
Stockport Central Library.

[453] **PENNINGTON MILL CO LTD**, cotton goods mfrs, Leigh, Lancs

Memorandum and articles of association 1877, 1962, directors' and shareholders' minute books (6) 1877-1948, rough minutes and agenda of directors' meetings (2 vols) 1949-67, registers of directors 1902-27, 1957-72, registers of mortgages, transfers of shares and debentures 1877-90, nd, share ledger and register 1922-9, share corresp, etc 1877-1960, annual returns 1947-56, managing director's letter book 1887-1938, secretary's corresp (3 vols and files) 1916-48, balance sheets and accounts 1880-1964, ledgers (6) 1886-1963, cash books (6) 1895-1903, 1933-63, petty cash book 1965-71, savings book 1962-72, bank statements 1962-8, order books (8) *c*1938-1962, lists of weaving prices, etc (8 vols) 1884-1971, yarn production records (16 vols) 1941-71, accident report books (7) 1948-62, corresp and papers rel to property, insurance and income tax 20th cent.
Wigan RO (D/DY Pe). NRA 30989.

[454] **PETTIGREW & DICKIE**, cotton weavers, Glasgow

Ledger 1812-13, day book 1814-15, cash book 1812-14, bill book 1812-14, bank book 1812-16, receipt books (2) 1812-15, rates of webs 1812-16, production journal and notebooks (4 vols) *c*1800, 1812-14, weaving book 1813-14, general account book of unemployed operatives fund, Kilmarnock and Irvine, 1842-3.
Strathclyde Regional Archives. NRA 17391.

[455] **J & N PHILIPS & CO LTD**, tape mfrs, Manchester, Upper Tean, Staffs and London

Buyers' meeting minutes 1929-39, ledgers 1806-1922, London accounts 1887-1907, cash books, etc 1938-63, sales figures 1870-94, corresp and orders (1 vol) 1753-69, stock records 1899-1939, patents 1944-51, staff instructions 1854-1930, travellers' records 1851-1911, deeds, valuations, rentals and plans 1748-1958 for property in various counties.
Manchester Central Library (M97). NRA 24109.

Statements of accounts 1770-1925, out-letter book 1904-7, corresp 1905-25, sales book 1870-3, orders (1 bundle) 1908-21, price lists (1 vol, etc) 1817-20th cent, stock and production books (5) 1771-1824, notebook rel to bleaching gardens *c*1849-60, export stamp impressions book 18th-20th cent, papers rel to stamping of weights (1 bundle) 1835-6, cost calculations, prices, dyeing recipes and memoranda (2 vols, 8 bundles) 1778-1925, staff contracts (17)

1751-60, wages books (4) 1813-1940, particulars, valuations, etc rel to premises 1774-1914, register of tape looms 1810, sick club account book 1807, misc papers 1806-1914.
Staffordshire RO (D 644). NRA 8750.

London branch (George Philips & Co) letter books (10) 18th cent-1830 incl private letter book of Sir George Philips 1820-30, ledgers (2) 1801-2, journals (3) 1801-4, bank book 1802-3, bill books (2) 1801-3, receipt book 1801-2, trading books (2 boxes) 18th-19th cent, misc corresp and papers 20th cent, family papers incl private accounts (5 vols) 1790-1846; articles of partnership of J & N Philips & Co and J Chadwick & Brother 1853.
Warwick County RO (CR 456). NRA 5911.

Philips family papers (195 items) 1805-1903 incl letters (10) from GA Lee to Sir George Philips 1806-22, Philips & Lee abstract of accounts to 1814, and papers (7 items) rel to business in India 1806, 1826.
Shakespeare Birthplace Trust RO, Stratford-upon-Avon (DR 198). NRA 27932.

Pattern books (5) 1900-12.
Greater Manchester Museum of Science & Industry (Acc 1975.5).

Pattern book 1906.
Quarry Bank Mill, Styal.

[456] **PLUM MILL LTD**, cotton mfrs, Heywood, Lancs

Letter books (4) 1905-7 rel to shares and building and equipping the mill, sales ledger 1930-4, misc corresp, delivery notes and invoices 1910-27, wages cards 1922-7.
Greater Manchester Museum of Science & Industry (TX 6). NRA 29510.

[457] **M & J POOL**, cotton merchants and brokers, Liverpool

Account books (2) 1811-22, 1816-18, purchase and sales account ledger 1811-16, Michael Pool's account book *c*1816-31 and notebook rel to business matters nd, misc corresp mainly rel to cotton trade (1 bundle, 18 items) 1803-*c*1820, list of cotton dealers in Kendal 1802, trade cards, price lists and circulars (1 bundle) *c*1830-40, deeds and other misc legal papers (9 items) 1790-1804.
Wiltshire RO (WRO 946). NRA 20411.

[458] **PORTSMOUTH COTTON CO LTD**, cotton mfrs, Cliviger, Lancs

Ledger 1845-59, journal 1845-56, cash book 1845-56.
Lancashire RO (NCPc). NRA 12638.

Time book 1855.
Lancashire RO (DDX 536).

[459] **PORTWOOD SPINNING CO LTD** (formerly **CEPHAS HOWARD & CO**), cotton spinners, Stockport, Cheshire

Ledgers and inventories (14 vols) 1868-1959, plans (29) 1833-*c*1960, photographs, misc papers.
Stockport Central Library.

Directors' and shareholders' minutes (1 vol)
1874-1933.
Manchester Central Library (M127).

[460] **REYNOLDS & GIBSON**, cotton brokers,
Liverpool and Manchester

Ledgers, journals and accounts from 1864.
Liverpool RO.

[461] **EDWARD & PICKLES RILEY & CO LTD**,
cotton weavers, Colne, Lancs

Annual balances 1899-1910, pricing books (19)
1904-24, schedule of orders 1896-9, notebooks (4) of
orders and quotations 1913-16, corresp (1 file) 1926-7,
sales ledger sheets 1937-52, working diary 1930-9 incl
a register of workpeople 1941, insurance inventories,
leases and misc papers 1917-56.
Lancashire RO (DDX 875). NRA 18061.

[462] **GEORGE ROBINSON & CO**, cotton
merchants, Manchester

Cash book 1847-52, petty cash books (3) 1847-79,
contract book 1847-55, lists (1 vol) of exports of yarn
and cotton goods to India and the Far East c1839-80,
stock book 1848-73, wages book 1865-76.
Manchester Central Library (MS F382.2 R1).
MD Wainwright and N Matthews, *Guide to Western
manuscripts and documents in the British Isles relating to
South and South East Asia*, 1965, pp313-14.

[463] **RODGETT & BRIERLEY**, cotton spinners,
Blackburn, Lancs

Articles of partnership and related papers 1833-63.
Lancashire RO (DDX 1041).

Register of young employees 1842-4.
Lancashire RO (DDX 577).

[464] **ROY MILL LTD**, cotton spinners, Royton,
Lancs

Directors' minutes (6 vols) 1905-53, shareholders'
minutes (1 vol) from 1929, register of directors
1905-19, shareholders' ledgers (2) nd, wages books
(10) 1932-66.
Shiloh plc. Enquiries to the Chairman and Managing
Director. NRA 31773.

[465] **ROYTON SPINNING CO LTD**, cotton
spinners, Royton, Lancs

Directors' minutes (2 vols) 1873-81, 1892-1901.
Shiloh plc. Enquiries to the Chairman and Managing
Director. NRA 31773.

[466] **RYLANDS & SONS LTD**, cotton spinners
and mfrs, and general warehousemen, Manchester

Records 1742-1969 incl minutes, annual reports and
accounts, ledgers, trade mark records, wages ledger,
deeds, catalogues, price lists, and photographs.
John Rylands University Library of Manchester. NRA
28631; BAC *Company Archives* no 181.

Profit and loss accounts 1847-54, stock sheets 1865,
machinery purchases and sales 1847-54, deeds and
corresp 1830-66, Joseph Rylands' account book
1847-54.
Wigan RO (D/DX E). NRA 19719.

Pattern book 1901.
Royal College of Art, London. Enquiries to the Textile
Design Department. NRA 32469.

[467] **BENJAMIN V SANDFORD** (afterwards
H NUTTER), grey cloth merchant, Manchester

Private ledger 1908-40, day book 1925-38, cash books
(2) 1928-40, returns and allowances for faulty goods
1909-38, order book 1928-40, contract book 1920-39,
stock book 1928-37, sample books (2) 1889-1938, diary
1927-9.
Manchester Central Library (M324). NRA 22536.

[468] **SHAW & SHAW**, cotton spinners,
Milnsbridge, Yorks

Corresp, bills, receipts and estimates (1 vol, 3 bundles)
1871-2, 1892-1904, wages sheets (11 items) 1896-1901.
West Yorkshire Archive Service, Kirklees (KC 26,
KC 137). NRA 26729.

[469] **SHILOH SPINNING CO LTD**, cotton
spinners, Royton, Lancs

Directors' minutes (8 vols) 1874-86, 1898-1901,
1907-41, 1944-53, shareholders' minutes (1 vol)
1929-53, balance sheets 1920-66, loan summary book
1926-40, log books (2) 1909-27, day book 1918-39,
weekly statements (2 vols) 1936-49, wages and other
employment records from 1927, press cuttings (5 vols)
from 1925.
Shiloh plc. Enquiries to the Chairman and Managing
Director. NRA 31773.

[470] **SIMPSON BROTHERS**, cotton spinners and
doublers, Ashbourne, Derbys

Records mid 19th-mid 20th cent incl letter books,
invoice books and price lists.
Derbyshire RO (D 710).

[471] **SAMUEL SLATER & SONS**, cotton mfrs,
Preston, Lancs

Trading accounts and balance sheets (33 items)
1908-25, schedules (4) of debtors and creditors 1924-5,
corresp 1920-5, stocktaking lists 1923-5, accounts,
corresp, plans and papers rel to building Waverley
Park and Tennyson Road mills 1909-15, insurance
receipts, etc 1919-21.
Lancashire RO (DDX 1306, DDX 1307). NRA 3510.

(472) **DUNDAS SMITH & CO**, muslin mfrs,
Paisley, Renfrewshire

Ledgers (3) and index 1790-1801, day books (3)
1790-1802, cash books (2) 1790-8.
Scottish Record Office (CS 96/1381-8). *Court of Session
Productions*, List & Index Society, special series vol
23, 1987, p104.

[473] **SMITH & WISEMAN**, cotton spinners, Colne, Lancs

Partnership accounts (4 vols) 1815-33 (Thornber & England), ledgers (4) 1818-71, day books (3) 1862-77, journals (4) 1838-79, cash books (3) 1852-79, cash account book 1858, cloth account book with details of mill machinery 1855-7, 1861, account books (5) 1833, 1861-85, payments book 1867-8, sundries ledger 1864-71, sales ledger 1841-2, invoice sales book and cash book 1850, order books (2) 1871-7, 1897-1900, delivery receipt book 1881-2, consignment books (6) 1814-35, stock books (2) 1883, 1886-90, production notebook 1826, corresp, cotton invoices and misc accounts (1 box, etc) 19th cent, wages book 1871-9, Vivary Bridge Mill sale catalogue 1886, personal account books, estate and executorship accounts of Thomas Thornber (10 vols) 1803-48.
Lancashire RO (DDWm). NRA 30525.

Inventory, etc of Thomas Thornber 1848, mill contracts and abstracts of title 1862-5.
Lancashire RO (DDBd/14/21). NRA 14637.

[474] **JOHN SPENCER & SON**, quilting and shirting mfrs, Manchester

Pattern books (3) of quiltings and dimities *c*1820, *c*1846, price lists (2) and address card 1817, sample card 1790.
Salford Museums & Art Galleries (52-56-1956). NRA 30500.

[475] **SPUR DOUBLING MILL LTD**, cotton doublers, Reddish, Lancs

Memorandum and articles of association 1919, balance sheets and misc accounts 1920-72, loan ledger 1908-44, loanholders' interest and balances 1909-42, corresp rel to debentures 1910-15, ledger 1880-1907, petty cash books (4) 1908-24, 1941-62, misc sales and production records 1935-70, wages book 1941-62 and misc employees' records 1913, 1954-68, letter book rel to new building 1908-9, estimates for machinery, etc 1907-8, insurance policies 1916-17, rent books 1958-62, visitors' book 1911-13.
Stockport Central Library (B/HH). NRA 27964 (vol 2).

[476] **STALEY & MILLBROOK LTD**, cotton spinners, Stalybridge, Cheshire

Secretary's letter books (7) 1897-1957 and misc corresp (2 bundles) 1874-1961, memoranda (1 bundle) 1873-6, reports, accounts and other corporate and share records (6 vols, many bundles) 1873-1970, balance sheets 1871-1952, cash books (5) 1886-1903, 1907-15, 1954-64, private journal 1904-23, misc account book 1878-1930, private receipt books (3) 1899-1907, 1925-30, 1957 and loose receipts 1900-8, vouchers (9 vols, etc) 1901-17, 1935-55, trade ledgers (2) 1947-57, analysis of plant accounts (1 vol) 1877, sales and purchase analyses (2 vols) 1949-71, stock book 1946-50, costing, production and other statistics (5 vols, 2 bundles) 1902-60, patent records (1 bundle) nd, income tax book nd, list of long-serving employees 1955, register of land and buildings 1881-1901, insurance records (1 vol, 6 bundles) 1883-1970.

Tameside Local Studies Library (DD SM). NRA 31005.

Statements of accounts incl general trade account, production statistics and costings, working expenses and property repairs (756 items) 1879-1934, comparative costs of both mills (21 items) 1887-1924.
Greater Manchester Museum of Science & Industry (TX 1). NRA 32348.

[477] **STOREY BROS & CO LTD**, cotton spinners, baize and leathercloth mfrs, Lancaster

Records 19th-20th cent.
Lancashire RO (DDSy). *Accessions to repositories 1982*, p27, *1988*, p25.

[478] **WG & J STRUTT LTD**, cotton spinners, Belper, Derbys

Letter books (3) 1824-7, 1864-6, 1888, ledgers (69) 1794-1894, cash books (30) 1780-1903, telegraph book 1879-82, wages and time books (69) 1784-1903, weekly and quarterly expenses books (11) 1809-93, statutory registers and age certificate books (42) 1836-1936, school records (104 vols) 1818-99, various records rel to services provided to employees (31 vols) 1813-1905, records of mill buildings and houses (15 vols) 1793-1865 and work on roads (16 vols) 1797-1885, maintenance of machinery, fuel, lighting, deliveries and tolls and watchman's reports (*c*60 items) 1789-1888.
Manchester Central Library. NRA 9852.

Standing books (2) rel to spindle work 1836-69, reeling book 1872, yarn store issue book 1872-4, spinning log books (2) 1874-86, accounts for stationery issue (4 vols) 1883-5, foreman's notebook *c*1896, misc notices, advertisements, photographs, etc 19th-20th cent.
In private possession. NRA 9852.

Strutt family corresp (several hundred items) 1748-1850, incl business letters, some rel to Jedediah Strutt's Derby Rib machine and the provision of mill schoolrooms.
Derby Central Library. NRA 20300.

Productivity figures for Belper and Milford mills incl wages paid 1880-2, patent records 1767, personal account books and other family papers 18th-20th cent.
Nottinghamshire AO (DD BK). NRA 30442.

[478A] **SUN MILL CO LTD**, cotton spinners, Oldham, Lancs

Minutes, printed reports and accounts, shareholders' registers and financial records *c*1860-*c*1960.
John Rylands University Library of Manchester: see *Bulletin of the John Rylands University Library of Manchester* 71, no 2, Summer 1989, p195.

[479] **JOSEPH SUNDERLAND, SONS & CO LTD**, cotton mfrs, Manchester

Minute books 1896-*c*1960, register of shareholders.
Courtaulds Spinning. Enquiries to the Company Secretary. NRA 30126.

[480] GEORGE SWINDELLS & SON LTD, cotton mfrs, Bollington, Cheshire

Deeds of partnership and related papers 1826-98, minute book 1834-42, personal account books (3) 1833-49 incl copies of business letters, diagrams and notes on mills, note of cotton prices 1828, production details 1841, corresp with factory inspector 1834, papers rel to mills incl costs and repairs 1834-1901, sale catalogue and plan of Clarence Mills 1882, family corresp, diaries and notebooks, etc 1804-1918.
Cheshire RO (D/2056). NRA 31590.

Private ledgers (2) 1887-91, 1898.
Courtaulds plc, Coventry (SWI). Enquiries to the Head of Archives. NRA 29343.

Plans (*c*100) from *c*1850.
In private possession.

Plans and construction details (30 items) 1894-1923.
Greater Manchester Museum of Science & Industry. NRA 29510.

[481] SYKES, ALLEN & CO (formerly **TAYLOR, SYKES & CO**), cotton brokers, Liverpool

Partnership agreement 1888, letter book 1872-84, JT Sykes letter book 1886-94 and other Sykes family papers 19th-20th cent.
Clwyd RO, Ruthin (DD/HB). NRA 26248.

[482] THOMAS TAYLOR & SONS, cotton spinners and doublers, Bolton, Lancs

Memorandum of agreement 1886, account book incl wages and applicants for work 1846-56, prime cost books (2) 1854-83, annual production and expenditure estimates 1883, cotton purchase and production book 1847-55, stock book 1848-80, letters patent for improving machinery for spinning and doubling 1876, valuations and plans of Grecian Mills 1882, *c*1900, *c*1910, schedule of deeds 1747-1841.
Bolton Metropolitan Borough Archives (ZTA). NRA 27220.

Register of members.
Courtaulds Spinning. Enquiries to the Company Secretary. NRA 30126.

[483] BENJAMIN THORNBER & SONS LTD, cotton mfrs, Burnley, Lancs

Deeds of partnership 1882, 1893, cash books (5) 1899-1937, production and mill record books (5) 1909-60, loom efficiency book 1919-20, wages books (8) 1896-1934, inventories (4 vols) of Danes House and Old Hall Mills 1937, 1957, probate of will of Benjamin Thornber 1885.
Burnley Central Library (M31). NRA 30746.

[484] ARTHUR THORP LTD, cotton spinners and mfrs, Rawtenstall, Lancs

Registers of young employees and certificates of fitness 1880, 1913.
Rawtenstall District Library (Rc 677 RAW). NRA 30888.

[485] TOLSON & GIBB, cotton spinners and doublers, Calver, Derbys

Summary ledger 1868-77, cost ledger 1867-74.
Derbyshire RO (2577B). NRA 25795.

[486] TOOTAL BROADHURST LEE CO LTD, cotton mfrs, Manchester and Bolton, Lancs

Minutes of board and general meetings (27 vols) 1888-1972, general management committee (1 vol) 1888-9, mill management committee (18 vols) 1888-1941, and finance committee (16 vols) 1888-1937; photographs.
Manchester Central Library (M461).

Ledgers 1864, 1882, stock book 1921, schedules, valuations, inspections, etc of Sunnyside and Bankfield Mills 1863-1962, Manchester Steam Users Association safety certificates 1917-32, part-time school attendance register 1950.
Bolton Metropolitan Borough Archives (ZTBL). NRA 27221; BAC *Company Archives* no 592.

Impersonal ledger 1966-8; ledgers, etc of subsidiaries from *c*1892.
Tootal Group plc. NRA 28631; BAC *Company Archives* no 592.

Pattern books (*c*200) *c*1840-1963 incl Gartside & Co and J Smith & Co.
Bolton Museum (IND.77.1980; IND.6.1982; IND.25.1982). NRA 29093.

Henry Tootal's diary and accounts 1852-68.
Greater Manchester RO.

[487] TOPLIS & CO, cotton mfrs, Cuckney, Notts

Apprenticeship register 1786-1805.
Nottinghamshire AO (DD 895/1).

[488] VINE MILL CO (ROYTON) LTD, cotton spinners, Royton, Lancs

Directors' minutes (9 vols) 1900-60.
Shiloh plc. Enquiries to the Chairman and Managing Director. NRA 31773.

[489] ROBERT WALKER LTD, cotton waste spinners, Bolton, Lancs

Directors' minute book 1906-10, corresp (3 files) 1966-71, private ledgers (4) 1896-1950, nominal ledgers (2) 1896-1931, credit and debit ledgers (3) 1946-65, ledger balance books (2) 1866-1960, day and cash books (7 vols) 1950-66, invoice, sales and contract records (26 vols, etc) 1913-75, stock books (2) 1938-72, spinners' weights (4 vols) 1948-69, wages books (4) 1947-63, age and school attendance certificates 1889-1939, specifications and plans 1898-1968.
Bolton Metropolitan Borough Archives (ZWA). NRA 27222.

[490] ALFRED WENNER LTD, cotton piece goods merchants, Manchester

Order books, sales ledgers, samples, etc from *c*1900.
Museum of the Lancashire Textile Industry, Helmshore.

[491] **WERNETH SPINNING CO LTD**, spinners of cotton and synthetic yarns, Oldham, Lancs

Directors' and general meeting minutes (9 vols) 1874-8, 1893-1966, agenda books (7) 1912-75, directors' reports (2 vols) 1889-1949, notes of board meetings (4 vols) 1920-45, registers of directors and members and other stock and share records (21 vols, files and items) 1874-1971, balance books (3) 1908-74, trading accounts (1 file) 1904-12, provisional accounts 1954-74, bank books (4) 1916-28, cotton purchase books (3) 1943-63, 1971-5, order books, stock books, stock reports, stocktaking notebooks and other production records (30 vols) 1906-79, staff and wages records (11 vols and files) 1920-70, valuations, insurance policies and other property records 1900-70. *Oldham Local Interest Centre* (MISC/42). NRA 29986.

[492] **GEORGE H WHEATCROFT & CO LTD**, tape mfrs, Wirksworth, Derbys

Memorandum and articles of association 1928, general account books, ledgers, day books and cash books 1917-58, bought ledgers 1941-56, purchase books 1904-11, 1940-61, order books (paper and twine) 1879-85, Canadian sales books 1914-31, stock books incl Canada and Australia 1871-1943, pricing memoranda books 1887-1920, price lists incl other firms 1859-1910, nd, production books with samples 1879-1903, 1949-54, dyeing and bleaching account books 1884-1914, sample books 1952-c1980, memorandum on manufacture of tapes 1851, cotton reports and statistics 1881-94, letters patent 1853 to James Tatlow for improvements in smallware looms, wages books 1944-61, inventory of Wirksworth and Derby mills 1927. *Derbyshire RO* (D 1262). NRA 30796.

[493] **ORMEROD WHITAKER & SONS LTD**, cotton spinners and mfrs, Manchester and Burnley, Lancs

Minutes 1901-48. *Coats Viyella plc*. Enquiries to the Company Secretary. NRA 32377.

[494] **DAVID WHITEHEAD & SONS LTD**, cotton mfrs, Rawtenstall, Lancs

Records c1807-1950 incl minute books, share registers, ledgers, account books, and corresp. *Rossendale Museum, Rawtenstall*. NRA 30829.

Diary of David Whitehead (2 vols) 1790-1851. *Rawtenstall District Library* (Rc 921 WHI). NRA 30888.

[495] **GEORGE WHITELEY & CO LTD**, cotton spinners and mfrs, Blackburn, Lancs

Directors' minutes 1899-1941, register of members, etc 1899-1941, annual returns 1934-66, ledger 1898-1963, winding master's order books (3) 1914-75, sort books (4) 1936-45, inventory 1911. *Lancashire RO* (DDX 868). NRA 18080.

[496] **W & S WILSON**, spinners of cotton, merino and angola yarns, Radford, Notts

William Wilson's business and general letter book 1835-40 and cash account books (27 vols) 1838-65, Radford mill bank book 1850-66, Wingfield mill accounts of cotton received and delivered, wages, etc 1856-7, valuations of Radford mill 1842, 1856, papers rel to sales of Radford and Wingfield mills 1853-67, Wilson family and estate papers 1802-1907. *Nottinghamshire AO* (DD WR). NRA 10258.

[497] **WOOD STREET MILL CO LTD**, cotton and yarn spinners, Bury, Lancs

Records from 1875 incl minutes, share registers, annual reports, balance sheets and accounts, letter book, private ledger, employee accident reports, factory registers, fire insurance papers, mill plans, weaving shed papers, and humidity register. *The Company*. NRA 28631; BAC *Company Archives* no 230.

[498] **R & J WORKMAN**, muslin and sewed work mfrs, Belfast

Overseas sales ledgers (3) 1820-45. *In private possession*. A microfilm is in the Public Record Office of Northern Ireland (Mic 142): see *Ulster textile industry*.

LINEN, FLAX AND JUTE

[499] **DAVID ACHESON LTD**, linen mfrs, Castlecaulfield, co Tyrone

Directors' minute book 1909-17, corresp (2 bundles) 1881-9, 1917-54, share records, balance sheets and other administrative papers (5 bundles, c130 items) c1919-1970, ledgers (9) 1880-5, 1939-67, day books (5) 1874-91, 1963-7, cash books (8) 1873-99, 1909-25, 1958-67, petty cash books (3) 1908-17, 1935-8, 1965-7, accounts received (c100 items) c1945-8, farm account book 1942-4, bill books (3) 1891-9, 1913-16, 1920-38, balance book 1925-70, bank books (15) and statements (c200) 1918-67, index books (2) nd, order books (9) 1880-1904, 1935-7, 1956-68, purchase and sales records (11 vols, etc) 1921-8, 1960-70, stock books (13) 1889-1938, costing books (2) c1935, 1965-8, tick book 1913-18, lot book 1959-70, cloth pattern books (3) 1906-13, 1922-8, cloth number book 1924-9, weekly production books (2) 1874-9, factory registers (12) 1895-1966, wages book 1917-27, notes (15 vols) by DA Acheson rel to cloth manufacture, etc c1932. *Public Record Office of Northern Ireland* (D 1699, D 2656). NRA 31448.

[500] **ADAMS family**, linen merchants, Ballyweaney, co Antrim

General and linen accounts and cash books c1780-1830. *Public Record Office of Northern Ireland* (D 1518/2): see *Ulster textile industry*.

[501] **ALEXANDER family**, linen merchants, Limavady, co Londonderry

Linen trade accounts 1757-67, letter book 1806-13, 1837-48.
Public Record Office of Northern Ireland (D 1491). *Deputy Keeper's Report 1960-5*, p160.

Corresp, balance sheets, stock accounts, etc 1797-1849.
Public Record Office of Northern Ireland (D 2587/8): see *Ulster textile industry*.

[502] **JAMES ALLISON & SONS (SAILMAKERS) LTD**, Dundee

Letter books (16 vols and files) 1933-54, private ledgers (6) 1894-1964, petty cash and bill books (3) 1880-1904, captains' and voyage account books (8) 1877-97, costing and stock books (20) 1918, 1928-62, time and wages books (11) 1890-1904, 1915-18, 1924-57, plans, etc (19 items) 1876-1954, misc papers 1876-1964.
Dundee University Library (MS 44). NRA 17674.

[503] **ALLISTRAGH FLAX MILLS LTD** (formerly **WILLIAM H ADDEY**), linen mfrs, Allistragh, co Armagh

Cloth despatch book 1786, corporate and financial records, etc 1861-1954.
Public Record Office of Northern Ireland (D 889/7, D 1142/B): see *Ulster textile industry*.

[504] **ARDS WEAVING CO LTD**, linen mfrs, Newtownards, co Down

Private ledger and journal (2 vols) 1889-1912, design book 1820s.
Public Record Office of Northern Ireland (D 2664): see *Ulster textile industry*.

[505] **ROBERT ATKINSON**, linen merchant, Moy, co Tyrone

Accounts and corresp 1798-1810.
Public Record Office of Northern Ireland (D 1721): see *Ulster textile industry*.

[506] **JAMES BANKS & SONS**, rope and twine mfrs, Perth

Ledgers (6) 1891-1920, 1946-70 some rel to fishing interests, balance sheets from 1944, cash books (2) 1903-11, 1931-6, order and despatch books (3) 1904-47, details of fish caught 1892, nd, corresp 1906-7, photographs 1895-c1930.
The Company. Enquiries to NRA (Scotland) (NRA(S) 1379). NRA 19760.

Balance and stock sheets 1921-43, netting samples nd.
Dundee University Library. NRA 19760.

[507] **BARCROFT & CO**, linen mfrs, Armagh and Tassagh, co Armagh

Corresp, ledgers, accounts, invoices, memoranda, etc c1875-1935.
Public Record Office of Northern Ireland (D 1257): see *Ulster textile industry*.

[508] **BARNAGORE JUTE FACTORY CO LTD**, London

Directors' minutes 1872-1900.
The Company. NRA 28631; BAC *Company Archives* no 151.

[509] **ROBERT BARR & CO**, thread, lawn, gauze and linen mfrs, Paisley, Renfrewshire

Letter books (3) 1777-1806, ledgers (4) 1771-1806, day books (3) 1784-94, 1805-6, cash books (3) 1794-1805, memoranda book 1795-6, waste book 1793-1806.
Scottish Record Office (CS 96/3432-46). *Court of Session Productions*, List & Index Society, special series vol 23, 1987, p64.

[510] **BARRY, OSTLERE & SHEPHERD LTD**, floorcloth and linoleum mfrs, Kirkcaldy, Fife

Board and shareholding records 1880-99, sales records 1900-30, trade brochures and price lists 1901-7, corresp and papers rel to trade, production and personnel 1885-1963, photographs 20th cent.
Kirkcaldy Museum & Art Gallery. NRA 18847.

[511] **BAXTER BROTHERS & CO LTD**, linen and jute mfrs, Dundee

Contracts of copartnery 1853, 1879, memorandum and articles of association 1892-1922, directors' and general meeting minutes (2 vols) 1873-1966, registers of members 1930-48, private letter books (2) 1898-1929, quarterly balances 1852-1927, private ledgers (4) 1853-1938, ledgers, journals and other accounts (65 vols) 1806-1974 incl Glamis spinning mill 1806-15 and private account book of Sir William Dalgleish 1891-1904, contract and order books, tenders and specifications (48 vols, etc) 1898-1971, representatives' report books (31) 1926-63, stock books 1953-64, calculation books 1850-1908, technical drawings (368) 1833-1957, wages/production books (8) 1841-1959, chief engineer's book 1878-1915, diary of Peter Carmichael, copartner 1833, notes on trade with France 1840-70, journals rel to flax weaving at Lille 1886, meteorological register 1891-1934, inventories and valuations, photographs from c1870.
Dundee University Library (MS 11). NRA 12255.

Plans and technical drawings (9) 1846-90.
Dundee Museums & Art Galleries, Human History Section (1981-400). NRA 12255.

Papers of Peter Carmichael incl his reminiscences 1816-90, notes and drawings rel to flax cultivation and linen manufacture, boiler and engine experiments 1837.
In private possession. Enquiries to NRA (Scotland) (NRA(S) 381). NRA 12259.

Deeds (1 box) incl contracts of copartnery with Peter Carmichael, etc.
In private possession. Enquiries to NRA (Scotland) (NRA(S) 723). NRA 16125.

[512] **ARCHIBALD BECK & CO**, cambric handkerchief mfrs, Portadown, co Armagh

Letter book 1871-6, bill books (2) 1860-9, 1887-97.
Public Record Office of Northern Ireland (D 1286/4): see *Ulster textile industry*.

[513] **BELFAST FLAX & JUTE CO LTD**, Belfast

Directors' reports 1922-45, letter books (3) 1939-45, business diary 1907, ledgers and other accounting records (9 vols) 1927-50, purchase, order and despatch records (23 vols, 4 bundles) 1926-53, stock books (6) 1930-49, work books and other production records (15 vols) 1923-49, time and wages books (9) 1932-49, register of young employees 1918-39, machinery books (2) 1885-1949, misc papers (1 box) 1867-1946, press cuttings book 1886-1949.
Public Record Office of Northern Ireland (D 1189). NRA 31442.

Corresp and papers (*c*100 items) 1882-94 of Alexander Taylor, proprietor of the Belfast Flax & Jute Co, incl some rel to business affairs.
Public Record Office of Northern Ireland (D 3658). NRA 31442.

[514] **BELFAST FLAX SPINNING & WEAVING CO LTD**, Belfast

Journal, salaries book and plan of Mulhouse Works 1897-*c*1944.
Public Record Office of Northern Ireland (D 2120/7): see *Ulster textile industry*.

[515] **BELFAST ROPEWORK CO LTD**, rope and twine mfrs, Belfast

Directors' minute books 1876-1965, registers of directors 1901-14, directors' reports and statements of accounts 1924-70, share registers 1932-*c*1970, ledgers (4) 1872-1941, bill book 1884-1944, travellers' accounts book 1928-51, stationery and label sample books *c*1920-70, wages book 1894-1903, machine inventory books 1887-1971, plans and photographs 1889-1972, misc papers 1886-*c*1950.
Public Record Office of Northern Ireland (D 2889). NRA 31464 (partial list); *Deputy Keeper's Report 1984*, p45.

[516] **THOMAS BELL & SONS OF DUNDEE LTD**, jute spinners and mfrs, Dundee

Minutes (2 vols) 1890-1933, agenda books (2) 1891-1926, registers (3) of members and transfers 1890-1928, letter book 1914-23, summary of capital and shares 1901-30, balance sheets and profit and loss accounts 1891-1932, ledger 1917-21, tradesmen's time books (2) 1939-42.
Dundee University Library (MS 66). NRA 12256.

[517] **TIMOTHY BELL & CO**, flax merchants, Belfast

Deed of partnership, bills of exchange, agreements, letters, etc 1866-74.
Public Record Office of Northern Ireland (D 638): see *Ulster textile industry*.

[518] **BESSBROOK SPINNING CO LTD**, flax spinners and weavers, Bessbrook, co Armagh

Records (over 600 vols, etc) 1851-1972 incl minutes 1878-1945, letter books 1865-1951, ledgers 1879-1939, journals 1860-1965, purchase and sales records 1909-74, order books 1900-70, stock books 1929-54, wages books 1905-66, and annual summaries of goods made, wages paid and hours worked 1851-1904.
Public Record Office of Northern Ireland (D 1133): see *Ulster textile industry* and *Deputy Keeper's Report 1984*, pp58-9.

Misc records 1776-1952 incl accounts 1776, 1791, managers' diary and report book 1898-1951, yarn price lists (1 bundle) 1900-47, and notebook rel to yarn prices 1922-30.
Public Record Office of Northern Ireland (D 2375). NRA 31436.

Medical certificates 1847-50, workers' time book 1878-9.
Public Record Office of Northern Ireland (D 2368/1). *Deputy Keeper's Report 1966-72*, p209.

[519] **BLACKSTAFF FLAX SPINNING & WEAVING CO LTD**, Belfast

Secretary's letter books (2) 1866-1916, reports and notices to shareholders *c*1862-1901, trial balance book 1834-1900, private vouchers book 1898-1951, yarn cost book 1887-9, spinning reports 1886-7, wages books (3) 1894-1905, 1917-63, agreement, plan, photographs of departments (61) *c*1940, 1967.
Public Record Office of Northern Ireland (D 2120). NRA 31451.

Cash receipt book *c*1867-84, typescript history of firm nd.
Public Record Office of Northern Ireland (D 1534): see *Ulster textile industry*.

[520] **BOASE SPINNING CO LTD**, flax, hemp and jute spinners and mfrs, Dundee

Articles of association 1866, minute book 1886-1920, ledger 1876-99, order book 1870, contract book 1898-9, production book 1906-50, specification book nd, photographs, etc 1866-1968.
Dundee University Library (MS 66). NRA 12256.

[521] **JOHN BOATH JUNIOR & CO LTD**, linen and jute mfrs, Forfar, Angus

Minutes, share register and share certificate book from 1916, letter books (15) 1909-11, 1917-52, balance sheets 1904-26, ledgers (7) 1852-9, 1863-1940 and index nd, statement books (3) 1884-92, bill book 1861-1946, order books (8) 1863-6, 1893-1956, orders and accounts (1 vol) 1843-1944, yarn buying book 1884-92, stock book 1865-71, specification and costing books (14) 1891-1958 and misc papers (3 folders) 1928-49, nd, wages books (10) 1881-3, 1912-22, 1933-48, inventory 1853, plan of works 1886, John Boath's notebook 1832.
The Company. Enquiries to NRA (Scotland) (NRA(S) 949). NRA 18268.

[522] **JAMES BOOMER & CO**, flax and cotton spinners, Belfast

Letter book 1826-30, day book 1845-51, journal 1848-54.
Public Record Office of Northern Ireland (D 2450/2). NRA 31458.

[523] **JOSEPH BOUCHER & CO**, linen merchants, Belfast

Ledger 1894-1914, cash book 1898-1914.
Public Record Office of Northern Ireland (D 2202/1/1, 3/1). NRA 31440.

[524] **BOYACK & BARCLAY LTD**, jute and flax merchants, Dundee

Day book 1876-98, journal 1899-1921, ledger 1909-27, cash book 1912-24, purchase book 1877-84, order book 1893-1927.
The Company. Enquiries to NRA (Scotland) (NRA(S) 423). NRA 13039.

[525] **HUGH BOYLE**, linen and general merchant, Warrenpoint, co Down and Armagh

Letter book, ledgers and account books 1838-43, 1851-89.
Public Record Office of Northern Ireland (D 266/321, 321A): see *Ulster textile industry*.

[526] **BOYLE & SON**, rope and twine mfrs, Leeds

Account books (4) 1852-73, 1882-1901, ledgers (7) 1863-1933, cash books (11) 1863-70, 1888-1916, bank books (7) 1863-85, 1907-9, 1921-2, list of bills payable 1901-31, order books (2) 1884-8, stock book nd, wages book 1851-89, misc legal, business and personal corresp and papers 1782-1906.
West Yorkshire Archive Service, Leeds (Acc 2162). NRA 21928.

[527] **BRAIDWATER SPINNING CO**, linen mfrs, Ballymena, co Antrim

Book of wages, costs, etc 1874-82.
Public Record Office of Northern Ireland (D 1492/8). NRA 31446.

Machinery book 1865-87.
Public Record Office of Northern Ireland (D 2297/X). NRA 31465.

Machinery book 1867-c1880.
Public Record Office of Northern Ireland (D 1189/93). NRA 31442.

[528] **BRITISH LINEN CO**, linen mfrs and bankers, Edinburgh and Saltoun, East Lothian

Records 1746-1972 incl proprietors', directors' and committee minutes, letter books, stock ledgers, journals and transfers, dividend books, ledgers, and cash books; Saltoun bleachfield general ledger 1768-73 and journals 1756-73.
Bank of Scotland, Glasgow Chief Office. Enquiries to NRA (Scotland) (NRA(S) 945). NRA 10784.

Corresp and papers of Lord Milton rel to the establishment, administration and finances of the company, the Saltoun bleachfield and the London warehouse (7 vols, etc) 1739-65; other papers mainly of Milton rel to manufacture of linen and woollens (26 vols) 1725-82.
National Library of Scotland (MSS 17560-77, 17579-86, 17594-17600; Ch 14879-83).

Business and family corresp, accounts and papers 1777-1817 of James Bell, the company's agent at Leith.
Scottish Record Office (GD 1/437). *Annual Report 1966*, p9.

[529] **BROADWAY DAMASK CO LTD**, linen mfrs, Belfast

Letter books (13) 1910-21, bill book 1914-35, order books (108) 1882-1948 and indexes (5 vols) from 1924, purchase ledgers (8) 1882-1947, sales ledgers (23) 1882-1950, linen prices (1 box) 1900-39, special prices (13 vols) 1912-46, shipping and invoice books (5) 1939-54, reference books (12) 1886-1946, yarn stock books (9) 1914-47, cloth books (2) 1931-49, goods received for finishing (1 vol) 1917-51, post book 1949, papers rel to boilers (2 folders) 1903-47, staff photographs (12) 1893-1901; New York office receipts and accounts (2 vols) 1925-47.
Public Record Office of Northern Ireland (D 1193). NRA 31444.

[530] **JOHN S BROWN & SONS LTD**, damask linen and handkerchief mfrs, Belfast and Edenderry, co Down

Out-letter book 1908-22, balance sheets and trading accounts 1915-20, purchase journal 1902-6, sales journal 1902-6, price lists 1901-2, map 1903 and photographs 1906-c1930 of St Ellen's Works.
Public Record Office of Northern Ireland (D 3484).

[531] **JOSEPH BRYANT LTD**, rope makers, Bristol

Private ledgers (2) 1903-63, ledgers (2) 1863-83, journal 1901-10, invoice book 1914-27, Bryant family deeds and papers 1747-1974.
Bristol RO (Acc 33302). NRA 19629.

[532] **BUIST SPINNING CO LTD** (formerly **LAING BROS & CO**), jute spinners, Dundee

Minute books (3) 1900-78, registers of members, shares, etc 1900-65, annual lists and summaries 1921-78, ledger c1954-77, jute purchase and sales books (2) 1929-79, stock books (4) 1926-79, yarns analysis 1962-79, jute used book 1971-9, wages books (10) 1957-68; Laing Bros & Co invoice book 1874-99.
Dundee University Library (MS 71). NRA 25437.

[533] **CALDERS**, sailmakers, Leith, Midlothian

Details of sails supplied (2 vols) 1823-1949.
National Maritime Museum (MS84/054). NRA 20623.

[534] HENRY CAMPBELL & CO LTD, flax spinners and linen thread mfrs, Mossley, co Antrim

Records (*c*25 vols and items) incl account books 1851-1909, ledgers 1879-97, costing books 1884-1935, and inventories 1877-93.
Public Record Office of Northern Ireland (D 2459).
Deputy Keeper's Report 1966-72, p69.

[535] JAMES CAMPBELL, flax seed and linen agent, Belfast

Business corresp and commission notes (4 vols, 4 bundles) 1860-4, 1867-8, cash book 1841-59, petty cash book 1859-69, sundries account book 1861, personal bank book 1865-72, misc corresp, receipts, press cuttings, etc (1 file) *c*1860-1924.
Public Record Office of Northern Ireland (D 2450/1).
NRA 31458.

[536] CANTER, WHALEY & CO, linen mfrs, Barnsley, Yorks

Specifications (8 vols) 1863-81, memoranda book 1853-77, rent accounts 1841-69, misc deeds and legal papers 19th cent.
In private possession. NRA 12362.

[537] JH CAPPER & CO LTD, linen goods mfrs, Belfast

Ledger 1870-90, private ledger 1890-1910, yarn price ledger 1900-16.
Ulster Folk and Transport Museum, Holywood (UFTM D4-9-14, D4-10-1, D4-10-5).

[538] CHAMPDANY JUTE CO LTD, jute mfrs, Glasgow

Directors' and general meeting minutes (8 vols) and agenda 1873-1921, balance sheets, profit and loss accounts, etc 1875-1931, 1947-61, corresp *c*1890-*c*1920, letter book 1910-15, Champdany Share Trust accounts 1902-22, mill indents 1890-1925, notebooks (4) rel to jute mills 1872-1900, inventories 1918, plans of Wellington and Champdany Mills *c*1883-1907.
Glasgow University Archives (UGD/91). NRA 23054.

[539] J & W CHARLEY & CO LTD, linen mfrs and bleachers, Dunmurry, co Antrim

Letter books (18) 1840-56, 1908-26, corresp files (20) 1951-64, ledgers (17) 1844-1952, journals (15) 1842-1926, private journals (2) 1892-1925, cash books (20) 1838-1928, 1945-61, petty cash book 1867-74, account books (2) 1937, 1950-6, entry books (9) 1896-8, 1905-12, bill book 1896-1946, bank books (2) 1936-45, invoice books (22) 1838-40, 1861-2, 1894-1911, 1916-25, order books (5) 1860-5, 1939-56, purchase, sales and stock records (*c*40 vols, parcels, etc) 1929-64, insurance policies and tax forms (1 bundle) *c*1845, time book 1945-7, wages books (2) 1947-61, deeds and leases (46 items) 1773-1862, 1935-50, price lists, maps and other printed material 19th-20th cent.
Public Record Office of Northern Ireland (D 1171, D 2242). NRA 31439.

[540] WILLIAM CLARK & SONS, linen mfrs, bleachers and dyers, Upperlands, co Londonderry

Letter books (4) 1877-99, 1904-17, 1954, corresp files (2) 1959-61, account book 1925-9, order books (10) 1900-2, 1937-65, purchase ledger 1922-5, production ledger 1903-22, samples book 1918-39, wages books (5) 1901-4, 1931-4, 1943-59.
Public Record Office of Northern Ireland (D 2659).
NRA 31462.

Diary of HJ Clark describing American sales trips *c*1900, misc corresp, notes, statistics, etc *c*1945, reference book 1919-53, inventory and valuation *c*1920, etc.
In private possession. Copies are in the Public Record Office of Northern Ireland (T 2329, T 2835, T 2990): see *Ulster textile industry.*

[541] COALISLAND WEAVING CO LTD, linen mfrs, Coalisland, co Tyrone and Belfast

Accounts and inventories (6 vols) 1906-43.
Public Record Office of Northern Ireland (D 1734).
Deputy Keeper's Report 1960-5, p72.

[542] COGGREY LINEN MILL, Doagh, co Antrim

Corresp, sales books, invoices, cinema records, etc (*c*100 vols) *c*1900-1957.
Public Record Office of Northern Ireland (D 1221).
Deputy Keeper's Report 1960-5, p133.

[543] WILLIAM COULSON & SONS, damask and linen mfrs, Lisburn, co Antrim

Account books (9) 1838-1908, 1931-49, weavers' account books (6) 1851-96, cash books (6) 1850-83, 1908-12, order books (8) 1846-60, 1884-*c*1904 and indexes (2 vols) 1884-90, *c*1910, despatch books (5) 1847-1913, 1959-64, invoices (19) 1900, weavers' books (9) 1834-43, 1852-97, bleach books (9) 1847-98, 1908-64, weft books (7) 1850-1913, yarn rolling books (2) 1838-82, cut book 1905-6, patterns (18 items) 1794-1829, 1946, grazing book 1851-2, rent books (2) 1853-97.
Public Record Office of Northern Ireland (D 1492, D 2360). NRA 31446.

[544] ANTHONY COWDY & SONS LTD, linen mfrs and bleachers, Loughgall, co Armagh and Banbridge, co Down

Greenhall Mill corresp, letter books, cash books, order and stock books, wages books, etc (*c*30 vols, *c*200 items) 1862-1933.
Public Record Office of Northern Ireland (D 1850).

Millmount Bleach Works ledgers (7) 1907-36, day books (2) 1896-1913, cash books (5) 1892-1944, bills receivable (2 vols) 1913-15, bank books (11) 1909-23, invoice books (8) 1907-57, purchase ledger 1924-33, bleachers' books (54) 1904-29, starchers' book 1937-40, brown room book 1934, dye process book 1937-8, bleaching piece time book 1937, mill furnishing book 1892.
Public Record Office of Northern Ireland (D 1872).
NRA 31473.

[545] COX BROS LTD (formerly **JAMES COCKS & SONS**), jute mfrs, Dundee

Minutes and related corresp (2 vols) 1893-1932, letter books (9) 1869-1923, register of seals 1906-10, register of members and other share and dividend records (4 vols) 1892-1933, balance sheets 1814-1932, ledgers (45) 1841-1928, account book 1872-4, journals (3) 1893-1921, cash books (2) 1913-21, bank books 1906-21, yarn sales book 1861-9, weaving order book 1914, stock books (3) 1906-10, 1921, notebook rel to production, etc 1886-1918, wages books (4) 1893-1921, misc administrative, business and legal corresp and papers 1811-1964.
Dundee University Library (MS 66). NRA 12256.

Letter books and diary of James Cox.
In private possession. BP Lenman and others, *Dundee and its textile industry 1850-1914*, 1969.

Letters from customers (1 vol) 1841-55.
Dundee Archive Centre (GD/X137). NRA 31624.

[546] CRAIKS LTD, linen and jute merchants and mfrs, Forfar, Angus

Minutes (2 vols) 1908-65, registers (3) of directors and shareholders 1908-47, private letter book 1909-25, general and furnishing ledgers (4) 1914-44, day and order books (7) 1920-44, yarn purchase books (2) 1877-80, stock books (2) 1935-46, cost book *c*1911-17, calculation book *c*1911-12, production books (5) 1956-62, weaving books (10) 1951-67.
Dundee University Library (MS 74). NRA 25436.

[547] JOHN DAVENPORT & SON, rope, twine and tarpaulin mfrs, Manchester

Business and family corresp and papers *c*1801-52.
Greater Manchester RO (1276 E19). *Accessions to repositories 1987*, p27.

[548] DON BROTHERS, BUIST & CO LTD, jute and flax mfrs, Forfar, Angus

Misc corporate and legal records, balance sheets, etc 1881-1987, letter books (8) 1804-17, 1840-2, 1896-1940, private ledger 1865-97, ledger 1885-97, journals (3) 1885-1917, 1925-57, cash books (4) 1835-9, 1845-52, 1870-6, order and specifications books (7) 1842-57, 1926-40, production analysis books (2) 1933-9, wages and salaries records (5 vols, etc) 1805-11, 1905-45, plans and diagrams of premises 1877-*c*1965, press cuttings and other printed material 1881-1988; Dundee Calendering Co Ltd misc corporate records 1898-1960.
Dundee University Library (MS 100). NRA 13034.

[549] D & R DUKE LTD, linen mfrs, Brechin, Angus

Minutes (2 vols) 1854-1962, letter books (6) 1863-1945, private ledgers (19) 1858-1959, cash books (7) 1851-1937, balance books (4) 1854-1926, private journal 1856-84, yarn purchase books (3) 1855-76, order books (24) 1902-60, cost books (7) 1864-1936, salaries books (6) 1910-52, valuation of machinery 1899, inventories 1918-30, rent roll 1941-67, visitors' book 1908-52, misc business and Duke family corresp and papers *c*1780-1954.
Brechin Public Library & Museum. NRA 21472.

[550] JAMES DUNCAN, grain and linen merchant, Dundee

Letter books (8) 1794-1820, journal 1793-1820, ledgers (2) 1808-20, cash books (9) 1794-1820, bill book 1795-1800, waste books (3) 1795-1807, postal and freight charges books (2) 1795-7, grain, seeds and meal purchase, sales and shipment records (13 vols) 1792-1820, farm ledgers (4) 1811-20, personal account book 1812-19, misc accounts (94 items) 1796-1800.
Scottish Record Office (CS 96/18-36, 52, 81, 1204).
Court of Session Productions, List & Index Society, special series vol 23, 1987, pp111-12.

[551] DUNS LINEN CO, linen mfrs, Duns, Berwickshire

Rules of partnery, minutes 1765-74, invoices 1767-8, corresp 1768-71.
National Library of Scotland (MS 3707).

[552] DURHAM STREET WEAVING CO LTD, linen mfrs, Belfast

Balance sheets and profit and loss accounts (1 box) 1896-1962, misc administrative and financial corresp and papers (*c*30 bundles and envelopes) 1878-1966, business diary 1906, ledgers (11) 1887-1950, cash and cash account books (12) 1891-1954, order books (31) 1895-1963, goods purchased books (10) 1907-55, invoice books (22) 1893-1907 and invoices (1 file, *c*100 items) 1897-1925, 1966, estimate book 1905-8, cloth delivery book 1924, stock and stock account books (40) 1933-62, damask instructions book 1928-30, denim bale book *c*1930, repair account 1940-1, notes rel to looms working (2 vols) 1941-7, wages summary book 1923, weavers' pay book 1945-6, particulars and valuations of premises and machinery 1895-1927, leases, plans and other papers rel to premises 1884-1959.
Public Record Office of Northern Ireland (D 1183, D 2202). NRA 31440.

[553] EDENDERRY SPINNING CO LTD, flax spinners, Belfast

Ledgers, cash books and yarn bale books (*c*200 vols) *c*1840-*c*1940.
Public Record Office of Northern Ireland (D 3487).

[554] EDINBURGH LINEN COPARTNERY, linen mfrs, Edinburgh

Letter book 1745-9, account and general ledgers 1745-66, journals 1745-67, cash book 1745-60.
Bank of Scotland, Glasgow Chief Office. Enquiries to NRA (Scotland) (NRA(S) 945). NRA 10784.

[555] **JAMES FAIRWEATHER & SONS**, sailcloth mfrs, Dundee

Spinning books (7) 1779-85, weaving and heckling books (8) 1779-85, buying book 1779-83, foreman's account book 1779-85.
Scottish Record Office (CS 96/1641-57). *Court of Session Productions*, List & Index Society, special series vol 23, 1987, pp74-5.

[556] **HUGH & SAMUEL FAULKNER**, bleachers and linen merchants, Wellbrook, co Tyrone

Corresp, expenses book, bill book, maps, plans, etc (*c*100 items) *c*1764-96.
In private possession. A microfilm is in the Public Record Office of Northern Ireland (Mic 21): see *Ulster textile industry*.

[557] **JOHN FERGUS & CO**, flax spinners and bleachers, Leslie, Fife

Business corresp and financial papers 1800-1933, ledger 1850-2, yarn journal 1860, memoranda books (2) 1862-74, diary 1876-1957, lists of wages 1880, plan of works nd, notes rel to history of firm 1957.
In private possession. Enquiries to NRA (Scotland) (NRA(S) 785, 2038-41). NRA 17554.

Letters received (*c*80) 1785-1883.
National Library of Scotland (MS 14298 ff160-302).

[558] **JAMES FERGUSON**, linen merchant, Belfast

Account book 1771-83.
Public Record Office of Northern Ireland (D 468): see *Ulster textile industry*.

[559] **WILLIAM FERGUSSON & SONS LTD**, jute mfrs, Dundee

Abstracts of accounts 1872-1915, ledger 1911-21.
Dundee University Library. NRA 19321.

Letters received (9) 1844-57.
National Library of Scotland (Acc 2908).

[560] **FINLAYSON, BOUSFIELD & CO LTD**, flax spinners, Johnstone, Renfrewshire

Board minutes (2 vols) 1898-1961, share certificate book 1908-69.
Glasgow University Archives (UGD/143). NRA 21537.

[561] **DOUGLAS FRASER & SONS LTD**, flax spinners, linen and jute mfrs, and engineers, Arbroath, Angus

Memorandum and articles of association 1905-60, minute books (3) 1905-68, register of directors 1903-61, letter books (3) 1880-1916, memoranda books (4) 1955-64 and index, private ledgers (7) 1878-1965, journals (6) 1878-1942, 1954-68, misc financial and legal corresp and papers 1857-1959, maps and plans 1837-1948, photographs *c*1920-1963.
Dundee University Library (MS 42). NRA 17171.

Notebooks (42) rel to engineering sub-contract work 1932-56, technical drawings 20th cent.
Giddings & Lewis-Fraser Ltd. Enquiries to Dundee University Library. NRA 17171.

[562] **GAFFIKIN & CO**, linen mfrs, Belfast

Letter book *c*1874-*c*1926, orders instruction book *c*1900.
Public Record Office of Northern Ireland (D 1796).
Deputy Keeper's Report 1960-5, p59.

[563] **GAILEY & TAYLOR**, flax commission agents, Londonderry

Corresp and papers of RA Taylor (8 boxes, etc) *c*1840-70, incl his business ledgers and stock books 1840s, and letters, accounts, etc to Gailey & Taylor *c*1857-69.
Public Record Office of Northern Ireland (D 1435). NRA 31445.

[564] **GARNOCK, BIBBY & CO LTD**, hemp and wire rope makers, Liverpool

Directors' and general meeting minutes (2 vols) 1892-1959, register of members, etc (2 vols) 1892-1959.
Doncaster Archives Department (DY.BRI/16). NRA 21369.

[565] **DAVID GILLIES**, net mfr and shipper, Lower Largo, Fife

Ledgers, accounts and cash books (9 vols, etc) 19th cent, letter and invoice books (7) 19th cent-1919, day book for supplying cord, twine and canvas 1873-96, quotation book and account of cotton received 1877-97, order and customers' books (7) 19th cent, delivery book 1885-1907, price lists of nets (1 vol) 1873-81, cotton testing book 19th cent, wages books (4) 19th cent, rates for guarding nets 19th cent, personal day book, ledger and cash notebooks, etc of David Gillies 1863, 1883-8, business and legal corresp and papers of Gillies family 1822-1934, misc papers and writs 1669-20th cent.
In private possession. Enquiries to NRA (Scotland) (NRA(S) 1503). NRA 20869.

[566] **GILROY, SONS & CO LTD**, jute spinners and mfrs, Dundee

Memorandum and articles of association 1890, minutes (3 vols) 1890-1933, agenda books (2) 1902-24, registers of directors, etc 1901-29, members 1917-23, shares 1931-2 and documents exhibited 1893-1924, balance sheets, etc 1890-1932, cash book 1920-1, misc business and legal corresp and papers 1867-1933, plan of Tay Works warehouses 1887, valuation 1901.
Dundee University Library (MS 66). NRA 12256.

[567] **GLENDINNING, McLEISH & CO**, linen merchants, Belfast

General meeting papers (37 files) 1906-60, balance sheets and annual accounts 1928-44, corresp (*c*300 files) 1913-51, Co Down Weaving Co debts papers (35 files) 1929-34, ledgers (13) 1883-93, 1909-54, day books (2) 1936-40, cash books (4) 1915, 1921-51, bank statements 1937-51, misc accounting records (6 vols) 1883-1945, order, costing and stock records (45 vols) 1925-44, pattern books (14) nd, cable code books *c*1900-14, 1933-8, wages and personnel records (12 vols

and bundles) 1905-51, deeds, legal papers and corresp rel to property (4 boxes) 1829-*c*1950, photographs and printing plates 1902-14.
Public Record Office of Northern Ireland (D 2424). NRA 31457.

[568] **WILLIAM GOODACRE & SONS LTD**, mats and matting mfrs, Holme, Westmorland

Bank book 1913-16, petty cash books (2) 1916-23, stock books (2) *c*1855-1861, 1885-6, 1897-1918, price lists and pattern books 1885-6, nd, production and despatch records (10 vols) 1910-75, wages books (4) 1866-1915, factory registers, school certificate books, accident records, etc (*c*20 vols) 1865-1974, rent books (2) 1916-68, property repairs book 1943-59, machine drawings, factory plans, etc.
Cumbria RO, Kendal (WDB/64). NRA 30972.

[569] **GOUROCK ROPEWORK CO LTD**, rope mfrs, Port Glasgow, Renfrewshire

Articles of association 1960, minutes (3 vols) 1774-1920, attendance book 1903-44, general meeting papers, annual reports and accounts, balance sheets, etc 1904-71, transfer books (8) 1904-33, letter books (13) 1736-46, 1900-38, office files (over 100) *c*1890-1972, ledgers (39) 1885-1937, account books, journals, etc (*c*13 vols) 1818-23, 1841, 1861-1937, purchase records (5 vols) 1862-1937, sales records (17 vols) 1900-33, warehouse charges books (3) 1912-30, stock book 1916-28, weight book 1897-1933, business and legal corresp and papers 1793-1941, salaries and wages books (4) 1870-88, 1903-12, 1919-43, fire insurance books (2) 1861-1920, rent books (6) 1911-41, inventories 1934, 1948, plant movements 1936-41, visitors' books (6) 1938-62; Gourock Ropework Export Co Ltd attendance book 1903-44, accounting records (5 vols) 1903-9, 1923-33, export book 1931-3.
Glasgow University Archives (UGD/42). NRA 10832.

Minutes 1903-40; Gourock Ropework Export Co Ltd minutes and register of members 1903-44.
The Company. A microfilm is in Glasgow University Archives (UGD/42/32).

Journals, statements of account, etc mainly for overseas branches (9 vols) 1934-71, sales brochures and other printed papers 1936-1960s.
Doncaster Archives Department (DY.BRI/18). NRA 21369.

[570] **GRACE family**, canvas weavers, maltsters, millers and corn merchants, Tring, Herts

Business and family papers 1766-1977 incl canvas weaving sales and purchase ledgers (2) 1791-1825, 1832-6 and notebook 1799-1805.
Buckinghamshire RO (D 109). NRA 30475.

[571] **DAVID GRAHAM & CO**, flax and tow spinners, Portadown, co Armagh

Ledgers, cash books, corresp, etc (*c*100 vols, files, etc) 1887-1904.
Public Record Office of Northern Ireland (D 1252/21): see *Ulster textile industry*.

[571A] **THOMAS GRAHAM & CO**, flax and linen mfrs, Harrington, Cumberland

Account book 1788-93.
Cumbria RO, Carlisle: see *Report of the County Archivist* June 1969, p3.

[572] **GREAT GRIMSBY COAL, SALT & TANNING CO LTD**, rope and twine mfrs, engineers and coal merchants, Grimsby, Lincs

Records 1873-1973 incl board and general meeting minutes, agenda, directors' attendance books, share records, reports and accounts, balance sheets, ledgers, bank books, corresp, legal papers, sales, production and branch records.
Cosalt plc. NRA 21353, NRA 28631; BAC *Company Archives* no 456.

[573] **THOMAS GREER & CO**, linen merchants and bleachers, Dungannon, co Tyrone

Family corresp (*c*850 items) 1717-1812 incl many letters from partners, agents and customers rel to linen manufacture and to trade in Ireland, England and America, misc customers' accounts (1 vol) 1785-1840, ledger for New Hamborough bleach green 1818-20, misc deeds, legal papers, family accounts, etc (*c*120 items) mainly 1729-1829.
Public Record Office of Northern Ireland (D 1044). NRA 31434.

Market book of Thomas Greer recording his cloth purchases 1758-9, agreement with Wakefield & Co 1794, corresp, deeds, etc 1738-1840.
In private possession. Copies are in the Public Record Office of Northern Ireland (T 1127/4, 6, T 1173): see *Ulster textile industry*.

[574] **EDWARD GRIBBON & SONS LTD**, linen mfrs, Coleraine, co Londonderry

Memorandum and articles of association 1902, letter books (5) 1878-94, 1910-12, 1914-48, corresp (2 bundles) 1925, 1928-33, ledgers (2) 1903-13, journal 1898-1915, day book 1906-10, cash books (8) 1847-8, 1880-4, 1892-1900, 1910-20, bank book 1909-10, financial report book 1905-23, invoices with some letters (3 boxes) 1861-1918, invoice books (19) 1911-22, order book 1924-5, sales books (6) 1902-22, receipt books (2) 1890s, 1916-19, linen price book 1909-10, stock books (4) 1904-21, general store book 1924, cloth books (4) 1876-80, 1900-3, 1906-9, work book 1870-3, run books (3) 1880-8, 1905-14, bleaching book 1918-23, notebooks (2) rel to prices, designs, etc *c*1907, *c*1920, time books (2) 1888-9, 1911-30, wages books (16) 1859-62, 1880-2, 1887-92, 1896-7, 1913-22, wages and insurance sheets 1921-2, machinery book 1906-7, inventory and valuation 1897, rent books (5) 1907-40, leases 1850-71.
Public Record Office of Northern Ireland (D 1191). NRA 31443.

[575] **J & AD GRIMOND LTD**, jute spinners and mfrs, Dundee

Minutes 1892-1933, registers of members, debentures and transfers 1893-1928, shareholders' ledger, papers, etc 1895-1932, letter books and files mainly rel to trusts 1898-1919, private ledgers (2) 1906-21, trust

cash book 1906-48, misc balance sheets 1892-1932, agents' agreements 1917-21, wages book 1912-22, register of accidents 1896-1935, inventories and valuations of Maxwelltown, Bowbridge and Holt Town Works 1892-1920 and Blairgowrie mills 1903, costs of alterations to buildings and machinery 1911-15, statistics, plans, etc; J & AD Grimond (Canada) Ltd minutes 1912-34; J & AD Grimond (New York) Ltd minutes 1912-21, corresp 1909-14.
Dundee University Library (MS 66). NRA 12256.

Grimond family papers *c*1797-1852 incl waste book and ledger of David Grimond 1797, waste books (5) 1835-42, day books (5) 1838-9, ledgers of Joseph Grimond 1838 and of AD Grimond 1839, receipts and payments book 1835, cash books (3) 1822-33, pocket book 1823-30, cheques of James Grimond 1835-8, notes on banking, business, etc (1 vol) *c*1838, account of sales of cloth (1 vol) 1828-31 with notes of payments and receipts 1826-36, corresp of James Grimond (9 vols) 1819-52, letter book of William Grimond, etc 1840, copies of letters of Thomas Saunders and William Grimond (1 vol) 1848-50; invoice book of Laurence Saunders, linen shipper, Dundee 1844-9; accounts of sales by JS Ormerod, Manchester (1 vol) 1849-50.
National Library of Scotland (Dep 365). NRA 29119.

[576] **GRIMSBY CORDAGE CO LTD**, trawl twine mfrs, Grimsby, Lincs

Records 1899-1979 incl directors' and general meeting minutes and reports, share records, financial statements, ledgers, deliveries book, register of plant and machinery, and corresp.
Cosalt plc. NRA 21353, NRA 28631; BAC *Company Archives* no 456.

[577] **JOSEPH GUNDRY & CO LTD**, fishing net mfrs, Bridport, Dorset

Letter book 1796-1812, ledgers (3) 1780-1894, journal 1811-17, cash books (2) 1807-19, petty cash book 1879-80, bank books (6) 1837-51, reports and accounts 1919-40, order book 1806-10, journey books (7) 1810-85, costing books for seines (3) 1755-71, production book 1815-53, stocktaking book 1793-1803, J Gundry's memoranda nd, misc corresp, price lists, etc 1728-1925, deeds 17th-20th cent.
Dorset RO (D 203). NRA 6592; *Accessions to repositories 1975,* p36.

[578] **JOHN GUNNING & SON LTD**, linen mfrs, Cookstown, co Tyrone

Corresp (48 boxes) 1920-52, ledgers (7) 1886-9, 1910-49, day books (13) 1921-46, cash books (20) 1908-50, order books (24) 1889-90, 1900-43, quotations and cloth samples (17 vols) 1923-49, cloth books (7) 1907-22, cloth contracts book 1939-53, yarn contracts (3 boxes) 1924-50, yarn and goods invoices, returns, credit notes, etc (18 boxes) 1923-51, wages books (21) 1883-1935, 1944-5.
Public Record Office of Northern Ireland (D 780). NRA 31433.

Letter book 1924, wages book 1955, deeds, etc *c*1780-*c*1850.
Public Record Office of Northern Ireland (D 2658/4): see *Ulster textile industry.*

[579] **R HOOD HAGGIE & SON LTD**, hemp and wire rope makers, Newcastle upon Tyne, Northumb

Memorandum and articles of association 1951, directors' minute book 1958-61, general meeting minute book 1901-63, directors' and shareholders' attendance registers (2 vols) 1901-63, registers of directors, transfers, etc (8 vols) 1901-66, annual reports and accounts 1902-59, wire rope order book 1918-19, memoranda books (4) 1909-33, *c*1955, consultants' reports 1959-62, corresp and papers rel to employees, property, etc 1905-61, inventories 1901, 1941, visitors' book 1959-72, catalogues, press cuttings, etc 1923-66, nd, photographs 19th cent-1972; Cardiff office records incl agent's private letter book 1909-12, customers' order book 1908-14, binder twine sales day book 1912-59, and wages book 1912-63.
Doncaster Archives Department (DY.BRI/20). NRA 21369.

[580] **HALE & MARTIN**, flax spinners and linen mfrs, Ballymoney, co Antrim and Dungannon, co Tyrone

Dungannon mill letter books (17) 1903-8, 1919-40, corresp files nd, ledgers (5) 1863-1920, ledger accounts from 1924, journal 1892-1929, cash books (3) 1872-1919, bill books (2) 1905-17, bank books (2) 1911-15, 1920-3, flax accounts 1924, order books (2) 1877-85, 1914-31, yarn contracts books (7) 1929-39, sales books (7) 1863-79, 1897-1904, 1924-39, invoice books (17) 1888-1937, flax and yarn returns book 1917, flax remark books (3) 1874-80, 1908-13, 1924-36, weigh-in books (2) 1905-10, turn-off book 1906-17, reelers' work books (3) 1904-12, 1917-21, 1932-7, wages and time books (24) 1864-1940, mill furnishings books (14) 1911-33.
Public Record Office of Northern Ireland (D 1064). NRA 31435.

Yarn book from 1937, coal and power costing books from 1929, rent books (2) 1890-1920 and from 1939.
Hale Martin & Co Ltd. NRA 31435.

[581] **WILLIAM HALLEY & SONS LTD**, jute and flax spinners and mfrs, Dundee

Minute books from 1921, balance sheets from 1909, partnership and other deeds 1828-1918, plans and diagrams *c*1832-1950, historical notes (1 vol) *c*1790-1976.
The Company. Enquiries to NRA (Scotland) (NRA(S) 422). NRA 13038.

[582] **HARRIS & CO**, linen merchants, Belfast

Insurance, customers' and orders notebooks and salary receipt book (4 vols) 1897-1928.
Public Record Office of Northern Ireland (D 2021): see *Ulster textile industry.*

[583] **JOHN HARRISON & CO**, rope makers, Whitehaven, Cumberland

Letter book 1824-45, journal 1824-45, account book 1834-43.
Cumbria RO, Carlisle (D/A). NRA 23766.

[584] **HAZELBANK WEAVING CO LTD**, linen mfrs, Laurencetown, co Down

Memorandum and articles of association 1922, letter books (3) 1938-55, corresp (3 bundles, 2 files) 1939-51, ledgers (2) 1917-40, day book 1905-47, cash books (2) 1909-42, rough account book 1932-40, bank books (3) 1932-49, order, invoice and advice records (15 vols, 11 bundles) 1904-62, material stock book 1902-c1930, stocktaking book 1924-49, cloth books (2) 1938-52, work books (4) 1943-54, turn-off sheets 1939, wages books (16) 1881-92.
Public Record Office of Northern Ireland (D 1764). NRA 31449.

[585] **A & S HENRY & CO LTD**, linen mfrs and merchants, Dundee and Manchester

Memorandum and articles of association 1889-1951, minute book 1953-72, directors' reports, balance sheets and accounts 1907-81, corresp (12 files) 1921-7, 1942-56, ledgers (2) 1953-68, misc leases, reports, notes, etc 1906-76.
Dundee University Library (MS 86/XIX, XX). NRA 31109.

Belfast branch foreign order book 1891-2, list of employees 1847-1955.
Public Record Office of Northern Ireland (D 824).
Deputy Keeper's Report 1954–9, p53.

Schedule of deeds 1810-1921, agreement rel to formation of a company as stuff merchants 1889, deed of dissolution of partnership 1899.
In private possession. A copy is in the Public Record Office of Northern Ireland (T 1346).

[586] **HEZLET family**, linen merchants, Coleraine, co Londonderry

Memoranda book, bleaching book and yarn buyers' notebooks (30 vols, etc) 1812-18, nd.
Public Record Office of Northern Ireland (D 668/20): see *Ulster textile industry*.

[587] **HILLSBOROUGH LINEN CO LTD**, linen mfrs, Hillsborough, co Down

Minute books (4) 1866-76, 1907-59, board business books (2) 1866-76, 1915-75, secretary's letter books (3) 1871-1920, lists of shareholders (3 vols) 1866-1965, share certificate books (3) 1890-1968, ledgers (4) 1868-71, 1916, 1922-63, cash books (5) 1927-49, 1960-6, bank books (8) 1894-1904, 1961-6, warehouse cheques journal 1961-6, order book 1906-24, sales book 1925-6, invoices (1 bundle) c1906-1914, corresp rel to invoices (1 file) 1942-5, stock book 1920, wages books (5) 1919-35, misc corresp and papers (3 boxes) c1870-c1920, map, plans and elevations 1836, 1874-c1880.
Public Record Office of Northern Ireland (D 2053). NRA 31482.

[588] **JOHN HIND & SONS**, linen mfrs, Belfast

Minute book, bank book, corresp, bankruptcy papers, etc 1833-89.
Public Record Office of Northern Ireland (D 1326): see *Ulster textile industry*.

[589] **HENRY HINDLEY**, linen cloth merchant, Mere, Wilts

Letter books 1762-70, 1773-5, corresp 1767-1813, accounts 1772-1808, stock inventory, etc 1783-4.
Wiltshire RO (WRO 372). NRA 6668.

[590] **WILLIAM HOUNSELL & CO**, net, cordage and canvas mfrs, Bridport, Dorset

Cash book 1777-1856, patent 1860.
Dorset RO (D 203). NRA 6592.

[591] **HUTCHISON & POLLOK LTD**, rope, twine and cord mfrs, Liverpool

Records 1896-1980.
National Museums & Galleries on Merseyside, Merseyside Maritime Museum: see *Accessions to repositories 1981*, p31.

[592] **ISLAND SPINNING CO LTD**, linen mfrs, Lisburn, co Antrim

Board minute books (9) 1866-1926, board business books (14) 1866-1908, share certificates (1 bundle) from 1867, dividend book 1925-34, summary of capital and shares (1 vol) 1868-1931, letter books (4) 1867-1926, private ledgers (5) 1867-1927, private journals (2) 1867-1903, bill books (2) 1899-1919, trial balance books (3) 1906-37, stock book 1867-76, further cash books, purchase records, invoices, stock records, wages books, etc c1920-40.
Public Record Office of Northern Ireland (D 1621). NRA 31447.

[593] **JAMES IVORY & CO**, flax spinners, Douglastown, Angus

Flax import book 1799-1803, bobbin flax books (2) 1799-1803.
Scottish Record Office (CS 96/3843-5). *Court of Session Productions*, List & Index Society, special series vol 23, 1987, p139.

[594] **JAMES JACK & SONS LTD**, net mfrs, Stonehaven, Kincardineshire

Directors' minutes (2 vols) 1904-20.
Scottish Record Office (GD 1/911).

Misc balance sheets, agreements, etc (2 files, 2 bundles) 1905-22.
J & W Stuart Ltd. Enquiries to NRA (Scotland) (NRA(S) 2159). NRA 23658.

[595] **JAFFE BROTHERS & CO LTD**, linen and yarn merchants, Dundee

Memorandum and articles of association 1920, minute book 1920-53, register of members 1920-34, directors' reports, balance sheets and accounts 1923-81, ledger 1909-59, private journal 1909-59, misc papers 1909-56.
Dundee University Library (MS 86/X). NRA 31109.

Accounts (12 vols) 1909-13.
Scottish Record Office (CS 96/2474-8, 2504-10).

[596] **PHILIP JOHNSTON & SONS LTD**, linen mfrs and flax and tow spinners, Belfast

Reports, minutes, shareholders' registers, ledgers, etc (c50 vols) c1880-1954.
Public Record Office of Northern Ireland (D 1851): see *Ulster textile industry.*

[597] **WILLIAM JOHNSTON & SON**, linen merchants, Lurgan, co Armagh

Stock receipt book 1858-1915, price book and lapping room book 1892.
Public Record Office of Northern Ireland (D 1619): see *Ulster textile industry.*

[598] **JONES & MORRIS**, sailmakers, Portmadoc, Caerns

Ledgers and accounts (with W Morris & Co) (6 vols) 1888-1920.
National Library of Wales (MSS 12088-93).

[599] **JONES & SHEWELL**, flax and hemp spinners, Hounslow, Mddx

Letter book 1818-22, letter book of receiver 1819-20, journal 1818-24.
Public Record Office, Chancery Lane (C 111/145).

[600] **JOSEPH KAYE & SONS**, rope and twine mfrs, Scisset, Yorks

Notebooks (6) containing bleaching and dyeing recipes, calculations, details of water supply, etc 1849-1927, formulae for polish and stain for fine twines (1 envelope) 1925, papers (1 bundle) rel to analysis of water supply 1913-29, photographs nd.
West Yorkshire Archive Service, Leeds (Acc 1510). NRA 19412.

[601] **WILLIAM KIRK & SONS**, linen mfrs, Keady, co Armagh

Business corresp (c500 items) c1830-70 incl some personal letters to William Kirk MP 1853-4, business corresp (3 files and some loose items) 1925-6, company register early 20th cent, business and personal accounts (c150 items) 1830-c1869, order books (3) 1907-10, 1920-3, nd, 'Drybetter Auxiliary Invoice Book' 1871-89, salary ledgers (2) 1884-1914, 1917-23.
Public Record Office of Northern Ireland (D 1185). NRA 31441.

[602] **KIRKCALDY LINOLEUM CO**, linoleum mfrs, Kirkcaldy, Fife

Share transfer register 1880-97, counting room rules nd, design particulars and misc papers 1885-7.
Kirkcaldy Museum & Art Gallery. NRA 18847.

[603] **KNOCKCLOGHRIM FLAX & TOW SPINNING CO**, Knockcloghrim, co Londonderry

Memorandum and articles of association, minutes, share applications list, expenses books, corresp, etc 1865-6.
Public Record Office of Northern Ireland (D 1905/2/153): see *Ulster textile industry.*

[604] **KNOX & POLLOCK**, linen merchants, Limavady, co Londonderry

Profit and loss accounts and papers rel to dissolution of partnership 1834-49, linen stock accounts of J Knox 1797-1836, and other Knox family and business papers 1830-73, nd.
Public Record Office of Northern Ireland (D 2587/8/3): see *Ulster textile industry.*

[605] **JOHN N KYD & CO LTD**, jute spinners, Dundee

Minute book 1920-33, share certificates 1921-5, share register 1929-31, balance sheets and profit and loss accounts 1913-32, journal 1902-16, cash book 1900-19, income tax returns and related corresp 1920, 1927, time books (2) 1897-1900, 1905-7, register of young employees 1901-2, extracted birth certificates of employees 1898-1928, history of Walton Works 1864-1931.
Dundee University Library (MS 66). NRA 12256.

[606] **JAMES LAMB**, yarn and linen mfr, Arbroath, Angus

Memorandum and waste book 1809-31, ledger 1824-31, bill books (2) 1824-30, winding book 1825-31, dressing book 1826-31, weaving book 1828-31.
Scottish Record Office (CS 96/3970-6). *Court of Session Productions*, List & Index Society, special series vol 23, 1987, pp205-6.

[607] **SAMUEL LAMONT & SONS LTD**, linen mfrs, Belfast

Cash account book 1858-65.
The Company. A copy is in the Public Record Office of Northern Ireland (T 2223). *Deputy Keeper's Report 1960-5*, p114.

Yarn book 1939-48.
Public Record Office of Northern Ireland (D 1942/9). NRA 31479.

[608] **LARNE WEAVING CO LTD**, linen mfrs, Larne, co Antrim

Ledgers (8) 1890-1967, cash books (2) 1941-50, 1960-70, bills payable 1902-20, bills receivable 1938-41, analysis books (2) 1958-70, order books (17) 1890-1946, delivery books (2) 1957-66, estimated cost book 1939-43, wages books (17) 1934-71, attendance register 1964-71.
Public Record Office of Northern Ireland (D 2690). NRA 31463.

[609] **WILLIAM LAWSON & SONS**, rope makers, Dundee

Letter book rel to rope orders, specifications and contracts 1875-7, list of tenders (1 vol) 1877-88, notebook of examples of quotations, prices and contracts 1882-1909, customers' address book c1880-c1900, notebook of tender and contract dates and prices 1898-1914.
Dundee Archive Centre (GD/Mus 104).

[610] **WILLIAM LIDDELL & CO LTD**, linen
mfrs, Donaghcloney, co Down

William Liddell's cash book 1856-71, chief engineer's
reports (1 vol) 1903-18, factory regulations and
conditions of service 1890, registers (12) of young
employees 1902-39, work and wages records (10 vols)
1910-20, 1937-48, Donaghcloney Factory Society for
the Sick records (4 vols) 1877-1921.
Public Record Office of Northern Ireland (D 1882).
NRA 31475.

[611] **LINEN THREAD CO LTD**, linen thread
mfrs, Glasgow, London and Belfast

Board, general meeting and committee minutes
(92 vols and folders) 1897-1964, board attendance
book 1947-68, board agenda book 1960-1, copies of
agreements 1897-1901.
Glasgow University Archives (UGD/143). NRA 21537.

Draft minutes, reports, memoranda, corresp and legal
papers (4 folders, 255 items) 1898-1936.
Scottish Record Office (GD 282/13). NRA 20359.

[612] **LINOLEUM MANUFACTURING CO
LTD**, Staines, Mddx

Minutes 1865-1949.
Greater London RO: see *Accessions to repositories 1983*,
p30.

[613] **WILLIAM LINTOTT & SONS**, hemp mfrs,
Romsey, Hants

Corresp, orders, bills, etc (c10 bundles) 1813-18, wages
book 1809-11.
Public Record Office, Chancery Lane (C 107/132).

[614] **WILLIAM LIVINGSTON & CO**, linen
merchants, Lurgan, co Armagh

Order and wages books, etc (5 vols) 1847-1930.
Public Record Office of Northern Ireland (D 1619).
Deputy Keeper's Report 1960-5, p122.

[615] **N & N LOCKHART & SONS LTD**, linen
mfrs, Kirkcaldy, Fife

Letter file 1858-1924, cash book 1851-1905, private
ledger 1907-29, payments book 1805-14, shirting
pattern book 1912, engine diagrams, etc 1859-1937,
corresp rel to machinery and plant 1857-74, misc
papers and photographs 1858-1978.
In private possession. Enquiries to NRA (Scotland)
(NRA(S) 1896). NRA 22370.

[616] **JOHN LOWE & BROS**, rope makers,
Wribbenhall, Worcs

Letter books (3) 1900-29 with loose letters 1887-97,
ledger 1875-c1904, cash books (7) 1845-1921 incl
partnership and rent agreements, cash day books (2)
1870-80, 1893-5, petty cash book 1894-1901, bank
books (4) 1874-81, 1892-1911, receipt stubs (1 vol)
c1940, accounts rendered (2 vols) 1868-1925, service
accounts 1877-8, account book 1888-92, ledger and

sales account 1880-1938, goods received ledgers (2)
1863-98, purchase ledger 1895, customers' ledger
1888-92, sales ledgers (2) 1880-98, order books (25)
1833-1934, stock books (2) and stocktaking accounts
1875-1911, memoranda book c1908-22, day book incl
wages 1877-99, wages book 1899-1908.
Bewdley Museum. NRA 30837.

[617] **JOHN LOWSON JUNIOR & CO LTD**, jute
mfrs, Forfar, Angus

Minutes 1898-1950, annual reports, balance sheets,
etc 1874-1955, private ledgers and journals (5 vols)
1898-1952.
Dundee University Library (MS 66). NRA 12256.

[618] **WILLIAM McCANCE**, linen merchant,
Ballyclare and Suffolk, co Antrim

Account books (2) 1796-1805, book of linen seals
c1850.
Public Record Office of Northern Ireland (D 823): see
Ulster textile industry.

[619] **SAMUEL McCRUDDEN & CO (BELFAST)
LTD**, fancy linen and handkerchief mfrs, Belfast

Ledgers (4) 1910-12, 1916-52, cash books (6) 1910-21,
1933-46, 1954-7, order books (5) 1939-60, purchase
day books (9) 1950-6, invoice books (3) 1953-5, price
lists 1915-18, 1929, lease 1910.
Public Record Office of Northern Ireland (D 2306).
NRA 31454.

[620] **McCRUM, WATSON & MERCER LTD**,
linen mfrs, Armagh

Letter books (2) 1861-1916.
Public Record Office of Northern Ireland (D 2518): see
Ulster textile industry.

[621] **JOHN McFARLANE & CO**, sailmakers,
Glasgow

Cash book 1841-7, job books (2) 1840-2.
In private possession. Enquiries to NRA (Scotland)
(NRA(S) 293). NRA 10843.

[622] **MALCOLM, OGILVIE & CO LTD**, jute
mfrs, Dundee

Directors' and general meeting minute books (6) from
1894, registers (3) of directors, shareholders and
transfers from 1894, transfer ledgers from c1920, cash
books (4) 1865-73 and from 1942, production books
(3) c1892-9, c1934-8, nd, wages book 1837, plant
register from c1920, corresp and papers rel to property
1897-1947, misc papers, photographs and press
cuttings 1843-1968.
The Company. Enquiries to NRA (Scotland) (NRA(S)
1056). NRA 19024.

[623] **MARSHALL & CO**, flax spinners, Leeds and
Shrewsbury, Salop

Private ledger of John Marshall 1791-1840, account
books (4) 1804-91, business notebooks (11) c1790-1900
and experiment books (4) 1788-1823 of members of
Marshall family, statistics and prices (1 vol) 1801, nd,

record of coal consumed and yarn spun 1823, stocktaking and balance sheets (1 vol) 1806-51, stock books (2) 1793-1804, 1828-40, record of new machinery (1 vol) 1810-23, plans of machinery, etc nd, register of employees nd, strike book 1871-2, minutes of Leeds & District Association of Factory Occupiers 1872-5, travel journals (3) of John Marshall 1800-29, misc business and family corresp and papers (7 envelopes) 1787-1887.
Brotherton Library, Leeds University (MS 200). NRA 30993.

[624] **JOHN & GEORGE METCALFE** (afterwards **FREDERICK ATKINSON**), flax spinners, Pateley Bridge, Yorks

Reeling accounts 1857-94, valuation 1864, designs, plans and related papers 1833-1982.
CJ Hawkesworth Esq. NRA 32318.

[625] **MILFORT SPINNING CO**, linen mfrs, Belfast

Machinery book 1869.
Public Record Office of Northern Ireland (D 2120/5). NRA 31451.

Order book 1894-8.
Public Record Office of Northern Ireland (D 2345): see *Ulster textile industry.*

[626] **MILLBROOK BLEACH & FLAX CO LTD**, Cookstown, co Tyrone

Private ledger 1901-40, ledger and details of yarn received 1929-41.
Public Record Office of Northern Ireland (D 1142/D): see *Ulster textile industry.*

[627] **JOHN MOIR**, merchant and mfr of canvas, sailcloth, bagging, etc, Dundee

Letter books (3) 1822-9, journal 1811-28, bill book 1823-8, cash book 1829-32, account book with agents 1822-8, sales, yarn and quarry book 1804-28, spinning books (2) 1822-9, quarry books (2) 1828-9.
Scottish Record Office (CS 96/4027–38). *Court of Session Productions*, List & Index Society, special series vol 23, 1987, pp167–8.

[628] **J MORICE & CO**, sailmakers, Liverpool

Day books (2) 1883-1904.
National Maritime Museum (SPB/19).

[629] **MICHAEL NAIRN & CO LTD**, floorcloth and linoleum mfrs, Kirkcaldy, Fife

Contracts of copartnery and other agreements 1858-1961, registers of directors and members and share ledgers (6 vols) 1893-1953, private letter book 1881-5, abstracts of costs, selling prices and sales 1857-64, 1882-91, price lists 1888, 1907, specifications and tender applications, etc 1907-c1955, drawing office job numbers description book 1929-51, pattern book c1880, sample books (3) c1850, 1876, 1905, diaries (3) incl patterns 1888-96, 1904, 1947, wages rates 1889-1962, work regulations 1872, lists of properties (2 vols) 1890-1964, leases and related corresp and legal papers (13 bundles) 1878-1970, plans and drawings from 1850, photographs c1900-59, minutes of the Linoleum and Felt Base Employers' Federation and other trade associations 1942-60, misc business and Nairn family papers 1828-1939.
Nairn Floors Ltd. Enquiries to NRA (Scotland) (NRA(S) 1898). NRA 22372.

Accounting records 1840-70, stock lists 1834, personnel records 1872-1907, drawings and photographs 1882-1972, records rel to Kirkcaldy, Elie and Kilconquhar 19th cent.
Kirkcaldy Museum & Art Gallery. NRA 18847.

[630] **NEW NORTHERN SPINNING & WEAVING CO LTD**, linen mfrs, Belfast

Letter books (4) 1890-7, 1902-6, 1918-20, copies of statements (3 vols) 1888-97, 1915-23, voucher book 1912-14, invoices (1 bundle) 1909-40 and invoice books (2) 1933-5, factory plan and valuations 1904-6.
Public Record Office of Northern Ireland (D 3546). NRA 31467.

[631] **OLD BLEACH LINEN CO LTD**, linen mfrs, Randalstown, co Antrim

Letter books (3) 1886-1908, 1912-15, private and general ledgers (4) 1863-91, directors' and family ledgers (5) 1905-20, journals (6) 1864-97, 1910-41, cash books (10) 1905-55, receipt book 1905-12, overseas invoice books (3) 1923-6, 1931-45, stock book 1909-33, wages book 1931-42.
Public Record Office of Northern Ireland (D 2103). NRA 31450.

[632] **ORR family**, linen merchants and bleachers, Aghadowey, co Londonderry

Business letter book 1797-9, cash book 1765-92, linen buyers' corresp and invoices (2 bundles) 1803-4, accounts of bleaching expenses 1788, 1792, misc family corresp and papers 1739, 1797-1834.
Public Record Office of Northern Ireland (D 664/O). NRA 19564.

[633] **JOSEPH ORR & SONS (CRANAGILL) LTD**, linen mfrs, Benburb, co Tyrone

Letter books (7) 1953-62, ledgers (7) 1918-65, expenditure book 1907-18, order books (3) 1903-43, sales day books (2) 1935-58, stock book 1907-51, cloth book 1910-65, cost books (3) 1876-1920, 1930-49, production book 1913-26, production or order book 1934-62, wages books (2) 1937-52, inventories and valuations 1920, 1935, 1956.
Public Record Office of Northern Ireland (D 2130). NRA 31452.

[634] **J & G PATON LTD**, flax and tow spinners, Montrose, Angus

Ledgers (7) 1818-43, 1864-1955, account books (4) 1825-54, 1909-42, day book 1832-5, waste books (3) 1919-1940s, cash books (11) 1827-60, 1921-50, 1961-7, import ledgers (12) 1861-71, flax purchase ledgers (12)

1868-70, 1900-50, sales registers (8) 1900-67, flax, tow and bleachers' order books (13) 1867-1918, raw materials contracts 1956-61, delivery books (6) 1870-1967, jute store book nd, production figures (11 vols) 1890-1904, 1924-63, spinning books (2) 1901-11, 1942-67, yarn books (5) 1841-8, 1924-8, weekly review of work 1836-7, misc wages records 1895-1963, rents ledger 1859-76, specifications for new premises 1830-4, misc business corresp and papers 1830-1954.
Montrose Public Library. NRA 12627.

[635] **WILLIAM PEACOCK LTD**, cord mfrs, Paisley, Renfrewshire

Private ledger 1894-1940, journal 1894-1952, bill book 1904-16, bank books (20) 1883-1945, order book 1924-54, sales ledger and cash book 1950-5, inventories (1 vol) of stock and premises 1898-1915, wages books (3) 1895-1924, 1936-44, misc papers 1938-52.
Glasgow University Archives (UGD/244). NRA 25891.

[636] **ROBERT PEAT**, linen mfr, Dundee

Flax purchases book 1804-12, weaving book 1809-13.
Scottish Record Office (CS 96/2926-7). *Court of Session Productions*, List & Index Society, special series vol 23, 1987, p166.

[637] **PEDEN family**, scutch and saw millers, Kilrea, co Londonderry

Accounts, corresp and deeds 1886-1904.
In private possession. Copies are in the Public Record Office of Northern Ireland (T 1590): see *Ulster textile industry.*

[638] **PHOENIX WEAVING CO LTD**, linen mfrs, Ballymena, co Antrim

Letter books (3) 1940-53, day books (6) 1930-8, journal 1919-56, cloth order books (6) 1908-48, yarn order books (3) 1912-47, invoice books (4) 1911-56, cloth sales book 1937-49, purchase books (3) 1933-51, yarn and cloth stock books (2) 1890-1909, cost books (8) 1891-1903, 1908-41, preparing yarn book 1934-44.
Public Record Office of Northern Ireland (D 1942). NRA 31479.

[639] **PILMER & PATON**, flax merchants, Dundee

Letter book 1873-6; Silvester Smith, merchant and commission agent, bill register 1835-65 and day book rel to flax purchase 1843-56.
Dundee Archive Centre (GD/Mus 103).

[640] **PORTADOWN LINEN CO**, linen mfrs, Portadown, co Armagh

Directors' minute book, liquidation papers and papers rel to sale of machinery 1873-7.
Public Record Office of Northern Ireland (D 1252/35/8, D 1769/22/2): see *Ulster textile industry.*

[641] **PYMORE MILL CO**, net, twine and thread mfrs, Bridport, Dorset

Register 1834, sales accounts 1842-51.
Dorset RO: see *Accessions to repositories 1971*, p30.

Building specifications and papers (23 items) 1843-61.
Dorset RO (D 203). NRA 6592.

[642] **THOMAS RAFFIELD**, sailmaker, London

Letters received (c75) c1802-13, ledgers (2) 1797-1805, rough day or cash book 1793-6, waste book 1793-6, warehouse day books (2) of supplies and repairs 1801-6; mathematical, accounting and penmanship exercise books (5) 1775-9, day book (?as apprentice to Peter Thompson, Monkwearmouth) 1776-9.
Public Record Office, Chancery Lane (C 114/132-3).

[643] **RAPHAEL & CO**, linen merchants, Galgorm, co Antrim

Misc papers 1845-1901 incl articles of agreement 1847, 1857, financial account with Philadelphia branch 1845, and order account book 1863-4.
Public Record Office of Northern Ireland (D 2011, D 3751/3). NRA 31480.

[644] **RATSEY & LAPTHORN LTD**, sail and flag makers, Gosport, Hants

Account and order book 1825-c1836, letter book 1887-92.
National Maritime Museum (MS87/068).

[645] **JN RICHARDSON SONS & OWDEN LTD**, linen mfrs, bleachers, dyers and merchants, Belfast

Register of directors and managers 1920-38, share registers and ledgers 1876-1947, private ledgers 1938-79, private journals 1930-76.
Public Record Office of Northern Ireland (D 1133). *Deputy Keeper's Report 1984*, pp58-9.

Report of shareholders' meeting 1909, balance sheet and directors' report 1917, notebooks (2) rel to firm's administration, shares, etc 1917-18, power looms private ledger 1867-84.
Public Record Office of Northern Ireland (D 2369). NRA 31470.

Corresp rel to establishment of spinning mill at Bessbrook 1845-9 and mill ledger 1865, papers rel to installation of mill machinery at Lisburn 1857, papers rel to mill at Buncrana 1864-7, diary of JN Richardson's sales trip to the United States 1889.
Public Record Office of Northern Ireland (D 2826). *Deputy Keeper's Report 1966-72*, p209.

Glenmore Bleach Works ledgers and other accounting records (5 vols) 1912-63, bleaching books (2) 1901-37, wetting books (39) 1911-46, kieve books (6) 1935-47, wages books (9) 1948-61.
Public Record Office of Northern Ireland (D 2370). NRA 31470.

Cash book 1784-9, 1815-17.
In private possession. A microfilm is in the Public Record Office of Northern Ireland (Mic 120): see *Ulster textile industry.*

[646] **HAMILTON ROBB**, linen and handkerchief mfrs, Portadown, co Armagh

Articles of association, bill book, copy deeds, etc c1830-1911.
Public Record Office of Northern Ireland (D 1251): see *Ulster textile industry.*

[647] **HM ROBB & CO LTD**, linen mfrs, Belfast

Private ledgers (2) 1886-1926 and other accounting records (5 vols) 1922-3, 1932-55, 1962-8, sales ledgers (4) 1908-64 and day book 1964-6, invoice book 1910-34, quotations, price lists and prices for cloth bought in (1 box, 3 vols) 1909-77, stock book 1926-35, incoming cloth books (3) 1927-37, 1949-68, sample book nd; stock book possibly of McBride & Williams 1900-6.
Public Record Office of Northern Ireland (D 2346). NRA 31455.

[648] **RICHARD ROBERTS**, flax spinner and linen merchant, Burton Bradstock, Dorset

Letter books (2) 1807-15.
Dorset RO (D 152). NRA 7828.

[649] **ROBINSON & CLEAVER LTD**, linen mfrs and merchants and general outfitters, Belfast

Memorandum of association 1900, register of directors 1928-30, share registers, etc (14 vols) 1900-59, directors' reports and statements of account 1931-61, private ledgers (4) 1898-1900, 1908-35, impersonal ledger 1955-60, private journals (2) 1898, 1901-16, cash received book 1952-71, bank books (3) 1933-9, 1952-65, monthly stock and cash account books (2) 1871-95, trading accounts 1901-12, register and index of foreign orders (3 vols) 1954-65, wages summary 1938-40, inventories and valuations of premises, machinery and plant 1900, 1921-2, 1930, title deeds 1825-1953.
Public Record Office of Northern Ireland (D 3678). NRA 31469.

[650] **G & R ROBINSON & CO LTD**, linen, sack and carpet mfrs, Leeds

Corporate, financial and misc records (24 boxes) 1875-1973 incl papers rel to incorporation 1901-3 and liquidation 1972-3, directors' and general meeting minute books (3) 1902-72, balance sheets, annual accounts and papers rel to general meetings from 1902, private ledgers (5) 1902-20, 1925-39, 1957-69 , nd, yarn stock book 1907-64, carpet stock book 1921-30, cloth tests books (2) 1923-72, and insurance policies, agreements and assignments 1875-1947.
West Yorkshire Archive Service, Leeds. NRA 31585.

[651] **ROSEBANK WEAVING CO LTD**, linen mfrs, Belfast

Letter books, yarn and stock books, wages books, etc (c200 vols) 1888-1960.
Public Record Office of Northern Ireland (D 3273).

[652] **JAMES RUSSELL**, linen merchant, Belfast

Letter and account books 1806-9, account of his personal estate 1819.
Public Record Office of Northern Ireland (D 2168/2-3): see *Ulster textile industry*.

[653] **ST MARTINS LANGDALE LINEN INDUSTRY**, Elterwater, Westmorland

Account book 1889-1924, order book 1884-1925, notebook 1896-1900, misc letters, photographs, etc late 19th-early 20th cent.
Cumbria RO, Kendal (WDB/73). NRA 30977.

[654] **JULIUS SALOMON & CO**, jute and linen merchants, Dundee

Out-letter books (24) 1897-1949, letters received (9 files) 1921-45, private ledgers (2) 1885-1944, ledgers (4) 1898-1929, account books (8) 1873-5, 1898-1945, journals (4) 1910-39, bill books (3) 1907-40, indexes (14) to missing ledgers, account books, etc nd, order books (12) 1899-1939, contract books (2) 1906-19, invoices (6 files) 1890-1, 1929-41, invoice books (5) 1899-1925, sales books (18) 1899-1945, prices book 1879-84, reports from overseas agents (1 vol) 1876-96, stock book 1911-20.
Dundee University Library (MS 12). NRA 19242.

[655] **SALTCOATS ROPEWORK CO**, Saltcoats, Ayrshire

Accounts 1772-1895, corresp 1802-c1844, valuations 1807, legal and misc papers 1734-1842, nd.
Cunninghame District Library, Ardrossan (CA 12). NRA 14148.

[656] **FRANK STEWART SANDEMAN & SONS LTD**, jute and cotton spinners and mfrs, Dundee

Directors' attendance book, reports, etc 1912-36, registers (2) of shares and members c1913-32, corresp 1903-20, trading accounts and misc financial papers 1912-24, jute stock book 1925-30, summary history of company 1858-1921 incl valuation of Manhattan Works 1908.
Dundee University Library (MS 66). NRA 12256.

Stanley Mills, Perthshire, cash book 1930-48, costings, specifications, names of employees, etc 1911-21, price lists 1922-33, workers' subscriptions 1924-48, plans 1785, 1831, misc personal and business papers c1825-1951.
In private possession. Enquiries to NRA (Scotland) (NRA(S) 1158). NRA 18755.

[657] **JR SAUNDERS**, importer of Irish linens, Manchester

Purchase ledger 1793-1824.
Manchester Central Library (MISC 706).

[658] **SCOTT & FYFE LTD**, linen mfrs, Tayport, Fife

Minutes (2 vols) 1907-75, letter book 1905-64, cash book 1919-60, bank books (2) 1917-75, monthly wages books (2) 1929-52, photographs.
The Company. Enquiries to NRA (Scotland) (NRA(S) 2029). NRA 23174.

[659] **H & A SCOTT LTD**, hessian and jute goods mfrs, Dundee

Memorandum and articles of association 1905, balance sheets and profit and loss accounts 1931-68, private ledger nd, general ledger 1914-32, cash books (4) 1937-55, inquiry book 1885-1921, warpers' order book 1861-4 incl inventory and valuation 1860 and production figures 1864-81, order books (3) 1887-1910, 1935-42, jute purchase books (2) 1882-1928, 1967-77, digest of production and costs (1 vol) 1950-63, time book 1880-1, wages books (18) 1916-57, misc papers (1 bundle) 1904-19.
Dundee University Library (MS 98). NRA 23008.

Account book 1832-69, salaries book 1902-25.
The Company. Enquiries to NRA (Scotland) (NRA(S) 2002). NRA 23008.

[660] **JAMES SCOTT & SONS LTD**, merchants, spinners and jute mfrs, Dundee

Articles of association 1923-50, board minute book 1903-65, letter books (3) 1897, 1900-57, corresp files (33) 1896-1969, annual returns, reports, accounts and balance papers 1922-65, Calcutta agency balance sheets (2 bundles) 1894-1933, dividend book 1918-65, investment lists (3 bundles) 1926-49, notebooks (20) rel to balances, costings, etc 1894-8, 1926-61, ledgers (10) 1915-62, misc account books, journals, etc (10 vols, 4 files, 5 bundles) 1876-1965, purchase book 1861-6, order books (3) 1876-9, 1964-6, stock books (9) 1921-67, additional cash and stock books 1904-54, costing records (c22 vols, files and bundles) 1938-66, production, batching, spin and reeling and winding books (42) 1908-13, 1920-64, wages and personnel records (10 vols, etc) 1867-88, 1897-1901, 1907-14, 1930-65, plans and engineering drawings 1871-1953, photographs c1880-c1970, misc papers 1874-1974.
Dundee Archive Centre. NRA 12257 (partial list).

[661] **SHIRRAS, LAING & CO LTD**, marquee mfrs and proprietors, Aberdeen

Directors' minutes (2 vols) 1903-48, corresp incl discharged bills, etc (6 bundles) 1888-1943, day books (3) 1943-5, sales and order books (4) 1932-62, lists of suppliers, price lists, stock valuations and oil contracts (9 bundles) c1886-c1945, wages books (11) 1913-48, bonus receipts (1 bundle) 1924-5.
The Company. Enquiries to NRA (Scotland) (NRA(S) 1434). NRA 20364.

[662] **J & J SMART (BRECHIN) LTD**, jute and flax mfrs, Brechin, Angus

Letter books from 1902, ledgers from 1838, cash books from 1879, private journal 1886-1901, bank books (2) 1903-8, order books (10) 1895-1905, manufacturing books 1867, 1885, 1895, 1900-12, production books from 1896, length books (4) 1899-1909, inventories 1858-80.
In private possession. Enquiries to NRA (Scotland) (NRA(S) 424). NRA 13037.

[663] **JAMES SMIETON & SON**, linen and jute mfrs, Carnoustie, Angus

Plans and drawings (113 items) of textile machinery, mill, etc 19th-20th cent.
Dundee University Library (MS 47). NRA 17578.

[664] **THOMAS & WILLIAM SMITH LTD**, rope makers, Newcastle upon Tyne, Northumb

Australian tramway order book 1887-1926, photographs (1 vol) early 20th cent.
Doncaster Archives Department (DY.BRI/30). NRA 21369.

[665] **ROBERT SMYLIE**, linen merchant, Camus, co Tyrone

Linen account book 1762-74.
Public Record Office of Northern Ireland (D 1075/1): see *Ulster textile industry.*

[666] **JOHN A SMYTH & CO**, flax merchants, Londonderry

Letter book with accounts 1868-82.
Public Record Office of Northern Ireland (D 2604). *Deputy Keeper's Report 1966-72*, p145.

[667] **SPENCE, BRYSON & CO**, linen mfrs, Portadown, co Armagh

Wages books (5) 1907-17.
Public Record Office of Northern Ireland (D 2662): see *Ulster textile industry.*

[668] **STEPHENS BROS & MARTIN LTD**, rope makers, Bristol

Corresp 1889-1961, private ledger 1925-68, wages book 1878-90, accident book 1938-40, apprenticeship indentures and related corresp 1913-20, inventories and valuations 1873-1923, deeds 1851-1951, plans 1904-c1950, photographs c1889-1924.
Bristol RO (Acc 33302). NRA 19629.

[669] **JOHN STEPHENS & SON LTD**, hemp and wire rope makers, Falmouth, Cornwall

Ledger 1821-46, account books (4) 1833-79 incl notes and inventories of stock, waste book 1838-41, apprenticeship indentures (12) 1837-80, misc letters and papers 1857-1965, machinery plan 1844, notes, etc rel to history of ropeworks 1939.
Cornwall RO (DD ST). NRA 24522.

[670] **WALTER STEVEN**, jute merchant, Dundee

Letter books (2) 1847-56.
In private possession. Enquiries to NRA (Scotland) (NRA(S) 723). NRA 16125.

[671] **ROBERT STOCKS & CO LTD**, linen mfrs, Kirkcaldy, Fife

Ledgers (3) 1823-62, 1873-9, day books (2) 1811-16, 1954-6, wages books (3) 1893-1901, 1912-13.
Scottish College of Textiles, Galashiels. NRA 31124.

[672] **WJ STRAIN**, linen merchants and mfrs, Belfast

Letter books (2) 1891-2, 1897, letters received (over 3,000 items) 1897-9, 1956-61, misc agreements, etc 1896-7, general ledgers (3) 1913-61, cash books (2) 1904-22, petty cash books (2) 1922-61, bank books (2) 1916-19, 1938-44, cheque book stubs and paid cheques 1896-1900, purchase and sales records (13 vols, bundles, etc) 1919-62, bleaching stock books (5) 1909-60, trade marks early 20th cent, design sheets (1 bundle) c1900-17, sample books (5) early 20th cent, inventory and valuation 1920, factory register 1909-17.
Public Record Office of Northern Ireland (D 2585). NRA 31461.

Letter book, ledgers, cloth order book, advice notes, contracts, wages book, etc (10 vols) 1890-1923.
Public Record Office of Northern Ireland (D 1504): see *Ulster textile industry.*

[673] **J & W STUART LTD**, net and twine mfrs, Musselburgh, Midlothian

Letter book 1882-1913, balance ledger 1843-68, private ledgers (2) 1878-1916, account books (6) 1871-6 incl lists of net prices, production and trading record 1909-11, net production book 1928-51, labour contracts book 1845-91, misc legal and business papers (9 bundles) 1859-1925.
The Company. Enquiries to NRA (Scotland) (NRA(S) 2159). NRA 23658.

[674] **WILLIAM TERRELL & SONS LTD**, rope makers, Bristol

Registers of directors and members (2 vols) 1886-1915, nd, register of transfers 1880-1932, share ledger 1888-1959, register of mortgages 1874-1950, balance sheets 1889-1958, private ledgers (2) 1879-1958, journal 1880-1961, cash books (3) 1920-63, bill books (2) 1843-1930, prices files 1940-64, estimate book 1908, cordage book c1814, stocktaking notebook 1925-53, policy register 1884-1915, valuation of plant and machinery 1878, site plans 1928, 1951, photographs (2 vols) 1920, 1950, misc papers 1875-1961.
Bristol RO (Acc 21790). NRA 15592.

Directors' minutes (4 vols) 1880-1962, misc corresp and papers 1940-64.
Doncaster Archives Department (DY.BRI/29). NRA 21369.

[675] **THOMSON, SHEPHERD & CO LTD**, jute spinners, Dundee

Board minute book 1896-1933, general meeting minute book 1897-1965, registers of directors (2) 1901-43, corresp file 1931-44, private ledger 1897-1959, general ledger 1930-9, cash book 1938-57, purchase and sales records (7 vols) 1929-65, stock books (4) 1883-1948, production records (4 vols) 1932-61, wages records (4 vols) 1932-56, factory school certificate books (2) 1868-70, memoranda book 1876-1906, press cuttings (1 vol) early 20th cent.
Dundee University Library (MS 85). NRA 18900.

Corresp file 1934-9, private ledgers (2) 1882-97, 1959-66, bill book 1916-57, accounts analysis books (5) 1934-58, purchase and sales records (2 vols, 1 parcel) 1948-58, wages records (7 vols) 1917-54.
The Company. Enquiries to NRA (Scotland) (NRA(S) 1019). NRA 18900.

[676] **THOMAS THOMSON LTD**, tarpaulin mfrs, Barrhead, Renfrewshire

Private letter books (2) 1902-12, ledger 1928-33, day book 1929-34, purchase book 1924-35, tracing 1843, plan c1890.
In private possession. Enquiries to NRA (Scotland) (NRA(S) 1050). NRA 19020.

[677] **RB TOPE & CO LTD**, flag and tent mfrs, Plymouth, Devon

Purchase ledgers (2) 1911-59, sales ledgers (3) 1911-53, sales and cash journal 1975-6, cheque register 1963-77, catalogue and price list nd.
West Devon Area RO (Accs 989, 1007). NRA 31496.

[678] **THOMAS TUCKER & CO LTD**, fishing net mfrs, Bridport, Dorset

Ledgers (2) 1782-5, 1819-1905, cash books (3) 1821-1918, outbraiders' book 1868-83.
Dorset RO (D 203). NRA 6592.

[679] **JOHN TUCKEY & CO LTD**, table linen mfrs, linen wholesalers and retailers, London

Directors' and general meeting minutes 1873-1985, royal appointments 1892, 1907.
Coats Viyella plc. Enquiries to the Company Secretary. Formerly with the National Linen Co. NRA 32377; and see BAC *Company Archives* no 176.

[680] **J & G TURNER LTD**, rope and twine makers, Bedford

Certificates of incorporation, etc 1917-78, ledger 1886-90, ropery guide c1930, photographs c1870-1970.
Bedfordshire RO (X 588). NRA 6970.

[681] **VICTORIA SPINNING CO LTD**, jute spinners and mfrs, Dundee

Minute book 1894-1920, yarn stock book 1959-62, spinning book c1945-8, wages books from 1971.
The Company. Enquiries to NRA (Scotland) (NRA(S) 1827). NRA 22000.

Wages books (c100) 1893-1971.
Dundee Archive Centre. NRA 22000; and see *Accessions to repositories 1987*, p43.

[682] **GEORGE WALKER & CO LTD**, flax and hemp spinners, Newtownards, co Down

Minute books (2) 1889-1972, letter book 1889-1918, private ledgers (5) 1870-1968, general ledgers (6) 1870-1971, journal 1889-1934, cash book 1934-68.
Public Record Office of Northern Ireland (D 2997). NRA 31465.

Letters received 1925-32.
Public Record Office of Northern Ireland (D 1905/2/107): see *Ulster textile industry*.

[683] **HARRY WALKER & SONS LTD**, jute spinners and mfrs, Dundee

Memorandum and articles of association 1892-1924, minutes (2 vols) 1892-1933, register of members 1892-1931, annual reports and balance sheets 1892-1932, letter books (2) 1885-1926, private ledger 1903-21, order books (3) 1847-51, costing books (17) 1851-1910, wages book 1911-12, misc papers, deeds and photographs 1856-1930.
Dundee University Library (MS 66). NRA 12256.

[684] **JABEZ WALL & SON**, rope and twine makers, Burford, Oxon

Ledgers (5) 1802-29, 1851-66, 1880-1940, account books (9) 1796-1850, 1859-1931, day books (2) 1851-85, order book 1807.
Bodleian Library, Oxford (MS. DD. Warner). NRA 5334.

[685] **WALTON & CO**, linen mfrs, Knaresborough, Yorks

Sales figures 1830-56, price lists 1863-early 20th cent, tally cards 1820, labels 1860s, specifications and tenders 1886, utensil ledger *c*1872, valuation 1899, rental 1881, ledger for rents, etc 1869-90, deeds, plans, photographs and maps 18th-20th cent, diary 1899-1901, misc corresp 1874-1913.
The Company. Enquiries to the Managing Director.

[686] **WATSON & ANDERSON**, merchants and linen-masters, Cullen, Banffshire

Ledgers (6) and indexes 1755-69, day and weaving books (5) 1759-70, journals (4) 1758-69, waste books (8) 1763-9, invoice book for flax from Rotterdam 1762-4, lint and yarn books (3) 1760-5, heckling and beating book 1765-6.
Scottish Record Office (CS 96/2912-14, 2918-22, 3051-71, 4908). *Court of Session Productions*, List & Index Society, special series vol 23, 1987, p44.

[687] **HENDERSON WATSON**, linen merchant, Lurgan, co Armagh

Bank book 1835, notebook rel to purchase of linen 1837-9, weavers' payment book 1837-9, etc.
Public Record Office of Northern Ireland (D 2516): see *Ulster textile industry*.

[688] **WEBSTER & CO LTD**, rope makers, Sunderland, co Durham

Private ledger 1882-1902, ledgers (9) 1848-1914, day books (23) 1820-1926, private journal 1882-1902, journals (2) 1864-93, cash book 1780-91, order books (3) 1890-1903, 1918-21, shipping and export ledger 1914-27, stock books (2) 1898-1904, 1915-20, stock account and valuation 1885, time books (8) 1865-1916, register of young employees, accidents, etc 1914-57, scrapbook 1906-23, misc business and legal corresp and papers, plans, photographs.
Tyne and Wear Archives Service (Acc 569). NRA 22975.

Memorandum and articles of association 1899, 1959, directors' minute book 1899-1959, registers of directors, mortgages, etc, share records and corresp 1907-68, factory register 1958-65, inventory and valuation 1935, catalogues.
Doncaster Archives Department (DY.BRI/30). NRA 21369.

[689] **FRANCIS WEBSTER & SONS LTD**, flax spinners and mfrs, Arbroath, Angus

Minutes from 1933, letter books (11) 1849-56, 1896-1932, balance sheets (4 bundles) from 1913, private ledgers (5) 1875-1916, ledgers, sales and other accounts (*c*35 vols, etc) from 1912, order books (15) 1911-65, material purchase book 1948-73, buying, hackling and spinning books (3) 1944-61, home and foreign consignment books (3) 1896-1955, stock books (10) from 1876, costing and specification books (*c*80) 1871-1952, yield book 1933-7, mill waste books (3) 1937-52, memoranda books and technical notebooks, wages records 1947-63, clerk apprenticeship book 1868-77, corresp and legal papers rel to property, plant and machinery *c*1905-70, plans, etc 1821-1912, address books 1868-*c*1886, misc business and family papers.
In private possession. Enquiries to NRA (Scotland) (NRA(S) 1223). NRA 19302.

[690] **WILLIAM WHITE**, sail and blind maker, Liverpool

Account book and journal 1860-5.
In private possession. A photocopy is in the National Museums & Galleries on Merseyside, Merseyside Maritime Museum.

Journal, etc 1900-10.
National Museums & Galleries on Merseyside, Merseyside Maritime Museum: see *Merseyside County Archives preliminary brief descriptive guide*, p10.

[691] **WHITEABBEY FLAX SPINNING CO LTD**, Whiteabbey, co Antrim

Notebook incl calculations rel to pricing, etc *c*1872.
Ulster Folk and Transport Museum, Holywood (UFTM D4-9-2).

Insurance register 1911-45.
Public Record Office of Northern Ireland (D 946).
Deputy Keeper's Report 1954-9, p100.

[692] **J & D WILKIE LTD**, jute mfrs, Kirriemuir, Angus

Stock books (15) 1889-96, 1907, costing book *c*1876-7, specification books (3) 1897-1907, 1913-16, minutes of workers' social meetings, etc 1872-93, rental of property owned by company 1866-84, specifications, etc (2 bundles) for building and extending factory 1868-86.
The Company. Enquiries to NRA (Scotland) (NRA(S) 1145). NRA 19354.

[693] **JAMES WILLIAMSON & SON LTD**, floorcloth, linoleum and table baize mfrs, Lancaster

Account books (6) 1838-47, 1854-61, 1868-9, day books (4) 1837-53, cash book 1837-46, receipt book 1844-52, order books (5) 1838-53, despatch books (4) 1845-62, corresp, orders, specifications of machinery, etc 1863, 1900-16, 1937-48, plans of Lune Mills *c*1900, *c*1930, press cuttings and notes on company history.
Lancashire RO (DDX 909). NRA 18059.

Laboratory and works trial reports 1931-60, research and technical committee minutes 1952-8.
Nairn Floors Ltd. Enquiries to NRA (Scotland) (NRA(S) 1898). NRA 22372.

[694] **JOHN WILSON & SONS**, buckram mfrs and linen merchants, Leeds

Letter books (24) 1754-1826, ledgers (9) 1754-1807, private ledgers (2) 1786, 1810-23, district ledgers (16) 1796-1830, day books (69) 1761-1825, cash books (11) 1754-1813, bill books (12) 1757-67, 1776-7, 1797-1831, bank books (7) 1778-82, 1789-95, 1801-12, 1820-3, porterage books (7) 1798-1804, 1812-19, warehouse books (5) 1754-7, *c*1770-84, memoranda of work done, costings, etc (28 vols) 1812-32, stock books (5) 1798-1813, inventories (12 vols) 1754-1809, nd, misc family papers early 19th cent.
West Yorkshire Archive Service, Leeds. NRA 6542.

[695] **WRIGHTS' ROPES LTD**, hemp and wire rope makers, Birmingham

Directors' minutes (6 vols) 1899-1954, registers of directors and members, share ledgers, etc 1923-64, annual reports and statements of accounts 1898-1963, representatives' price lists 1912-16, nd, production record book 1915-25, patent specifications 1796-1906, misc administrative corresp 1950-64, catalogues and historical and publicity material 1880-1964, Wrights' Ropes Charitable Trust minute book and annual accounts 1945-64.
Doncaster Archives Department (DY.BRI/31). NRA 21369.

[696] **YOUNG family**, linen and general merchants, Fenaghy, co Antrim

Family and business records (*c*400 vols and items) 1715-1956 incl balance sheets 1834-9, general merchant's cash book and day book 1776-1817, letter books and invoices rel to shipment of linen 1813-16, account book 1885-90, and corresp, legal papers and deeds rel to bleach green and other property 1715-*c*1904.
Public Record Office of Northern Ireland (D 1364, D 1658). *Deputy Keeper's Report 1960-5*, p188; *Ulster textile industry.*

SILK

[697] **J & R ALLAN LTD**, silk mercers and drapers, Edinburgh

General meeting minute book 1879-1953, private ledger sheets 1949-50.
Glasgow University Archives (UGD/98/14-15). NRA 19964.

[698] **ANDERSON & ROBERTSON LTD**, silk mfrs, Glasgow

Articles of association 1904, minutes (3 vols, etc) 1895-1964, register of members and debenture holders 1925-30, annual returns, etc 1957-63, nd, letter books (15) 1876-81, 1930-42, private ledgers (2) 1896-1945, cash books (8) 1877-1963, bill book 1912-39, misc accounts (4 vols) 1940-64, purchase, package and sales accounts (7 vols, etc) 1933-64, costing book 1931-55, wages books (2) 1936-63, misc papers incl scrapbooks 1921-32.
Glasgow University Archives (UGD/29). NRA 13689.

Glemsford Mill plans and corresp 1895-1953.
Suffolk RO, Bury St Edmunds (HC 525). NRA 3517.

[699] **JOHN BARRACLOUGH**, silk spinner, Triangle, Yorks

Notebooks 1845-91, corresp 1845-69 incl drawings and plans of technical processes, receipts and invoices 1862-95, business and introduction cards nd.
West Yorkshire Archive Service, Calderdale (SPL 203). NRA 19148.

[700] **BATCHELOR, HAM & PERIGAL**, silk weavers, London

Pattern books (12) *c*1755-1826, incl successors Harvey, Perigal & Ham and Jourdain & Ham.
Victoria & Albert Museum, Department of Textile Furnishings & Dress (T.374-382-1972, T.385-1972, T.89-1973). NRA 28420, NRA 30151.

[701] **BENTLEY SILK MILLS LTD**, silk spinners, throwsters, etc, Meltham, Yorks

Ledger accounts books (2) 1858-65, 1875-80, sales day book 1864-83, purchase day book 1866-70, lot book 1854, costing book 1872-1904, wages book 1848-53.
West Yorkshire Archive Service, Kirklees (KC 278). NRA 31062.

Memorandum of association 1900, minutes (2 vols) 1890-9, 1906-15, plans 1891, 1901, 1959, 1968, catalogue of plant, etc 1891.
In private possession.

[702] **JAMES BENTLEY**, silk mfr, Manchester

Corresp with John Bentley, his son, trading in silk in South Africa (29 items) 1855-8, invoices (6) 1853-7, misc legal papers 1801, 1866.
Manchester Central Library (M221). NRA 19442.

[703] **BERISFORDS LTD**, mfrs of ribbons, labels, trimmings, etc, Congleton, Cheshire

Partnership records, articles of association, agreements, etc (3 envelopes, 3 packets) 1879-1961, directors' minutes (1 vol) 1916-46, general meeting minutes (1 vol) 1947-61, annual returns and balance sheets 1916-64, papers rel to reduction of share capital (1 packet) 1928, private ledgers (4) 1915-56, cash books (2) 1922-61, misc accounts (4 packets) 1945-75, sales day book and stock book 1865-97, sales book 1915-64, silk shipping book 1926-47, stocks and

balances (1 vol) 1916-31, contract records (4 vols) 1910-41, costing book 1911-20. Congleton Weavers list of prices 1843-98, weaver's design book 19th cent, pattern particulars book 1914-29, misc wages and pension fund records (2 vols, 2 packets) 1911-66, inventory and valuations 1913-15 and insurance records 1913-15, 1936-60, executorship records *c*1880-1910.
The Company. Enquiries to the Company Secretary. NRA 30104.

[704]　**BOLINGBROKE, JONES & CO**, poplin mfrs, Norwich, Norfolk

Account and costing books (19) 1859-88, pattern books (18) *c*1850-1890.
Bridewell Museum, Norwich. NRA 30575.

[705]　**J & T BROCKLEHURST & SONS LTD**, silk mfrs, Macclesfield, Cheshire

Minute book 1968, committee minute book 1945-70, partnership accounts 1756-89, ledgers (2) 1901-11, *c*1951-7, bank books (3) 1924-9, despatch book 1906-7, order records (3 parcels) 1968-70, pattern books (132) containing textile samples *c*1844-1958, nd, pattern books (17) containing prints on paper *c*1935-63, nd, files of patterns, loose sheets and design cards (1 box, 40 files, 7 folders, 3 drawers) nd, memoranda book *c*1870, inventory of stock 1789, inventory and valuation 1934, insurance records 1955-62, account of Hurdsfield water supply 1898, deeds 17th-20th cent; pattern books (20) of misc English, Scottish and French firms *c*1830-1962, nd.
Cheshire RO and *Brocklehurst Fabrics Ltd.* Enquiries to Cheshire RO. NRA 30216.

[706]　**BROUGH, NICHOLSON & HALL LTD**, silk mfrs, Leek, Staffs

Partnership agreements, etc (23) 1869-1941, board minutes (7 vols) 1907-10, 1930-76, general meeting minutes (1 vol) 1908-30, registers of members and other share records (7 vols) 1907-32, register of mortgages 1904-7, annual reports and balance sheets 1856-1969, letter books (6) 1886-1927, corresp file 1947-53, general ledger 1873-84, impersonal ledgers (9) 1903-47, private ledgers (3) 1904-9, 1921-30, 1943-60, nominal ledgers (4) 1932-79, private journals (9) 1930-62, cash books (48) 1847-1978, bank books (27) 1835-1930, sales ledgers (2) 1815-30, 1836-47, customers' account ledger 1905-33, supplies ledger *c*1960, purchase book 1947-8, despatch book 1950-3, analysis of monthly production figures (3 vols) 1870-97, patent records (57 files and items) 1878-1928, trade marks and samples book nd, salaries and wages books and staff registers (*c*45 vols) 1845-54, 1874-1985, sprinkler plans (47) 1924-7, valuation of plant 1847, deeds, etc 1832, 1887-1932.
Staffordshire RO (D 4241, D 4382, D 4640). NRA 29524.

Summary accounts 1815-46, annual balance sheets 1832-55, ledger 1828 incl new silk factory expenses 1844, corresp 1850-80, Brough family papers.
Staffordshire RO (D 538/4/B pt). NRA 6138.

[707]　**BRUNT, FYNNEY & CO LTD**, sewing silk mfrs, London

Directors' and shareholders' minutes 1903-6, register of shares 1903-5, nominal ledger 1900-6, private ledger 1903-6, order book of Henry Brunt & Co 1879-86, quotation books (2) *c*1931-49.
Staffordshire RO (D 1227). NRA 16677.

[708]　**CARTWRIGHT & SHELDON LTD**, silk mfrs, Macclesfield, Cheshire

Letter books (6) 1927-79, private ledgers (6) 1916-44, nd, cash books (4) 1912-77 and other accounting records 1921-81, order books (*c*30 vols) 1930-81, nd, sales, delivery and despatch records nd, index of customers and address books (10 vols) nd, invoices 1912-26, 1974-7, price lists 1873-20th cent, stock books (11) 1940-*c*1980, nd, weavers' production records (*c*40 vols) 1924-79, costing books (3) 1927-39, warp and yarn books 1940-81, nd, pattern books and samples 20th cent, wages books (2) 1912-24, apprenticeship records 1875-*c*1970, workers' agreements 20th cent, register of machinery 1944-75 and other premises records 20th cent, misc notebooks and papers 20th cent.
Macclesfield Sunday School Heritage Centre Silk Museum. NRA 30203.

[709]　**J & J CASH LTD**, ribbon and tape mfrs, Coventry, Warwicks

Memorandum and articles of association, etc (1 vol, etc) 1895-1951, directors' minutes (11 vols) 1895-1965, executive meeting minutes (1 vol) 1931-6, private minutes (1 vol) 1895-7, register of directors (2 vols) 1925-49, register of members, share ledgers and other share records (24 vols, etc) 1895-1965, annual reports, balance sheets, etc 1898, 1925-70, letter book 1917-40, private ledgers (6) 1857-1928, 1934-50, cash book 1919-25, misc financial records 1857-92, order books (2) 1891, 1901-7, advertising contract books (4) 1960-7, stock book 1868-1900, register of trade marks, patents and designs 1879-1928, cost books (3) 1889, 1899-1936, wages ledgers and payrolls (4 vols) 1925-39, 1951-67, staff pension register 1934-67, employees' aid and benefits' book 1910-40, Kingfield Mutual Improvement Society minutes (1 vol) 1868-9 and other benevolent fund records 1883-9, nd, valuations of machinery and buildings (1 vol) 1882-1900, plans 1856-1959, photographs 19th-20th cent, historical notes 20th cent, misc Cash family business corresp and papers 1836-1970; J & J Cash Proprietory Ltd, Australia records 1914-71 and other papers rel to Australian and New Zealand interests 1877-1971.
Coventry City RO (Accs 562, 738). NRA 30535.

[710]　**COURTAULDS LTD**, crape, dress fabric and artificial silk mfrs, London

Records mainly from 1891 incl board, international consortia, divisional and committee minutes, agenda books and related papers, annual reviews of divisions and subsidiary companies, directors' attendance books, reports, accounts and balance sheets, share records, letter books and corresp, private, nominal and other ledgers, cash books, registers of contracts,

production and sales statistics, corresp, drawings, designs, records of experiments, etc on the production and spinning of viscose, salaries and wages books, files rel to working conditions, plant ledgers, inventories, valuations, deeds, papers of chairmen and directors chiefly Samuel Courtauld (1876-1947), Sir John Hanbury-Williams (1892-1965) and Sir Dallas Bernard (1888-1975); records of home and overseas subsidiaries 19th-20th cent.
Courtaulds plc, Coventry. Enquiries to the Head of Archives. NRA 29343.

London Office: partnership deeds 1841-94, balance sheets and annual accounts (6 vols) 1829-81, private ledgers (7) 1828-91, general journal and ledger 1880-91, partners' cash withdrawal book 1866-91, assignment book 1885-95, silk book 1873-6; Bocking Works, Essex: annual accounts (1 vol) 1833-62, letter books (5) 1893-1923, production registers (34) 1829-1936, records of trials in crape finishing (1 vol) 1853-66, in silk (1 vol) 1886-8 and in dyeing (14 items) 1857-72, work abstracts (8 vols) 1888-1926, notebooks (70) on technical experiments, plant, labour conditions, etc 1862-1925, registers of employees and applicants (4 vols) 1860-1921, staff instructions (1 vol) 1863-94, wages books (11) 1827-1940, papers on labour 1860-1922 incl strike of weavers 1860, reports on boilers at Bocking, Chelmsford and Halstead mills (1 vol) 1864-94, register of engines incl specifications 1866-99, contracts register of suppliers of machinery 1895-1901, misc papers and corresp 19th-20th cent incl some rel to dissolution of partnership 1817; Halstead and Earls Colne Works, Essex: records 1852-1982 incl letter book 1873-91, production book 1912-25, mill manager's diary 1888, registers of employees and applicants (28 vols) 1831-1925, wages books (80) 1852-1953, and ledgers of the Taylor family incl throwing and sale of silk 1799-1802 and of Remington Mills & Co 1819-25; Braintree Works: registers (2) of young employees 1907-14, school certificate books 1879-91.
Essex RO, Chelmsford (D/F). NRA 21783; *Accessions to repositories 1983,* p25.

Sample and design books (*c*200) 1897-1959, nd, Bocking Works cost and construction books (8 boxes).
Courtaulds plc, London. Access restricted. Enquiries to the Design Library, Courtaulds Textiles. NRA 30957.

Castle Works, Flint: registers of young employees 1910-42 and of hands 1934-49, wages books 1917-31, factory inspection records 1922-35, misc reports. accounts and papers *c*1930-73.
Clwyd RO, Hawarden: see *Annual report 1971* p15, *1974* pp25-6, *1979* p24, *Accessions January 1973-March 1974* p6.

Staff associations and Bocking works committee records *c*1920-1977.
Warwick University Modern Records Centre (MSS 31, 201). NRA 19095, 22796.

Salaries books (6) *c*1940-1950; records of subsidiaries.
Courtaulds Spinning. Enquiries to the Company Secretary. NRA 30126.

Foleshill deeds 1767-1877.
Coventry City RO: see *Accessions to repositories 1983,* p36.

Family corresp.
In private possession. See *Courtauld family letters 1782-1900,* ed SA Courtauld, 8 vols, Cambridge 1916.

[711] **EAGLE SILK MILL**, Leek, Staffs

Ledger 1872-6, wages accounts 1890-4.
Staffordshire RO (D 1452). NRA 3515.

[712] **FORD, AYRTON & CO LTD**, silk spinners, Low Bentham, Yorks

Directors' minutes (4 vols) 1909-70, general meeting minutes (1 vol) 1951-69, register of members, share ledger, etc (3 vols, etc) 1909-69, annual reports, profit and loss accounts and balance sheets 1915-69, letter books (7) 1899-1901, 1905-28, 1945-6, corresp files (*c*37) 1913-58, 1970, accounts (5 vols, 11 files) 1871-83, 1913-69, ledger 1871-80, private ledgers (4) 1883-1970, journals (3) 1876-1907, cash and day books and other accounting records 1925-71, trade ledgers (5) 1870-1902, 1909-26, order books (52) 1871-1970, invoice records and delivery notes (*c*22 vols and bundles) 1887-1970, index of customers nd, contract notes, licences, quotation book, etc (7 vols and bundles) 1919-54, transportation cost records (3 vols) 1934-46, 1955-9, stock sheets 1937-49, silk prices and yields (5 vols) 1898-1968, costing ledgers (2) 1881-1913, dressers' balance books (13) 1898-1955, yarn particulars (1 vol) 1884-1905, machinery repair records, inspection reports, test notes, etc (10 vols and bundles) 1898-1953, wages records (*c*85 vols) 1871-1949, 1961-70 and other employment records (*c*16 vols and bundles) 1916-70, rent book 1902-38, plans of premises and machinery with misc related papers (16 boxes and some loose items) 1831-1935.
West Yorkshire Archive Service, Leeds. NRA 31028.

[713] **WILLIAM FRANKLIN & SON LTD**, ribbon mfrs, Coventry, Warwicks

Register of seals, petty cash and invoice books 1943-5, order and instruction records (6 vols, 1 file) 1932-44, warping prices (1 vol) 1933-40, calculations books (7) 1908-35, sample and order books (54 vols and folders) for neckwear, labels, badges, etc from *c*1860, production books (4) *c*1940-58 nd, weavers' ledgers (3) 1914-49, sample labels and badges.
Herbert Art Gallery & Museum, Coventry (88/274). NRA 32342.

Minute book 1913-23, pattern book *c*1933-43, pattern cards *c*1961-8, specimens of lines weaving (1 vol) nd, sample book of ribbons nd, sample cards.
Coventry City RO (Acc 597). NRA 30532.

[714] **WILLIAM FROST & SONS LTD**, silk throwsters, Macclesfield, Cheshire

Ledgers (2) 1876-1938, day book credits (1 vol) 1891-1919, order book 1918-25, customers' day book 1926-31, production book 1882-1924, warping book 1907-22, 1932, weekly production figures (2 vols) 1912-1932, analysis book *c*1924-5, commission accounts (1 vol) 1933-5, deeds (5 bundles) 1767-20th cent, press cuttings books (7) 1932-53.
Gradus plc. Enquiries to the Chairman. NRA 32468.

[715] **HT GADDUM & CO LTD**, silk and man made fibre yarn and waste importers and merchants, Macclesfield, Cheshire

Minute books from 1940, letter books (5) 1879-1928, ledgers (11) 1833-55, c1875-1929, day books (2) 1865-9, 1892-1905, journals (3) 1876-1931, waste book 1882-1909, account book 1883-94, produce book 1882-1909, silk books (3) 1882-1918, summaries book 1859-1900, stock lists, balances, etc (52 files) 1875-1939, information rel to other firms, customers, etc (1 vol) 1875-1900, staff book 1875-1916, valuation 1882 and deeds 1881-1920 of Manchester warehouses, corresp and deeds rel to failure of Josiah Smale & Sons Ltd 1914-19, letter books, diary and account books of HT Gaddum (12 vols) 1854-1905, private corresp of FE Gaddum 1863-6, family corresp (1 box) 19th cent, notebooks and misc papers 1856-1950. *The Company and AH Gaddum Esq.* All enquiries to AH Gaddum Esq. NRA 30069.

Quotation sheets and printed papers. *Macclesfield Sunday School Heritage Centre Silk Museum.* NRA 30202.

[716] **GAUNT & LUCAS**, silk mfrs, Leek, Staffs

Sales ledgers (3) 1789-1831. *Staffordshire RO* (D 1227). NRA 16677.

[717] **STEPHEN GOODWIN & TATTON LTD**, silk mfrs, Leek, Staffs

Articles of association 1946, board minutes (2 vols) 1904-69, general meeting minutes (1 vol) 1942-69, registers of directors, members, shareholders and transfers (4 vols) 1904-64, private ledgers (3) 1910-42, nominal ledger 1932-41, patent for improvements in thread making 1896, certificates of transfer 1896-1910 and registration c1911-1943 of trade marks, estimates of rebuilding costs 1941. *Staffordshire RO* (D 4241/9, D 4640/E). NRA 29524.

[718] **GROUT & CO LTD**, silk mfrs, Great Yarmouth, Norfolk

Partnership agreements, etc (5 files, etc) 1819-1918, minutes and related papers (4 vols, etc) 1894-1946, share registers (18) 1894-1935, statements of partnership profits, annual reports and balance sheets (7 files, etc) 1825-1950, private ledgers (2) 1829-37, 1874-91, general ledgers (3) 1894-1907, abstract ledgers (2) 1889-94, trading and other accounts (10 vols) 1856-8, 1938-50, silk purchase totals 1888-9, warping particulars and weaving costs 1857, hosiery reports, accounts and samples (1 file) 1930, 1937-9, specifications and contracts, corresp and apprenticeship indentures (32 files, etc) c1821-1949, stock analysis (1 bundle) 1860-93, valuations of factories and stock (2 bundles) 1834, 1840-59, 1889, rough accounts rel to machinery and equipment (1 bundle) 1867-8, 1905-11, deeds and related papers (13 bundles) 1692, 1769-1934, legal papers (10 files) c1833-1932. *Norfolk RO* (Y/D60). NRA 27668.

Valuation of Ponders End factory 1823, deeds and related corresp and papers 1749-1920. *Enfield Local History Library.* NRA 27668.

[719] **WALTER HANDS & CO**, ribbon dressers and waterers, Coventry, Warwicks

Sample books (4) of silk ribbons before 1864. *Herbert Art Gallery & Museum, Coventry* (53/43). NRA 32342.

[720] **HICKLIN & MILLER**, silk merchants, London

Misc accounts and corresp with overseas suppliers of raw silk, throwsters and weavers in Macclesfield and Derby, retailers and others (9 bundles) 1770-80. *Public Record Office, Chancery Lane* (C 107/77).

[721] **GEORGE HILTON**, silk spinners and mfrs, Leigh, Lancs

Sample books (47), patterns and point papers mainly 19th cent. *Wigan Pier Heritage Centre.*

[722] **ADAM HIND & SONS**, silk weavers, Bradford, Yorks

Pattern books (5) 1859-63, c1896, 1903-4, 1906, nd. *Brocklehurst Fabrics Ltd.* Not available for research. NRA 30216.

[723] **FRANCIS HINDE & SONS LTD**, silk and artificial silk fabric mfrs, Norwich, Norfolk

Account and costing books (8) 1828-60, pattern books (11) 1846-64, dyeing records and other records of manufacturing processes (c50 vols, etc) 1867-1964, photographs c1920-c1950. *Bridewell Museum, Norwich.* NRA 30575.

Directors' and general meeting minutes, etc 1924-71. *Courtaulds plc, Coventry* (FRH, TRE). Enquiries to the Head of Archives. NRA 29343.

[724] **IVES, BASELY & ROBBERDS**, silk merchants, Norwich, Norfolk

Account book c1790, pattern books (3) 1791-9. *Bridewell Museum, Norwich.* NRA 30575.

[725] **LE GROS & CO**, silk mfrs, Tewkesbury, Glos

Receipt book 1859-65, wages sheets 1854, circulars 1862-3. *Gloucestershire RO* (D2641). NRA 16917.

[726] **MACCLESFIELD SILK MANUFACTURING SOCIETY LTD**, silk mfrs, Macclesfield, Cheshire

Directors' and shareholders' minutes 1941-75, share registers (3 vols, 1 file) 1888-1971, balance sheets, etc 1888-1976, administrative papers and corresp 1904-76, rule books (9) 1902-70. *Warwick University Modern Records Centre* (MSS 162). NRA 21673.

Pattern books 1888-1975. *Macclesfield Sunday School Heritage Centre Silk Museum.* NRA 30202.

[726A] **D & T MILNE**, silk merchants, Edinburgh

Letter book 1809-18 incl specimens of silk.
National Library of Scotland (Acc 7467). NRA 29189.

[727] **WILLIAM MILNER & SONS LTD**, sewing
silk mfrs, Leek, Staffs

Minutes (2 vols) 1907-70, registers of directors and
shares (5 vols) 1907-64, annual reports and accounts
1908-62, ledgers, cash books and bank books (6 vols)
1913-69, schedules and valuations of buildings and
machinery (2 vols) 1943, misc financial and legal
papers 20th cent.
Staffordshire RO (D 1214, D 1227, D 1262). NRA
16677.

[728] **T & V MYATT LTD**, sewing silk mfrs, Leek,
Staffs

Directors' minutes (2 vols) 1905-70, registers of
directors and shares (5 vols) 1905-70, agendas, reports
and balance sheets 1905-33, 1948-58, private ledgers
(2) 1905-39, 1945-55, nominal ledgers (2) 1906-26,
accounts 1910-19 incl William Stannard & Co Ltd,
cash books (3) 1918-59, summaries of transfers to sales
and nominal ledgers 1912-33, purchase and sales
ledgers (2) *c*1907-31, quotation book 1932-58,
customers' trade book 1914-25, index of customers
nd, corresp rel to trade marks (2 files) 1905-6, wages
books (2) 1925-37, deeds 1829-1932; papers rel to
shares in Coltness Iron Co Ltd 1942-52.
Staffordshire RO (D 1227, D 1262). NRA 16677.

[729] **THOMAS PEAKE**, ribbon weaver, Bedworth,
Warwicks

Time book 1873-4, samples 1873-84.
Warwick County RO: see *Accessions to repositories 1967*,
p101.

[730] **JAMES PEARSALL & CO LTD**, silk thread
mfrs, Taunton, Somerset

Agreements and certificates of registration, etc
1907-75, group managing director's reports (2 vols)
1965-9, secretary's files (6) 1920-32, annual reports,
balance sheets and profit and loss accounts 1865-74,
1899-1953, accounts 1896-1938, 1963-7, ledger
1900-26, cash books (8) 1874-1953, bank books (5)
1875-1932, price books and lists (6 vols, etc)
1885-1930, nd incl Australia and New Zealand,
specifications and orders *c*1903-44, details of stock and
despatch *c*1890, 1923-45, production records (9 vols,
etc) late 19th cent-1951 incl details of labels and skein
tickets, weekly turn off details 1908-42, shade cards,
samples and catalogues (5 boxes, 1 vol, etc) 1935-75,
employment certificates 1894-1907, deeds etc
1748-1971, photographs 20th cent.
The Company. Enquiries to the Business Archives
Council. NRA 26751.

[731] **JL PHILIPS & BROTHER**, silk and cotton
mfrs, Manchester and Tideswell, Derbys

Accounts, etc 1789-1819, diary 1814, Philips family
papers and corresp 18th-20th cent.
Manchester Central Library (M84). NRA 14283.

Summary accounts for spinning and building new mill
at Cressbrook 1814-16, deeds 18th-19th cent.
Derbyshire RO (507B) NRA 13543.

[732] **MORRIS POLLOK**, silk throwster, Glasgow

Ledger 1839-62 incl accounts and memoranda rel to
silk factory in Govan and experiments in silk growing
in America, and other Pollok-Morris family business
corresp and papers 1514-1934.
In private possession. Enquiries to NRA (Scotland)
(NRA(S) 905). NRA 17389.

Statistics of sales 1861-70.
In private possession. Enquiries to NRA (Scotland)
(NRA(S) 457). NRA 13689.

[733] **JOSIAH SMALE & SON LTD**, silk mfrs,
Macclesfield, Cheshire

Ledger and stock book 1862-89, account books, cash
books and ledgers (8) 1940-63.
Macclesfield Sunday School Heritage Centre Silk Museum
(L 3246-54). NRA 30206.

[734] **THOMAS STEVENS (COVENTRY) LTD**,
woven label mfrs, Coventry, Warwicks

Memorandum and articles of association 1946, board
minutes (2 vols) 1923-69, general meeting minutes (1
vol) 1906-69, registers of directors, members and
transfers (4 vols) 1906-64, private ledger 1922-45, cash
book 1937-45.
Staffordshire RO (D 4241/10, D 4640/D). NRA 29524.

[735] **STONE & KEMP**, silk mfrs, London

Pattern books (6) *c*1840-1860.
*Victoria & Albert Museum, Department of Textile
Furnishings & Dress* (T.392-397-1972). NRA 28420,
NRA 30151.

[736] **WILLIAM THOMPSON & CO LTD**, silk
mfrs, Galgate, Lancs

Records 1793-1971 incl letter book, ledgers, day, cash
and bill books, stock books and accounts, sales books,
yarn order books, waste purchase and delivery books,
silk run books, details of patent yarns, silk production
notebooks, yield books, production weekly weights,
sample book, wages books, apprenticeship papers,
factory registers, inventories, building and machinery
books, plans, etc of gas plant, and scrapbooks.
Lancaster Central Library. NRA 28631; BAC
Company Archives no 103.

Records 1869-1971 incl articles, directors' and
shareholders' minutes, register of shareholders, share
transfers, balance sheets, private ledgers, cash books,
stock book, yarns produced for war purposes,
employees' registers and record cards, and inventory
and valuation.
Patons & Baldwins Ltd. NRA 28631; BAC
Company Archives no 103.

[737] **JOHN TUTHILL & SON**, silk merchants,
Norwich, Norfolk

Pattern books (3) *c*1790-*c*1800.
Bridewell Museum, Norwich. NRA 30575.

[738] **J VANNER & SON**, silk weavers, Sudbury, Suffolk

Private ledgers (4) 1854-95, private journals (3) 1840-1900, cash books (8) 1858-74, 1892-1906, cash ledger 1874-86, bought ledger 1865-80, summary of goods, private, cash and bought ledgers (2 vols) 1896-1900, Vanner family accounts, diaries and other papers (45 vols, etc) 1839-1909.
Midland Bank plc. Enquiries to Midland Bank Group Archives. NRA 3825.

Pattern books *c*1706-30, *c*1820-6 incl designs by James Leman, apprenticeship indenture of John Vanner 1774.
In private possession. Enquiries to the Victoria & Albert Museum, Department of Textile Furnishings & Dress. NRA 3825 (partial list).

[739] **WARDLE & DAVENPORT LTD**, sewing silk mfrs, Leek, Staffs

Partnership agreements 1867-83, articles of association, etc 1899, directors' and shareholders' minutes (8 vols, etc) 1899-1970, registers of directors and secretaries (3 vols) 1917-70, shareholders' ledgers (16) 1899-1959, annual reports, accounts and balance sheets 1877-1970, corresp rel to establishment of firm and early trading 1899-1907, out-letter books (2) 1899-1910, 1950-1, corresp 1914-56, account book 1868-81, private ledgers (4) 1898-1936, ledgers and day books (18 vols) 1866-1965, receipts (1 vol) 1879-97, bill book 1907-41, analyses of income and expenditure 1890-1914, 1937-48, 1961, misc accounting records 1898-1970, sales cash books, ledgers, etc (25 vols) 1860-9, *c*1900-69, analyses of purchases, sales and production (12 vols, etc) 1900-65, purchase ledgers, credit books, etc (4 vols) *c*1924-50, quotation books (3) 1901-31 incl for dyeing from Joshua Wardle Ltd, stock sheets 1929, 1940-69, costing calculations 1947-62, trade mark registers and corresp 1898-1972, patents applications 1892-1948, trade catalogues *c*1900-50, wages books (16) 1928-66, deeds 1874-1954, plans (24) 1906-26, nd, schedules, specifications, etc for plant and machinery 1916-67, photographs 1859, *c*1900-60, misc papers 19th-20th cent.
Staffordshire RO (D 1214, D 1227, D 1262). NRA 16677.

[740] **WARNER & SONS LTD**, silk and furnishing textiles mfrs, London and Braintree, Essex

Ledger 1869-91, order books (22) from 1909, invoice register 1934-42, stock register *c*1874-82, hand and power loom record and piece books and other production and costing records (over 100 vols) from 1876, designs (over 7,000) 1870-1970, sketch and design books (7) 19th cent-1920, fabric samples (*c*30,000), paper designs and tracings (*c*6,000), pattern, dye and sample books (over 100) 18th-20th cent, photographs of samples and some point papers *c*1850-*c*1930 for Daniel Walters & Sons, Norris & Co, Keith & Co, Cohens, and H Scott Richmond & Co, weavers' ledgers (24) 1864-1938, register of warpers 1932-68, piecework computation book *c*1904-48, payment books (4) incl designers 1869-1911, notebooks, misc papers, corresp, deeds, photographs and press cuttings 19th-20th cent.

The Company. Enquiries to the Company Archivist. NRA 21789.

Handloom production records (17 vols) 1884-1930, French order book 1760-4, pattern books (26) of various firms *c*1755-mid 19th cent, point papers (*c*180) 18th cent-1849, paper designs (*c*40) *c*1895-1933.
Victoria & Albert Museum, Department of Textile Furnishings & Dress (T.373-701-1972; T.89-1973). NRA 28420, NRA 30151.

Photographs of designs, press cuttings, corresp, etc 1893-1972 incl corresp with Amalgamated Silk Weavers Union 1914, deeds 1714-1926.
Essex RO, Chelmsford (D/F 24). NRA 21789.

Pattern book 1925-36, with others collected by the Cotton Board, some possibly Warners'.
Royal College of Art, London. Enquiries to the Textile Design Department. NRA 32469.

[741] **WATSON & CO (LEEK) LTD**, mfrs of sewing silks, threads, braid and hose, Leek, Staffs

Minutes (2 vols) 1905-49, annual lists and summaries of capital and shares 1910-50, share ledger 1906-48, register of mortgages 1896-1935, ledgers (5) 1896-1948, journals (2) 1898-1955, cash book 1944-50, bank book 1934-6, raw silk purchase book 1889-1914, sales ledgers, day books, etc (49 vols) 1910-64, bought ledger payments books (2) 1940-55, stock books (23) 1914-68, general mixing book 1881-1956, costing books (6) 1922-81 and misc production records (11 vols) *c*1920-1956, wages books and other staff records (18 vols and files) 1907-56, inventories and valuations 1920, *c*1940, leases and related papers 1882-98.
Staffordshire RO (D 4310). NRA 29528.

[742] **JOHN WESTMACOTT & BROS**, silk throwsters, Blockley, Glos

Accounts (3 vols) 1824-38.
Birmingham University Library: see *Accessions to repositories 1971*, p3.

[743] **EDWARD WILLETT, NEPHEW & CO**, dress fabric mfrs, Norwich, Norfolk

Design and dye book *c*1860-70.
Bridewell Museum, Norwich. NRA 30575.

Pattern books from 1767.
Untraced. Sir Frank Warner, *The silk industry of the United Kingdom: its origin and development*, 1921.

[744] **J & R WILLMOTT LTD**, silk throwsters, Sherborne, Dorset

Articles of copartnership 1764, dissolution of partnership 1769, letter books (2) 1782-1804, letters received 1776-97 incl inventory of stock 1787, ledgers (4) 1769-1833 incl accounts of silk received and thrown, day books (2) 1782-98, cash books (7) 1776-97, Robert Winter's account with William Willmott 1776-8, payments to out-winders 1793, accounts of silk thrown (1 vol) 1830-41, solicitors' bills for purchase of silk mills, etc (5 items) 1769-94, deeds of mills, apprenticeship indentures, etc (40 items)

1725-1816, Willmott family corresp and accounts (70 items) 1774-96.
Dorset RO (Museum Collection, 6367-7009). NRA 30193.

Letters 1772-82.
Sherborne Museum. NRA 30193.

[745] **AJ WORTHINGTON & CO (LEEK) LTD**, silk and braid mfrs, Leek, Staffs

Memorandum and articles of association 1909, 1936, partnership and agency agreements and other legal papers 1851-1938, board minutes (2 vols) 1909-10, 1923-36, share certificates 1909-12 and transfers 1906-50, balance sheets and profit and loss accounts 1896-1944, corresp (20 files) 1912-44, ledgers (6) 1874-1916, 1937-52, cash books (2) 1917-32 and receipts (2 bundles) 1910-41, bank books (2) 1918-32 and statements 1931-5, order book, price calculation books and price lists (6 vols) 1937-41, nd, stock books and related papers (10 vols) 1843-1915, 1940-5, production records (5 vols) 1876-1943, memoranda of agreements for employment (1 vol) 1845-6, valuations of Portland Mills (5 vols) 1875-1941, schedule of deeds nd.
Staffordshire RO (D 4316). NRA 29568.

Order books (2) nd, orders memoranda (1 vol) 1908-9, price lists 1941, pattern book nd, misc wages records (22 items) 1928-48.
Macclesfield Sunday School Heritage Centre Silk Museum (1226-54). NRA 30205.

LACE

[746] **THOMAS ADAMS LTD**, lace mfrs, Nottingham

Records 1865-1953 incl memorandum and articles of association, board minutes (3 vols), corresp with Companies Registration Office (1 file), diary of transactions and business enquiries, summary of monthly bank balances, day book of payments and receipts, petty cash books (2), wages and salaries books (13), and lists and returns of staff.
Nottinghamshire AO (M 10689-10751). NRA 30741.

[747] **BARRETT family**, gold and silver lace mfrs, London

Articles of partnership, agreements, etc 1736-1809, cash books (2) 1740-86, accounts with Floyer & Price for gilt and silver wire (2 vols) 1776-85 and with Messrs Coutts 1801-3, copy petitions to prohibit weaving of gold and silver lace c1760, annual inventories of stock 1758-98, receipts, legal papers, etc (96 items) 1751-1803, family and estate papers 1576-1910.
Berkshire RO (D/EBt). NRA 803.

[748] **BODEN & CO LTD**, net lace mfrs, Derby

Business and personal account books (5) and loose papers 1815-76, petty cash book 1852-64, register of letters and orders 1857-62, consignment book and related papers 1824-5, despatch register 1838-52, stock books (5) 1828, 1831-7, 1840-64 and papers (26 items) c1831-45, costing books (3) 1849-57, 1866-8, 1877-89, winders' book 1825, list of lace made 1825, general memoranda books (2) 1825-51, young employees' register 1877-9, factory chapel preachers' books (2) 1886-1919, misc letters, legal papers, deeds, etc 1825-95, typescript history of firm.
Nottingham University Library (Bo). NRA 12398.

[749] **ROBERT FRANCIS BROWN & CO LTD** (formerly **SEELIG & CO LTD**), lace merchants, Nottingham

Memorandum and articles of association and related papers 1910-33, shares book 1910-24, ledger 1910-21, account books (3) 1899-1921, cash books (3) 1914-32, receipted bills, etc (1 bundle) 1904-51, business corresp rel to shares, orders, etc 1905-48, wages book 1899-1904, insurance salaries book 1912-20, insurance papers 1916-33, apprenticeship indentures 1923, misc agreements 1924, papers rel to charges of trading with the enemy 1915-17, plans of factory 1941-3, account book of RF Brown 1917-20.
Nottinghamshire AO (DD 888). NRA 30739.

[750] **JAMES BURGH**, lace and fringe mfr, London

Ledger 1799-1812, journals (2) 1819-27, waste books (8) 1827-30, order books (4) 1824-32, executorship accounts (2 vols, 1 bundle) 1801-9.
Public Record Office, Chancery Lane (J 90/55-9).

[751] **CHARD LACE CO LTD**, lace and plain net mfrs, Southampton

Nottingham branch day books (6) 1908-25 incl notes and costings, ledger 1913-25, cash account book 1908-24 incl bills and receipts, petty cash book 1908-24, cash payments (1 vol) 1905-11, bank book 1908-23, piece work books (3) c1900-1920, amended costings and notes on costings c1912-24, delivery notes for pieces sent from Ilminster and Eynsham (2 vols, 649 items) 1907-24, register of pieces sent to Nottingham (5 vols) 1909-24, order books (5) 1908-24 incl copy letters, letter book giving quotations to various companies 1906-15, corresp with suppliers, customers, etc (401 items) c1920-1925, mending book 1911-19, stocktaking book 1909-21.
Nottinghamshire AO (DD PH). NRA 30740.

[752] **CUCKSON, HASELDINE & MANDERFIELD LTD**, lace mfrs, Nottingham

Pattern book c1900-10, misc photographs and printed material 1949-61, nd.
Nottingham University Library (L/C). NRA 16249.

[753] **JAMES FISHER & CO**, lace mfrs, London and Nottingham

Rough account books (2) 1876-c1888, stock books (8) 1826-7, 1860-74, 1885-1908, business and personal corresp (4 bundles) 1843-89, solicitors' bills (19 bundles) 1817-58, 1877, letters of attorney in favour of Hamburg and New York agents (2 bundles) 1830-49, personal accounts, diaries, etc (16 vols and bundles) 1825-1902.
Nottingham University Library (Fi). NRA 7887.

[754] **WILLIAM FLETCHER & SONS (DERBY) LTD**, lace mfrs, Derby

Ledgers (2) 1912-39, journals (3) 1898-1943, cash book 1898-1933, bought ledger 1898-1906, wages books (2) 1902-4, time book 1898-1901, corresp, specifications, plans, etc 1897-1913.
Derby Central Library. NRA 27879.

[755] **GODFREY BROS**, lace mfrs, Nottingham

Ledgers (2) 1917-54, cash books (2) 1915-53, order books (10) 1914-53, shipping book 1903-54, pattern books (4) 1913-32, assortment book 1918-53, cost book 1912-53.
Nottingham University Library (L/G). NRA 16249.

[756] **JOHN HEATHCOAT & CO LTD**, lace and textile mfrs, Tiverton, Devon

Balance sheets and profit and loss accounts 1823-40, ledgers (3) 1826-38, 1849-64, 1933-44, journal 1822-5, cash book 1854-1929, John Heathcoat's account with the firm (1 vol) 1826-8, account books (2) 1933-70, misc financial papers, letters, agreements, etc (19 bundles and items) c1825-1957, stock book 1840-4, patent specifications 1804-43, agreements with employees 1816-28, time book 1852-3, insurance register 1954-66, misc legal papers, deeds, etc 1791-1840, 1955-73, family papers 1797-1957.
Devon RO (4302 B). NRA 30634.

Business and family papers c1790-c1980 incl log books containing notes, press cuttings, etc rel to the firm 1898-1970, weaving overlookers' pattern books c1900-80, pension fund register 1906-10, notebooks rel to operation of sewing machinery 20th cent, and machinery drawings 19th cent.
Tiverton Museum. NRA 30634.

[757] **HERBERT & CO**, gold lacemen and army accoutrement makers, London

Ledgers (5) 1809-1927 incl details of lace and uniform items with loose bills and samples, drawings of shabracques (1 vol) c1858 with costings and photographs.
National Army Museum (6807-497). NRA 28106.

[758] **T LESTER & SONS**, lace mfrs, Bedford

Drafts, patterns, sample books, etc from 1800.
Cecil Higgins Art Gallery & Museum, Bedford: see Anne Buck, *Thomas Lester: his lace and the East Midlands industry 1820-1905*, 1981.

Drafts post-1850.
Luton Museum & Art Gallery: see Anne Buck, ibid.

TEXTILE FINISHING

[759] **WILLIAM ADAM & SON**, bleachers, Hogganfield, Lanarkshire

Corresp, sale plans, etc 1854, 1882, chemical reports and plans 1865, 1892, cloth samples (1 vol) 1844-1900.
Strathclyde Regional Archives (T-HB). NRA 14673.

[760] **AINSWORTH MERCERISING CO LTD**, Bolton, Lancs

Order books (2) 1959-64, stock books (3) 1896-1900, 1906-14, 1937-45, corresp and papers rel to dyeing recipes, advertising, wage rates, machinery, etc 1880-1974, address/sample book 1924-33, training manuals and working instructions (4 folders) 1946-73, wages book c1920-44, plans 1926-67, photographs of works and machines 20th cent, drawings of mercerising machine 1950-60, scrapbook 1927-44.
Bolton Metropolitan Borough Archives (ZAJ). NRA 27087.

Share transfers (1 folder), private ledgers (4) c1909-45, nominal ledgers (3), private cash book 1916-45, wages books (2) 1918-37.
Courtaulds Spinning. Enquiries to the Company Secretary. NRA 30126.

Estimates, contracts and plans for works extensions 1929-30, valuation and inventory 1944, machine drawings nd.
Courtaulds plc, Coventry (AIN). Enquiries to the Head of Archives. NRA 29343.

[761] **RICHARD AINSWORTH, SON & CO LTD**, bleachers, Halliwell, Lancs

Accounts (10 vols) 1805-62, wages books 1810-13, valuation book 1833-41, misc papers incl price lists and details of employees 1834-71.
Quarry Bank Mill, Styal. NRA 27727.

Account book (Peter Ainsworth & Sons) 1801-19 and other Ainsworth family personal and business accounts 1780-1819, 1835-65, diaries, journals and letter books of JH Ainsworth (44 vols) 1819-65 incl corresp with Thomas Ridgway, Bridson & Sons and other bleaching firms 1853-65, deeds etc 18th-20th cent.
Bolton Metropolitan Borough Archives (ZAH). NRA 27088.

Account books (3) 1830-42, 1886-1906 (probably of Richard Ainsworth, Son & Co Ltd), stock book 1861, wages book 1829-34, time book 1840-3 incl details of employees, inventory 1833.
Bolton Metropolitan Borough Archives (ZZ/109, ZZ/200). NRA 19836.

[762] **ALBION MILL CO (PUDSEY)**, cloth finishers and dyers, Pudsey, Yorks

Minute book 1822-55.
West Yorkshire Archive Service, Leeds (Acc 2149). NRA 31010.

[763] **JAMES ARMITAGE & SONS**, cloth finishers, Leeds

Ledger 1873-8, day books (3) 1873-88, letter books (5) 1877-84, order books with copy letters (4 vols) 1878-87, stock book 1878-85, record of lots dyed incl samples (1 vol) 1873-87.
West Yorkshire Archive Service, Leeds (AM). NRA 31027.

[764] HENRY ASHWELL & CO LTD, bleachers, dyers and finishers, Nottingham

Articles of association from 1908, directors' minutes 1909-68, corresp and reports from 1909, share ledgers (2) 1909-17, 1940-6 and other share records 1949-1960s, annual statements 1909-73, profit and loss accounts (1 vol) 1909-38, day book 1909-73, trimmers' rates 1915, plans 1870s-1960s, inventory, valuations, etc 1965-71, corresp, speeches and articles (several folders) 1840s-1908, photographs and misc papers. *GJ Murfet Esq.* NRA 32372.

[765] GP & J BAKER LTD, importers and wholesale merchants of oriental carpets, mfrs of and dealers in printed fabrics, and commission agents, London

Records 18th-20th cent incl block books, drawing books, roller books, pattern books, etc from Swaisland's Printing Co Ltd, and designs and samples. *The Company.* Not normally available for research. *From East to West. Textiles from GP & J Baker*, Victoria & Albert Museum, 1984.

Pattern books (c70 vols) 19th-20th cent incl Swaisland's Printing Co Ltd and Mair & Sons. *Royal College of Art, London.* Enquiries to the Textile Design Department. NRA 32469.

Baker family papers and corresp incl letter books rel to import and export trade with Turkey c1876-88. *In private possession:* see *From East to West*, ibid.

Pattern book of silk ribbons early 19th cent. *Victoria & Albert Museum, Department of Textile Furnishings & Dress* (T.671-1919). NRA 30151.

[766] BAKER, TUCKERS & CO, silk handkerchief printers, London

Pattern books (4) c1760-late 19th cent. *GP & J Baker Ltd.* Not normally available for research. *From East to West. Textiles from GP & J Baker*, Victoria & Albert Museum, 1984.

[767] BANFORD BLEACHWORKS CO LTD (formerly **BENJAMIN HAUGHTON & CO**), Gilford, co Down

Copies of out-letters (5 vols, 1 folder) 1922-34, 1938-48, 1956-7, ledgers (5) 1884-1962, cash books (3) 1856-7, 1919-57, bill book 1925-45, statement books (2) 1926-43, invoice books (17) 1870-1949, receipt books (6) 1950-5, order book 1874-83, sales book 1881-4, despatch and delivery books (10) 1935-61, stock books (11) 1884-8, 1913-63, price book 1956-63, brown books (8) 1878-83, 1919-63, full books (8) 1862-3, 1871-9, 1926-49, bleach books (8) 1863-5, 1873-7, 1915-50, bleachers' handbooks (12) 1895-1900, 1907-38, finishing records (2 vols) 1961-3, costs records (3 vols) 1882-1951, wages, time and rent books (10) 1863-5, 1894-1962, address books and other misc records (8 vols) 1931-63; James & William Gamble ledger 1845-53. *Public Record Office of Northern Ireland* (D 1136). NRA 31437.

[768] BATLEY CARBONIZING CO LTD, Batley, Yorks

Memorandum and articles of association 1896, directors' minutes 1897-1902, balance sheets, trading accounts, etc 1897-1900, share ledger 1896-1902, share certificates (1 vol) 1897-1900, valuation papers and plan 1896-7, 1902. *West Yorkshire Archive Service, Wakefield Headquarters* (C149). NRA 24385.

[769] AC BEALEY & SON LTD, bleachers, Radcliffe, Lancs

Partnerships deeds 1875, 1879, minute book 1871, resolutions, memoranda, etc 1837-48, letter books (2) 1894, nd, account book 1875, cash books (3) 1842-54, 1869-77, 1896-7, bank books (17) 1836-55, 1908-22, commission account book 1868-73, misc accounts 1849-1931, notebooks (4) of orders and samples 1889, 1899, price lists 1872-1906, trade marks and pattern block books (7 vols, etc) 1891-7, nd, clerks' salaries (6 vols) 1865-98, inventories and valuations (6 vols, etc) 1789-1869, nd, plans and drawings (c110) 1870-1911, nd, chapel, school and hospital papers 1852-1932, misc corresp 1882-1906 incl orders and complaints, financial and other family papers 19th-20th cent. *Bury Central Library.* NRA 27970.

Account books (2) 1834-42, 1887-1907, cash book 1813-19, half-yearly balances (2 vols) 1900-12, percentage books (3) 1884-1912, receipt book 1957-65, stock accounts (1 vol) 1788-1817, registers (2) and lists of employees 1795-7, 1864-1928, nd, valuation 1887, deeds and plans 1861-1936, misc corresp and papers c1825-1912, nd. *Quarry Bank Mill, Styal.* NRA 27727.

[770] BLEACHERS ASSOCIATION LTD, Manchester

Articles of agreement, etc 1900, minutes of board of management, managing directors, finance and trading committees (30 vols) 1900-63, agenda papers, annual reports, etc (6 vols) 1904-63, register of directors 1901-24, directors' signatures (2 vols) 1900-69, share records (6 vols) 1900-29, ledgers and analysis books (11 vols) 1900-76, statistical surveys (5) 1917-51, notebook of prices 1931-42, copies of trade marks, etc 1876-1962, staff record 1900-26, salaries book 1900-7, wages books (3) 1900-12, employees' long-service certificates (8 vols) 1927-67, staff pension fund 1932-7, inventories and valuations incl branch companies (69) 1898-1914, press cuttings (5 vols) 1900-69, misc papers incl historical notes of A Haggas Brown 1947-59. *Quarry Bank Mill, Styal.* NRA 27727.

[771] BOASE & CO LTD, bleachers, Dundee

Memorandum and articles of association 1892, contracts of copartnery 1865, 1870, directors' reports 1931-66, ledger 1838-59, day book 1833-8, cash book 1833-8, misc patent records 1855-6, wages book 1856-9. *Dundee University Library* (MS 10). NRA 12264.

[772] **THOMAS BOYD (LEEDS) LTD**, millers, finishers, waterproofers and embossers, Leeds

Ledgers 1896-1923, cash books 1889-1932, finishing books 1893-1913, employment and wages records 1891-1917.
Brotherton Library, Leeds University: see Hudson.

[773] **BRADFORD DYERS ASSOCIATION LTD**, Bradford, Yorks

Minutes of board meetings (4 vols) 1898-1983, general meetings (2 vols) 1899-1981, managing director (6 vols) 1905-69, executive committee (5 vols) 1910-45, managing committee (1 vol) 1958-62 and managers of employees' bonus register (1 vol) 1918-66, USA minutes 1919-58, register of directors 1926-63, annual reports 1900-60, secretary's notes (1 vol) c1917-64, trading guidelines, prices and administration procedures 1900, 1907, private journal 1965-83, frame wrapping book 1904-12, salaries book 1904-23, employment agreements 1899, schedule of deeds (2 vols) 18th-20th cent, misc papers 1905-51.
Coats Viyella plc. Enquiries to the Company Secretary. NRA 32377.

Corresp (1 file) c1960-70, corporate and misc financial records of subsidiaries c1899-1971 incl William Aykroyd & Sons Ltd, Fentona Cotton Supply Co Ltd, John Holt & Son Ltd, Lowmoor & Water Lane Ltd, Meadow Road Dyeworks Co Ltd, Thornton, Hannam & Marshall Ltd, and Westside Dyeing & Finishing Co Ltd.
Lancashire RO (DDVc). NRA 30810.

Dye patterns, recipe books, laboratory notes, etc 19th-20th cent incl W Grandage & Co.
The Colour Museum, Bradford.

Papers rel to patents and superannuation fund (6 boxes) 1866-1982; records (15 boxes) c1910.
West Yorkshire Archive Service, Bradford.

Wages books (2) 1923-33.
Brotherton Library, Leeds University: see Hudson.

[774] **ISAAC BRAITHWAITE & SON LTD**, dyers, rope mfrs and drysalters, Kendal, Westmorland

Articles of association 1888, 1909, annual reports, balance sheets, etc 1889-1965, board minutes 1964-5, business corresp 1804-53, letter book 1857-91, account books and cash books (7) 1737-42, 1771-1813, 1854-1920, ledgers (10) 1767-1938 incl dyehouse ledger 1856-8, vouchers 1734-1857, 1946-7, dyehouse statements 1820-42, indigo book 1815-47, indigo sale book 1824, dye book 1840-58, register of prices current for drysaltery articles 1823-45, stock book 1837-50, twine, hemp and hair book 1859-60, grinding costs book 1840-58, quotations and calculations book 1852-84, shipping registers (2) 1823-58, papers rel to processing of Elfive cloth 1966, patent records 1888, 1897, dyehouse wages book 1834-60, wages and salaries books (5) 1909-44, misc pension records 1930-45, valuation book for machinery, etc 1920-36, insurance book 1824-31, rent roll 1859-1930, misc leases and other property records 1849-1928, family papers 18th-20th cent.

Cumbria RO, Kendal. NRA 30974 (partial list); *Report of the County Archivist* June 1971 p7, Dec 1974 p7, May 1979 p8, March 1980 p5.

[775] **BRITISH COTTON & WOOL DYERS ASSOCIATION LTD** (afterwards **CAWDAW INDUSTRIAL HOLDINGS LTD**), dyers, bleachers, printers and sizers, Manchester

Registers of directors incl subsidiaries (27 vols) to 1982, registers of directors' interests 1967-81, mortgages 1900-75 and shares 1900-60, minutes of board meetings (2 vols) 1900-50, executive directors (11 vols) 1900-46, executive board (7 vols) 1950-67, sealing committee (3 vols) 1900-70 and shareholders (1 vol) 1900, annual reports and statements 1901-81, misc financial records 1919-77, secretary's cash book 1938-67, salaries books (7) 1901-67, inventories and valuations (9 vols) 1929, agreements, leases and corresp (4 boxes) nd, press cuttings (5 vols) 1901-80, diary of R Atherton, company registrar, 1912-39; Cawdaw Industrial Holdings Ltd various records (c32 vols) c1946-82; Eagle Dyeing Co Ltd minutes (1 vol) 1904-18; Holwell Co Ltd minutes (2 vols) 1903-42; Kearns, Allen & Co Ltd inventory and valuation (1 vol) 1893.
Manchester Central Library (M464).

[776] **JAMES BURT-MARSHALL LTD**, bleachers, Luncarty, Perthshire

Records of work (87 items) 1889-1939, bleaching process book nd.
Perth and Kinross District Archive (MS 63). NRA 18284.

Valuation nd, plans 1801, 1914, historical notes 20th cent.
Burt-Marshall, Lumsden Ltd. Enquiries to NRA (Scotland) (NRA(S) 930). NRA 18284.

[777] **JAMES BURY & CO**, calico printers, Manchester and Sabden, Lancs and London

Articles of association and related deeds 1790-1815, balance sheets, private and other accounts (124 items) 1793-1817, stock books (9) 1803-15, sample book nd, John Bury's notebooks (2) 1811-16 incl samples and information on stock, etc, corresp (73 items) c1790-1815, lists of property c1808, legal papers 1764-1815.
Manchester Central Library (L4). NRA 10013.

Stock sheets with printed cotton samples 1800-12.
Victoria & Albert Museum, Department of Textile Furnishings & Dress (T. 304-1960). NRA 30151.

[778] **CALICO PRINTERS ASSOCIATION LTD**, Manchester

Agreements (2 vols, etc) 1899-1969, minutes of directors, board, shareholders and committees (91 vols) 1899-1982, agenda book 1899-1900, board and finance committee regulations (1 vol) 1913-18, questionnaire on workings of the board (1 vol) 1930-1, minutes of joint conferences between directors of CPA, BDA and BA (1 vol) 1917, evidence of CPA before

the Cotton Inquiry Sub-Committee of Civil Research (1 parcel) 1929, reports, etc (2 vols, etc) 1906-13, 1944-6, research department reports and minutes (280 files, etc) 1920-43, nd, register of directors and managers of member firms 1899-1905, retirement of directors (1 vol) 1900-69, seal books (15) nd, pattern books for French prints (102 vols) 1820-1915, woven silks (32 vols) 1889-1908, flannelettes (25 vols) 1897-1911, dress goods (5 vols) 1860, 1900-10, misc pattern, receipt and swatch books (23 vols) 1820-1935 incl Rossendale and Grafton collections, engraving books (3) 1934-54, tickets and stamps for goods (various firms) 1902-12, registers of employees, service agreements and secrecy declarations (5 vols) 1900-68, employment department files (4 boxes) c1940-60, valuations, etc of printworks (242 vols, 6 files) 1904-68, nd incl United Turkey Red Co Ltd (19 vols) 1912-51, plant machinery record (1 vol) c1944-60, press cuttings, notes, etc.
Manchester Central Library (M75).

Records 1899-1961 incl accounts, ledgers, journals, cash books, and royalties book; Belfield Printing Co Ltd private ledger 1912-39; Daniel Lee & Co Ltd ledger 1905-24.
Tootal Group plc. NRA 28631; BAC *Company Archives* no 592.

Pattern, sample and recipe books (21 vols) 1795-1946 from Rossendale, Thornliebank and Birch Vale Works, photographs.
Greater Manchester Museum of Science and Industry. NRA 29510.

Pattern books (9) 1808-52, 1900-2 incl Rossendale collections; account book 1798, with samples c1820-30, of Duffy & Co, Ball's Bridge Printworks.
Gallery of English Costume, Manchester.

Pattern books (10) 1840-1920 incl Rossendale collections.
Salford Museums & Art Galleries.

Patterns and misc records.
The Colour Museum, Bradford.

Sample books 1933-70.
Victoria & Albert Museum, Archive of Art & Design.

Dye recipe books (7) with samples, from various member firms incl F Steiner & Co Ltd and Brinscall Hall Printworks, 1925-c1933.
Victoria & Albert Museum, Department of Textile Furnishings & Dress (T.270-276-1971). NRA 30151.

Designer's sketch and scrapbooks (2) 1890s-1915 incl samples.
Manchester Polytechnic Library (F 746 6 CAL).

Design book c1950.
Lancashire RO (DDHs). NRA 19214.

Deeds of Cheshire, Derbys, Lancs and London printworks 1687-1905 incl valuation and plan of Newton Bank Works (FW Ashton & Co) 1850; Kinder Printing Co schedule of design numbers and dates 1899.
Manchester Central Library (M159). NRA 19565.

[779] **CARGILL & CO LTD**, bleachers and yarn merchants, Dundee

Directors' minutes (2 vols) 1895-1976, registers of members, directors, etc (4 vols) 1895-1972, directors' reports and accounts 1946-76, private journals and ledgers (2 vols) 1936-46, 1956-69, employees' registers (2) 1951-74.
Dundee University Library (MS 86/XI). NRA 31109.

[780] **J CHADWICK & CO LTD**, calico printers, dyers, bleachers and finishers, Oldham, Lancs

Memorandum and articles of association 1888-1955, directors' and general meeting minutes with reports, etc (7 vols) 1888-1953, register of directors 1901-43, agenda book 1908-41, ordinary share book 1954-73, share transfer certificates 1880-1975, annual returns, balance sheets and trading accounts 1899-1977, general ledger 1874-82, impersonal ledgers (8) 1888-1980, ledger containing customer and dividend accounts 1895-1934, private ledger 1946-64, journal 1888-1941, cash book 1888-99, Mr Chadwick's petty cash book 1892-3, accounting analysis 1919-37, private receipts and corresp 1895-1929, costing and production figures 1903-34, patent 1852, index book c1890, inventories and valuations of premises and plant 1905-46, rent book 1929-62, misc corresp, agreements and legal papers 1899-1979, photographs c1890, c1940-70.
Oldham Local Interest Centre. NRA 29989.

Register of members and share ledger 1953-73.
Coats Viyella plc. Enquiries to the Company Secretary. NRA 32377.

[781] **JB CHAMPION & CO LTD**, bleachers, Farnworth, Lancs

Corresp (74 items) 1902-35, nd, monthly trading accounts and statements 1909-31, drawings and blueprints (98) 1899-1930, nd, printed and misc items 1898-1926, nd.
Bolton Metropolitan Borough Archives (ZCH). NRA 27085.

[782] **RICHARD COBDEN & CO**, calico printers, Manchester, Sabden and Chorley, Lancs

Balance sheets (7 vols) of Francis Sherriff, Richard Cobden, George Gillett, George Foster and James Hindle, copartners 1833-9, balance sheets, account books and cash account books (18 vols) of Richard and FW Cobden 1840-54, accounts probably of Sabden Works (2 vols) 1832-47, receipts for rent for Sabden Works 1833-9, account book for salaries and wages paid at Manchester 1833-48, corresp, rent statements, accounts, etc (1 vol) rel to printworks, etc in Manchester 1832-63, agreements, leases, tax assessments, etc 1833-87, letters to Richard and FW Cobden rel to business affairs 1825-57, misc financial papers 1832-41.
West Sussex RO (Cobden Papers). *The Cobden Papers: a catalogue*, 1964.

Cobden family papers (c290 items) 1817-87, incl business corresp and papers of Richard and FW Cobden (76 items) 1825-53.
Manchester Central Library (M87). NRA 14284.

Book of dye recipes of George Foster c1820-30 incl prices for printing and rules for Sabden Works 1838.
Victoria & Albert Museum, Department of Textile Furnishings & Dress (T.5-1978). NRA 30151.

[783] **ROBERT CREIGHTON**, dyer, Kilwinning, Ayrshire

Waste books (3) 1821-34.
Scottish Record Office (CS 96/3819-21). *Court of Session Productions*, List & Index Society, special series vol 23, 1987, p344.

[784] **JOHN CROCKATT LTD**, dyers and cleaners, Leeds

Business and family records 19th-20th cent.
West Yorkshire Archive Service, Leeds: see *West Yorkshire Archive Service Report 1985-6*, p57, *1986-7*, p66.

[785] **EB DUDDING**, furniture printers, London

Pattern book c1800-14.
Victoria & Albert Museum, Department of Textile Furnishings & Dress (T.86-1964). NRA 30151.

Pattern book c1815-20.
GP & J Baker Ltd. Not normally available for research. *From East to West. Textiles from GP & J Baker*, Victoria & Albert Museum, 1984.

[786] **DAVID EVANS & CO LTD**, silk printers, Crayford, Kent

Directors' and general meeting minutes from 1894, register of members from c1950, dividend book 1961-2, ledgers, journals and account books (11 vols: ?some from Swaisland's Printing Co Ltd) 1844-60, 1869-70, 1911-12, 1922-4 mainly reused to mount paper design samples, balance books (2) 1934-40, ledgers, cash books and invoices from c1942, shipping ledger c1928-36, invoice books (2) 1906-28, order books c1920-40, production books (3) 20th cent, files of samples, prints and designs (see also above) 20th cent, wages ledgers (22) 1861-1936 and other employment records from 1936, insurance records from 1843, rent accounts 1926, Thomas and David Evans executors' and trustees' ledgers and cash book (6 vols) 1884-1924.
The Company. Enquiries to the Company Financial Director. NRA 29554.

[787] **R DALGLISH FALCONER & CO LTD**, calico printers, Glasgow

Directors' and shareholders' minute book 1892-1901, share ledger 1895-9.
Manchester Central Library (M75).

[788] **JAMES & WILLIAM FERGUSON**, bleachers, Belfast

Letter book 1847, bankruptcy papers c1881.
Public Record Office of Northern Ireland (D 1905): see *Ulster textile industry*.

[789] **FIELDING, BENTLEY & STOUT**, calico printers, Bridgewater Printworks, Clitheroe, Lancs

Recipe books 1835, wages book 1838-47.
Lancashire RO (DDX 28).

[790] **HENRY FIELDING & BROS**, calico printers, Catterall and Bowker Bank Printworks, Blackley, Lancs

Catterall (and Rose Bank Works) production notes with dyed samples (1 vol) 1818-42, experiment books (2) 1822, 1825-34, sample book c1830.
Arthur Sanderson & Sons Ltd. Access restricted. Enquiries to the Company Archivist. NRA 30127.

Catterall Works print pattern book with dye recipes 1824.
Victoria & Albert Museum, Department of Textile Furnishings & Dress (T.12-1956). NRA 30151.

Bowker Bank Works wages book 1845.
Manchester Central Library (M75).

[791] **RICHARD FORT & CO**, calico printers, Oakenshaw Printworks, Lancs

Recipe and trial books, etc (6 vols, etc) of John Mercer c1830-c1848.
Museum of the History of Science, Oxford (MSS North). PJT Morris and CA Russell, *Archives of the British chemical industry 1750-1914*, British Society for the History of Science, Monograph 6, 1988.

Pattern book of John Mercer c1847.
Manchester Central Library (M75).

Articles of agreement, corresp, tax assessments, etc (1 vol) 1802-26.
British Library of Political and Economic Science, London (COLL MISC 236). NRA 28876.

[792] **FOSTER & CO**, calico printers, Bromley Hall Printworks, London

Pattern books (3) 1760-1800 incl Robert Maxwell, Merton Abbey Printworks.
Musée de l'Impression sur Etoffes, Mulhouse, France.

Copperplate impressions (1 vol) 1760-1800.
Victoria & Albert Museum, Department of Designs, Prints & Drawings (E.458 (1-223) -1955).

[793] **ANDREW FOULDS**, bleacher, Springfield, Midlothian

Cash book 1810-13, bill book 1808-10, bleaching books (3) 1805-16.
Scottish Record Office (CS 96/4494-8). *Court of Session Productions*, List & Index Society, special series vol 23, 1987, p170.

[794] **WILLIAM FULTON & SONS LTD**, bleachers and dyers, Paisley, Renfrewshire

Minutes 1896-1951, corresp 1899-1907, cash books, etc 1930-62, order and stock books 1931-51, wages and staff records 1907-57, inventories 1898-1918.
Strathclyde University, Department of History. NRA 13492.

Registers of transfers 1944-70.
Coats Viyella plc. Enquiries to the Company Secretary.
NRA 32377.

Photographs (1 vol) 20th cent.
Lancashire RO (DDVc). NRA 30810.

[795] **WILLIAM GILLESPIE & SONS**, textile
printers, Anderston Printworks, Glasgow

Day books (6) 1806-8.
National Library of Scotland (MSS 17962-7).

[796] **GOVAN DYE WORK CO**, Glasgow

Ledger, journal, cash book and wages book 1821-2.
Scottish Record Office (CS 96/1611, 1668-70). *Court of
Session Productions*, List & Index Society, special series
vol 23, 1987, p334.

[797] **JAMES HARDCASTLE & CO LTD**,
bleachers, Bolton, Lancs

Letter books (2) 1869-91, corresp 1871-94, pattern
books (8) 1837-1901, nd, notes on prices and processes
(2 vols, etc) 1882-1901, trade mark papers 1878-1903,
Bradshaw Works rules and regulations 1875, plans
and photographs 1845-1950, misc accounts and papers
1898-1956.
Quarry Bank Mill, Styal. NRA 27727.

Pattern books (2) 1836-46.
Bolton Museum (D.2-3.1969). NRA 29093.

[798] **THOMAS HARDCASTLE & CO**, bleachers,
Bolton, Lancs

Accounts (3 vols) 1864-83.
Bolton Metropolitan Borough Archives (ZZ/109). NRA
19836.

[799] **ALEXANDER HARGREAVES**, calico
printer, Adlington, Lancs

Pattern books (2) c1830-40, printing recipe 1839.
Lancashire RO (DDX 389). NRA 17138.

[800] **HARGREAVES, DUGDALE & CO**,
(afterwards **FW GRAFTON & CO**), calico printers,
Broad Oak Printworks, Accrington, Lancs

Trial books (9) 1831-61, receipt books (12) 1831-71,
swatch books (8) 1841-71, pattern books (8 vols, etc)
1830-3, 1841-72, nd, patent specifications 1850-70,
Lightfoot family notes and memoranda (11 vols, etc)
1818-69, press cuttings 20th cent.
Manchester Central Library (M75).

Thomas Lightfoot corresp rel to calico printing, etc
1860-4, private account books (2) 1856-66, cash book
1866, notebook nd, half-yearly stock account book
1856-66, grant of patent 1864, patent and specifications
1859, 1864.
West Yorkshire Archive Service, Leeds (Acc 1726).

[801] **HAWLEY & JOHNSON LTD**, dyers and
finishers, Leicester

Copy memorandum of agreement 1879-80, directors'
minute book 1915-66, balance sheets and capital
statements 1888-97, corresp rel to property and general
administration of company (6 files) 1917-60, papers
rel to trade marks, insurance certificates and valuations
1887-1932, photographs, etc 1868-c1940.
Leicestershire RO (DE 2139). NRA 26187.

[802] **HAYFIELD PRINTING CO LTD**, calico
printers, Hayfield, Derbys

Colours and examples of work done (3 vols) 1865-84,
general information 1876.
Manchester Central Library (M75).

[803] **SAMUEL HEAP & SON LTD** dyers and
finishers, Rochdale, Lancs

Memorandum and articles of association and related
papers 1893, directors' minutes from 1893, agenda
books 1894-1951, lists of shareholders and directors
1894-1950, letter books (2) 1895-1905, corresp (c70
files, 150 packets) from 1893 rel to chemical contracts,
insurances, patents, lawsuit with Bradford Dyers
Association Ltd, etc, copy letters from Thomas and
William Heap to Richard Howarth in Canada 1817-51,
corresp rel to Charles Heap's American ventures
c1880-99, balance sheets, etc from 1920, account book
1813-24, private ledgers and cash books from 1894,
nominal ledgers (2) 1894-1934, loan and other ledgers
(8) 1887-1952, bill book 1897-1933, stocktaking
records 1885-93, wages books (21) 1841-53 and from
1894, rent book 1839-99, photographs c1920-30,
deeds.
Courtaulds Fabrics. Enquiries to the Company
Secretary. NB Harte, 'A history of Samuel Heap &
Son Ltd 1823-1964', typescript, 1967.

Legal papers (4 boxes) 1895-1912, 1924.
Rochdale Local Studies Department. NRA 31058.

[804] **JAMES HOLROYD & SON**, cloth finishers
and dyers, Leeds

Letter book 1784-1827, ledger 1783-1825, day book
1812-21, bill book 1788-1807.
West Yorkshire Archive Service, Leeds: see Hudson.

[805] **JACKSON, WATSON & GREIG**, calico
printers, Rose Bank Printworks, Ramsbottom, Lancs

Rose Bank (and Catterall Works) production notes
with dyed samples (1 vol) 1818-42, experiment books
(2) 1822, 1825-34, sample book c1830.
Arthur Sanderson & Sons Ltd. Access restricted.
Enquiries to the Company Archivist. NRA 30217.

Dye recipe and print pattern books (2) 1823, 1836.
Bolton Museum (IND.42.1983). NRA 29093.

Pattern books (6) c1835-9.
Rossendale Museum, Rawtenstall. NRA 30829.

[806] **JENNENS, WELCH & CO LTD**, cloth shrinkers, Huddersfield, Yorks

Directors' minutes (2 vols) 1898-1956, register of directors and annual returns (3 vols) 1930-55, members' journal (2 vols) 1898-1956, shareholders' ledger 1930-63, audited accounts (2 bundles) 1911-56, nominal ledger 1971-2, cash books (2) 1956-70, insurance book 1898-1968, misc papers 1898, 1926-60. *West Yorkshire Archive Service, Leeds* (Acc 2448). NRA 24550.

[807] **KILWEE BLEACHING CO LTD**, Dunmurry, co Antrim

Letter book 1903-5, desk diaries (73) 1896-1953, workers' account books (17) 1895-1940, misc papers (14 items) 1894-1909. *Public Record Office of Northern Ireland* (D 1158). NRA 31438.

[808] **KIRKPATRICK BROS**, bleachers, dyers and finishers, Ballyclare, co Antrim

Ledgers (6) 1899-1901, 1909-12, 1916-17, 1919-20, 1927-31, cash books (23) 1900-41, journal 1902-18, bill books (11) 1902-25, bank pass books (11) 1909-26, statements of accounts (10 vols) 1920-5, 1936-46, purchase analysis books (16) 1900-47 and ledgers (4) 1905-44, sales ledgers (12) 1905-57 and other sales records (29 vols) 1918-38, order books and goods received (4 vols) 1921-36, damages and allowances records (6 vols) 1903-8, 1911-37, price record book 1913-19, stock books (2) 1906-25, customers' cloth stock books (11) 1905-6, 1909-10, 1912-28, stock return books (3) 1928-42, shipping returns 1918, dyers' reduction and rebate book 1924-30, wages books (48) 1884-8, 1892-1937, wages summary and analysis (2 vols) 1928-37, fuel book 1913-14. *Public Record Office of Northern Ireland* (D 2047). NRA 31481.

Purchase book 1908-30. *Public Record Office of Northern Ireland* (D 1580). *Deputy Keeper's Report 1960-5*, p112.

[809] **LAMBEG BLEACHING, DYEING & FINISHING CO** (formerly **RICHARDSON & CO**), Lambeg, co Antrim

Letters received from 1898, letter books from 1891, memoranda books 1871, 1875-6, 1882, balance ledger 1871-5, journals (5) 1882-92, 1897-1919, cash books (6) 1896-1916, 1924-38, petty cash books and vouchers (4 vols) 1903-19, bank books (11) 1908-45, Lambeg stores cash book, vouchers, etc 1903-23, goods ledgers (2) 1896-1917, brown goods received (3 vols) 1914-24, received and delivery book 1902-4, advance book 1914-16, chemical stores stock book 1904-7, bleaching ledgers (4) 1884-5, 1888-92, 1896-1908, bleaching department day books (6) 1900-8, dyeing department day books (4) 1900-14, wages books (10) 1884-1908, maps and plans c1957, photographs c1920-60. *Public Record Office of Northern Ireland* (D 1770). NRA 31472.

[810] **JOHN LEACH, BENNETT & CO**, calico printers, Merton Abbey Printworks, Surrey

Treatise by John Leach on calico printing 1792. *Victoria & Albert Museum Library* (L.34-1982).

[811] **EDWARD LONGBOTTOM**, dyer, Batley, Yorks

Pattern books (4) 1849, 1873, nd, recipe books (15) 1831-85, nd, day books of work done and recipes (8 vols) 1841-63, loose recipes, accounts, notes, etc 1837, c1850. *Brotherton Library, Leeds University*. NRA 18164.

[812] **LONGWOOD FINISHING CO LTD**, scourers, millers, dyers and shrinkers, Longwood, Yorks

Directors' and general meeting minute books (2) 1923-53, register of directors and annual returns 1946-66, share corresp file 1895-1927, share certificate registers (2) 1920-39, ledgers (6) 1898-1964, balance books (3) 1902-47, cash books (7) 1923-71, expenditure analysis books (2) 1957-65, wages books (7) 1911-31, wages analysis books (some with Parkwood Mills Co Ltd) (12) 1927-31, 1940-60, inventories, valuations and reports (9) 1916-75, insurance register 1924-6. *West Yorkshire Archive Service, Kirklees* (KC 17). NRA 31065.

Records 1887-1923 incl minutes and balance sheets, directors' reports and general meeting papers, balance book, private ledgers, mill cash book, journals, and wages books. *Brotherton Library, Leeds University*. NRA 28631; BAC *Company Archives* no 579; and see Hudson.

[813] **LOVE CLOUGH PRINTING CO LTD**, calico printers, Rawtenstall, Lancs

Printworks Library and Club records (1 box, 1 file) 1892-1944, invoices 1838. *Rawtenstall District Library* (RC 027.4 LOV, RC 366 LOV, RC 677 LOV). NRA 30888.

[814] **LUMSDEN, MACKENZIE & CO**, bleachers, Huntingtower, Perthshire

Minute books (2) 1930-62, draft minutes (1 vol) 1933-58, register of members (2 vols) 1930-61, share record books (2) 1930-61, letter book 1916-47, general ledgers (9) 1911-62, journals (6) 1908-71, private journal 1879-83, cash books (14) 1913-52, purchase day book 1945-8, general instructions to beetlers 1904, note on mercerising 1915, inventories incl farm stock (55) 1918-53, nd, plans 1914, photographs 19th-20th cent, misc legal and financial papers, corresp, etc 1872-1965. *Perth and Kinross District Archive* (MS 62). NRA 18282.

[815] Number not used.

[816] **A & J McNAB LTD**, dyers and cleaners, Stirling

Cash books, diaries and recipe books of Charles McNab (11 vols) 1880-1929. *National Library of Scotland* (Acc 8633).

[817] **J MARSDEN & CO LTD**, bleachers, Manchester and Bolton, Lancs

Analysis book and quarterly accounts 1872-1903.
Quarry Bank Mill, Styal. NRA 27727.

[818] **MILLER & MUTER** (formerly **PATRICK MITCHELL**), textile printers, Milton Printworks, Dunbarton

Account book 1840, 1855-61, day books (2) containing details of experiments and developments in production of colours 1809, recipe books (26) for colours 1790-c1845 and misc recipes 1844-5, notebook 1810-45.
National Library of Scotland (MSS 17961, 17968-97).

Letter books (2) 1845-64, cash books (3) 1817-45, cash books (2) of Thomas Muter 1869-82, goods day book 1848-68, consignment book 1875, stock records 1858-62, pattern book (James McDowall & Son) ?1780s, dye recipe book 1822-6, legal papers, corresp and other Muter family papers 1766-1896.
Glasgow University Archives (DC90/8-9). NRA 21743.

Invoice book 1848-61, receipt books (2) 1848-64, voucher book 1840-53, vouchers 1828-58.
Glasgow University Archives (UGD/86). NRA 21941.

[819] **MOORE, JOHNSTONE & MASON**, textile printers, London

Pattern book 1814-16.
Victoria & Albert Museum, Department of Textile Furnishings & Dress (T.85-1964). NRA 30151.

Pattern book nd.
GP & J Baker Ltd. Not normally available for research. *From East to West. Textiles from GP & J Baker*, Victoria & Albert Museum, 1984.

Pattern book nd.
Royal College of Art, London. Enquiries to the Textile Design Department. NRA 32469.

[820] **THOMAS A NICHOL & SONS LTD** (afterwards **PETERGATE FABRICS LTD**), woollen cloth dyers, Huddersfield, Yorks

Minute books (2) 1907-71, register of members and share ledger 1907-36.
Lancashire RO (DDVc). NRA 30810.

[821] **GEORGE NUSSEY & SONS**, dyers and woad growers, Leeds, and Algarkirk and Sutterton, Lincs

Deeds of dissolution of partnership 1867, cash books (9) 1843-54, 1874-1929, accounts and memoranda (6 vols) rel to woad and chicory grown and sold 1843-58, 1899-1923, stock book 1843-57, Leeds agent's letter book 1907-21, wages books (10) 1843-7, 1869-1932, rent books (2) 1847-54, farm account book 1852-7, George Nussey executorship records 1879-80, title deeds, schedules, plans, etc 1717-1925.
Lincolnshire AO (HD 25). NRA 31852.

[822] **PEEL & CO**, calico printers, Church and Bury, Lancs

Corresp and papers 1821-45 incl some rel to arrangements with Frederick Steiner, statements of account 1833-4, bill book 1823-32, misc accounts 1836, nd, stock books (2) incl samples 1806, 1831-4, pattern book 1836-50 incl details of customers, orders and costs, building books (2) 1812, 1821, valuation of printing and bleaching machinery 1822, valuation of machinery, buildings, etc c1837, papers rel to Plantation Mill 1837, calculation of expenses of rebuilding Accrington Mill c1841, apprenticeship indentures 1768, 1806, 1838, Peel of Knowlmere family papers, diaries and account books 18th-19th cent.
Lancashire RO (DDP1).

Pattern book c1807-21 incl details of printing methods and dyes.
Bolton Museum (D.1.1971). NRA 29093.

Pattern book c1826.
The Colour Museum, Bradford.

[823] **J PENDER**, calico printers and merchants, Glasgow and Manchester

Samples of print designs (6 files) 1857.
Royal Museum of Scotland, Chambers Street, Edinburgh.

[824] **PERROTTS LTD**, clothworkers and shrinkers, Leeds and London

Minute book 1944-51, ledger 1913-24, private and nominal ledgers (12) 1951-74, journals (2) 1902-11, cash books (9) 1950-71, purchase, sales and analysis books (6) 1938-69, wages books (6) 1916-65, history of firm c1980; F Farr & Co Ltd minutes 1924-43, register of members and shares 1924-54, journal 1902-71 and other accounts 1947-72.
West Yorkshire Archive Service, Leeds (Acc 2448). NRA 24550.

Partnership and premises deeds 1845-1903.
Guildhall Library, London (MSS 14158-9, 14161, 17358).

[825] **ALLAN POLLOK**, bleacher, Wellmeadowfield, Lanarkshire

Invoice books (2) 1799-1804.
Scottish Record Office (CS 96/1298-9). *Court of Session Productions*, List & Index Society, special series vol 23, 1987, p139.

[826] **EDMUND POTTER & CO LTD**, calico printers, Dinting Vale Printworks, Derbys

Dinting Vale prints (8 vols, 1 parcel, etc) 1890-1960, assorted pattern books (9) 1850-1948, nd (some from Brickton Vale), sample books (6) nd, recipe books (5) from 1904, technical memoranda book 1917, printer's notebooks (4) c1898-1953, technical notes of JG Hurst, chemist, from c1930 and MS of his book on Edmund Potter c1948, notes on Thornliebank process 1930, weekly analysis record 1920, printing prices 1910-14, Dinting Vale Printworks Sick and Burial Society annual balance sheets 1903-11, plans of Dinting Works 1835, 1853, 1878, nd, photographs, press cuttings.
Derbyshire RO (D 1589).

Dye book 1848-c1860.
Victoria & Albert Museum, Department of Textile Furnishings & Dress (T.398-1972). NRA 28420; NRA 30151.

[827] **J PULLAR & SONS LTD**, dyers and cleaners, Perth

Minute books from 1911, share registers from 1911, register of directors from 1948, balance sheets from 1911, annual returns from 1949, purchase ledger 1939-58, laboratory notebooks 1892-1920, 1935-63, pattern books 1894-5, c1900-7, visitors' book 1876-1932.
The Company. Enquiries to NRA (Scotland) (NRA(S) 867). NRA 17168.

Petitions, warrants, agreements, etc (c12 bundles) 1871-1976, abstracts of accounts and balance sheets, analysis books, turn-over records, etc (30 vols) 1897-1976, general, cash, shop expenses and misc ledgers (50) 1936-75, journals, cash books and statements (24 vols) c1928-1972, misc accounting records (c36 vols and bundles) 1928-76, sales records (5 vols) 1944-78, returns records (7 vols) 1919-32, 1948, 1964-8, departmental report books (25 vols) 1889-1975 incl benzine stills (4 vols) 1889-1937 and laboratory reports (4 vols) 1895-1933, cleaning and dyeing record book 1951-68, notes on dyeing processes with samples and patterns 1893-1902, corresp, specifications, engineering drawings, maintenance diaries and other technical records (c112 vols, bundles and items) 1897-1976, wages records (c20 vols, etc) 1898-1972, registers of employees, insurance, pensions and sick society records, etc (c85 vols, etc) 1903-76, inventories of buildings and plant (8 vols) 1869-1931, plans of premises (96 bundles) 1902-76, misc property records 1882-1966, catalogues, advertising scrapbooks, press cuttings and other printed material c1870-c1980.
Perth and Kinross District Archive (MS 51). NRA 17168.

[828] **THOMAS RIDGWAY & CO LTD**, bleachers, Horwich, Lancs

Wages book 1785-8, price list 1803, misc papers 1797-1841, nd.
Quarry Bank Mill, Styal. NRA 27727.

[829] **EDWARD RIPLEY & SONS LTD**, dyers and finishers, Bradford, Yorks

Register of shareholders, etc 1901-71, loose minutes, etc 20th cent.
Lancashire RO (DDVc). NRA 30810.

Wages books 1831-1950.
Brotherton Library, Leeds University: see Hudson.

Papers, plans, deeds, etc 17th-20th cent.
West Yorkshire Archive Service, Wakefield Headquarters (C325). NRA 24876.

[830] **T ROBINSON & CO LTD**, dyers and finishers, Ramsbottom, Lancs

Ledgers, orders, corresp and wages records 1926-69.
Greater Manchester RO.

Wages books (16) 1913-39, stock book 1936-41.
Bury Archive Service (GRO). NRA 30196.

Sample book, shade cards, etc 1930s-1940s.
Bury Art Gallery & Museum. NRA 31020.

[831] **SLATER & CO LTD**, bleachers and finishers, Bolton, Lancs

Directors' minutes (3 vols) 1896-1965 and attendance book 1967-8, registers of shares and debenture holders (2 vols) 1896-1968, private ledgers (4) 1896-1960, ledgers (5) 1864-1968, day books (2) 1879-82, 1959-69, cash books (3) 1908-18, 1949-71, debit notebook 1959-70, order book 1878-1931, stock books (2) 1957-61, kier book 1971-3, wages books (4) 1891-9, 1945-57, inventories and valuations 1860, 1891, misc corresp 1939, 1948-53.
Bolton Metropolitan Borough Archives (ZSL). NRA 27219.

[832] **GEORGE & JAMES SLATER LTD**, bleachers, Dunscar, Lancs

Ledgers (2) 1783-1811, cash books (2) 1824-40, misc accounts c1790-1835, chemic and bean book 1831-43, valuation of stock 1792, apprenticeship agreements, deeds and photographs 1784-c1869.
Quarry Bank Mill, Styal. NRA 27727.

Account books (2) 1848-67, 1878-84, patents and licence 1815-94.
Bolton Metropolitan Borough Archives (ZZ/200). NRA 19836.

[833] **JOHN SMITH JUNIOR & CO LTD** (formerly **THOMAS RIDGWAY, BRIDSON & SONS**), bleachers, Little Lever, Lancs

Out-letter book 1926-8, account and memoranda books (2) 1836-1933, general ledgers (4) 1865-1922, analysis books and ledger (5 vols) 1864-70, 1909-27, cash books (7) 1873-1921, sundry sales books (2) 1875-1930, stock books (2) 1900-13, merchandise receipt book 1924-30, returns book 1922-6, bleaching journals (2) 1894-1922, makers' and crofters' washed-up books (8) 1911-35, finishing books (2) 1899-1906, white piece day books (3) 1919-29, piece work ledgers and wages books (10 vols) 1864-92, 1908-20, pay lists (3) 1857-78, datal hands wages and time books (5) 1868-1931.
Bolton Metropolitan Borough Archives (ZLB). NRA 26470.

Memoranda book 1821-30, misc price lists and papers 1821-68.
Quarry Bank Mill, Styal. NRA 27727.

[834] **SPITTAL DYEWORKS**, Edinburgh

Ledger, etc 1797-1801.
Bank of Scotland, Glasgow Chief Office. Enquiries to NRA (Scotland) (NRA(S) 745). NRA 10784.

[835] **SPRINGFIELD HOSIERY FINISHING CO LTD**, bleachers, dyers and finishers, Nottingham

Directors' minutes 1972-6, balance sheets 1873-6, 1881-6, profit and loss accounts 1915-18, letter book 1920s, business and private corresp 1839-1900, ledgers (8) 1826-1916, day books (3) 1861-70, 1920-25, 1936-7, cash books (4) 1851-67, 1892-1909, 1919-26, 1945-62, bill book 1857-86, bought, sold and purchase books (5) 1873-1938, invoice books (4) 1915-46, monthly

sales 1910-64, chemical stocktake 1915-65, production
for individual firms 1923-40, bleaching, scouring and
milling work book from 1874, wages books (6)
1848-1922, inventory and valuations 1920-66,
photographs and misc records 1924-72.
GJ Murfet Esq. NRA 32373.

[836] **JOHN STANNING & SON LTD**, bleachers,
Leyland, Lancs

Directors' minute book 1890-1900, letter to
shareholders 1900, price list 1863.
Quarry Bank Mill, Styal. NRA 27727.

[837] **STEAD, McALPIN & CO LTD**, calico
printers, Cummersdale, Cumberland

Balance sheets and other accounts 1852-65, account
books (2) 1835-63, day books (6) 1835-60, cash books
(4) 1835-68, ledger balances (1 vol) 1874-1908, ledger,
day book and returns book rel to goods sent to London
1852-68, stock books (2) 1843-51, fabric samples,
patent for improvements in textile printing machinery
1852, weekly wages books (2) 1835-56, child
employment certificates 1862-71, accounts (1 vol) for
refitting Cummersdale Mills 1835-6, valuations of
machinery, stock, property, etc (3 vols) 1848-1902,
papers (2 vols) rel to settlement of Thomas McAlpin's
estate 1849-57, private account book of John Stead
1852-60.
John Lewis Partnership Archives. Access restricted.
Enquiries to the Company Archivist. NRA 31115;
Lorna Poole, 'British business archives-1. The John
Lewis Partnership', *Business Archives* 37, Dec 1972,
pp11-16.

Printers' work books (15) 1885-90, 1903-43.
Cumbria RO, Carlisle (DB/82). NRA 30982.

[838] **STEVENS & BAILWARD**, dyers,
Bradford-on-Avon, Wilts

Bill book 1762-96, pattern books (2) 1768-75.
Bath Reference Library. NRA 25737.

Register of bills of exchange 1762-99, dye recipe book
1768-74.
Wiltshire RO (WRO 1610). NRA 3523.

[839] **SAMUEL STOCKS JUNIOR & CO**,
bleachers, Heaton Mersey, Lancs

Letter, memoranda and account book of Samuel
Stocks 1813-34.
Stockport Central Library (S/J 42). NRA 9716.

[840] **STRINES PRINTING CO**, calico printers,
Strines, Cheshire

Registered patterns (8 vols) 1868-81.
Manchester Central Library (M75).

[841] **CHARLES SWAINSON & CO**, calico
printers, Bannister Hall Printworks, Higher Walton,
Lancs

Memoranda books (2) 1818-19, 1822-35, patterns and
designs mainly 1802-40.
John Lewis Partnership Archives. Access restricted.
Enquiries to the Company Archivist. NRA 31115;
English chintz, Victoria & Albert Museum, 1960.

[842] **SWAISLAND'S PRINTING CO LTD**, textile
printers, Crayford, Kent

Records 18th-19th cent incl designs for shawls and
dress fabrics (25 vols), registered strike-off patterns (3
vols), designs and strike-offs of handkerchiefs (6 vols),
volumes of samples of printed dress fabrics, etc from
1815, cutting department register from 1870, dye
recipes *c*1850-60, and account book from 1830; pattern
books of various firms from *c*1760 incl Henry Cooke,
William Fenning & Sons, Howard, Rivers & Co,
Nixon & Co and Tagg & Whitehead.
GP & J Baker Ltd. Not normally available for
research. *From East to West. Textiles from GP & J
Baker*, Victoria & Albert Museum, 1984.

Pattern books (3) 1841-5, nd.
Maidstone Museums & Art Gallery (3-1961).

Pattern books (*c*8) 1847-58, nd.
Royal College of Art, London. Enquiries to the Textile
Design Department. NRA 32469.

Rules for the drawing shop, etc *c*1845.
Victoria & Albert Museum Library (L.774-1964, Box
III, 86 DD (x)).

Scrapbook of impressions for prints using wooden
rollers late 18th-early 19th cent.
*Victoria & Albert Museum, Department of Designs, Prints
& Drawings* (E.2229-1966).

Impressions from copper pin blocks for printing
textiles early 19th cent.
*Victoria & Albert Museum, Department of Designs, Prints
& Drawings* (E.259-320-1924).

[843] **SWANWICK & JOHNSON**, calico printers,
Manchester

Patterns of printed cottons sent to the Great Exhibition
1851.
*Victoria & Albert Museum, Department of Textile
Furnishings & Dress* (T.57-1938). NRA 30151.

[844] **SYDALL BROS LTD**, calico printers,
Chadkirk, Cheshire

Receipts, costs of printing, patterns, etc (2 vols) from
1851, order book 1860-72, samples *c*1929.
Manchester Central Library (M75).

[845] **SYKES & CO LTD**, bleachers, Edgeley,
Cheshire

Letter book 1815-18, private cash and account books
(2) of William Sykes 1786-1809, cash books (3)
1804-37, banking ledger 1813-24, account book
1812-25, balance sheets 1852-78, misc accounts
1793-1862, stock book 1808-15, price lists 1854-65,
notebook of Richard Sykes rel to prices, costings and
processes 1851, valuations 1839-68, deeds 1828-72,
plans 1882, misc corresp and papers rel to rentals, etc
1843-87; production statistics (1 vol) for William
Sykes' cotton weaving factory at Millgate 1807-20,
executors' letter book 1866-98.
Stockport Central Library (B/HH/7). NRA 27964
(vol 1).

Letter and memoranda books (2) 1819-39, 1900-1, nominal ledger 1805-24 and cash books (2) 1812-38 of William Sykes, price lists 1809, 1860-78, 1893, nd, valuation 1827, misc receipts, corresp, etc c1814-78.
Quarry Bank Mill, Styal. NRA 27727.

[846] **THOMSON, CHIPPINDALL & CO**, calico printers, Clitheroe, Lancs

Ledgers (4) 1810-53.
Lancashire RO (CYC 3/46-9). NRA 15239.

Samples of printed cloth 19th cent.
Manchester Central Library (MS BR F 667.2 T4).

[847] **THORNLIEBANK CO LTD** (formerly **ALEXANDER CRUM & CO**), calico printers, Glasgow

Directors' and shareholders' minute book 1886-1900.
Strathclyde Regional Archives (TD 585).

Pattern books (2) 1814.
Manchester Central Library (M75).

Sample book c1814.
Gallery of English Costume, Manchester.

[848] **TODD, SHORTRIDGE & CO**, calico printers, Levenbank, Dunbarton

Pattern books (3) incl shawls, furnishings and garments 1792-1802.
Royal Museum of Scotland, Queen Street, Edinburgh.

'Carlisle' pattern book 1780-5 (probably Todd, Shortridge & Co).
Victoria & Albert Museum, Department of Designs, Prints & Drawings (E.1348-2008-1921).

[849] **WILLIAM TOLSON LTD**, bleachers, and dyers, Fazeley, Staffs

Customers' order book 1897-1900, corresp 1871-3, 1905, estimates 1872, 1910, advertising leaflets 1871, nd, employees' school attendance certificates 1875-7, plans and sketches nd.
Staffordshire RO (D 813). NRA 10935.

[850] **TURNBULL & STOCKDALE LTD**, textile printers, dyers, bleachers and finishers, Rose Bank Printworks, Ramsbottom, Lancs

General account book 1916-39, cash book 1908-52, order, sales and stock records 1926-67, wages books (16) 1907-36, piece work details book 1920-4, machinery account book 1882-91, photograph and plans of factory c1900-20.
Lancashire RO (DDX 924). NRA 18063.

Sample books (5) 1930-9.
Bury Art Gallery & Museum (1979.39). NRA 31020.

[851] **J TWISSE & CO**, dyers and finishers, Bolton, Lancs

General and impersonal ledgers (6) 1914-39, cash books (3) 1926-35, 1962-78, invoice ledgers and analysis books (22 vols) 1905-73, order and purchase books (12) 1939-66, dyers' journal 1959-61, wages book 1898-1940.
Bolton Metropolitan Borough Archives (ZTW). NRA 32008.

[852] **UNITED TURKEY RED CO LTD**, dyers and calico printers, Alexandria, Dunbarton

A Orr Ewing & Co letter book 1868-90, private ledgers (2) 1845-1900, day book 1858, journals (2) 1845-97, private journals (2) 1895-1924, current account book 1845-98; William Stirling & Co private ledgers (2) 1881-9, private journals (3) 1881-97; United Turkey Red Co Ltd general ledger 1898, journal 1895, monthly statements 1929-39, sales books (2) 1895-7, production books (4) 1898-1932, sample books (10) c1850-1949, dyeing calculation book 1873-92, dyestuff quantities book 1875-9, ticket books (10) nd, recommendation book 1898-1906, factor book 1931-50, pay book 1845-7, trade disputes book 1912-16, legal papers 1878-1905, map of Dalquhurn Dye Works 1909, press cuttings 1898-1920.
Glasgow University Archives (UGD/13). NRA 21578.

Sample books, misc order books, etc (c200 vols) c1840-1930 incl records of A Orr Ewing & Co and J Orr Ewing & Co.
Royal Museum of Scotland, Chambers Street, Edinburgh.

Samples (c200) 19th cent, scrapbooks (3) of export labels 20th cent.
The Colour Museum, Bradford.

Export ticket books (3) c1870s-1890s, 1897-1919 mainly for William Stirling & Co.
Greater Manchester Museum of Science & Industry (Acc 1973.16/1-3).

Pattern book c1860-80.
Victoria & Albert Museum, Department of Textile Furnishings & Dress (T.133(1-31)1976). NRA 30151.

[853] **VINT & GILLING**, textile printers, Crayford, Kent

Pattern books (5) c1803-10 incl bills and notes of payment.
GP & J Baker Ltd. Not normally available for research. *From East to West. Textiles from GP & J Baker*, Victoria & Albert Museum, 1984.

[854] **JC WADDINGTON & SONS LTD** (formerly **WILLIAM BRAYSHAW & SONS**), woollen and worsted dyers, Leeds

Accounts 1822-64, ledgers 1878-1947, cash books 1915-47, bill book 1822-94, sales and purchase records 1908-c1959, dyeing and sample books 1816-82, c1903-45, wages books 1863-1929.
Brotherton Library, Leeds University: see Hudson.

[855] **JOSHUA WARDLE LTD**, silk dyers, Leekbrook, Staffs

Vouchers (over 270) 1829-73, receipts 1835-46, orders for dyeing (c200 items) 1872-4, inventories of stock (2) 1838-9, corresp c1830-45 mainly rel to Thomas Wardle's accounts, lists of dye colours and misc papers c1825-40.
Staffordshire RO (D 1313). NRA 17363.

[856] SIR THOMAS & ARTHUR WARDLE LTD, printers and dyers, Leek, Staffs

Memorandum and articles of association 1921, 1949, agreements, reports, etc 1949-78, directors' minutes 1955-62, balance sheets and profit and loss accounts 1898-1915, 1937-61, share register 1967-9, corresp 1968-76, day book 1881-91, bank book and accounts 1888-91, 1905-17, nominal ledgers (2) 1920-42, purchases record 1956-60, commission accounts 1925-7, 1945-63, business addresses *c*1905-8, chemical process notebook 1888-1908, memoranda 1896-1906, wages and salaries books (5) 1882-92, 1902-7, 1940-70 and other employment records 1968-76, machinery purchased to late 1940s, deeds 1940-70.
GJ Murfet Esq. NRA 32371.

Corresp and papers of Sir Thomas Wardle (2 vols, 248 items) 1874-98 incl letters from William Morris rel to production and processes of dyeing, standards and prices, and record (1 vol) of spectral analysis of dyes from Indian plants.
William R Perkins Library, Duke University, Durham, North Carolina: see *Guide to the cataloged collections*, 1980, p604. Copies of the Morris letters are in Staffordshire RO (618) and the Victoria & Albert Museum Library.

Pattern books (16) 1875-*c*1909.
Whitworth Art Gallery, Manchester (T.R. M.15).

Sample book 1888-90, dye books and manuals.
Victoria & Albert Museum, Department of Textile Furnishings & Dress.

[857] JOSEPH & MARY WARE, calico printers, Crayford, Kent

Order book incl samples 1773-5.
The Colour Museum, Bradford.

[858] WHALLEY ABBEY PRINTING CO LTD, calico printers, Wiswell, Lancs

Records incl summaries of capital and list of members 1890-9 and valuation 1874.
Lancashire RO (DDX 2/32-55 *passim*). NRA 3510.

Receipts, trials and notes, with patterns (2 vols) 1911-19.
Manchester Central Library (M75).

[859] JOHN WHEADON & CO, dyers, ?Chard, Somerset

Ledger, accounts and misc corresp 1791-1804.
Birmingham University Library. NRA 19138.

[860] WILLIAM WHISTON & SON LTD, silk printers, Langley, Cheshire

Cash book 1881-5, pattern books (*c*180 vols, etc) 19th-20th cent, dye and dyeing record books (28) *c*1850-1920, lists of paper impressions and travellers' samples (2 vols) 1860-5.
Cheshire RO (DLA/1166). NRA 31656.

Account book *c*1843-70, designs (2 vols, etc) for shawls, flags, kerchiefs, etc *c*1843-early 20th cent.
Victoria & Albert Museum, Department of Designs, Prints & Drawings (E.378-380-1964).

[861] JOHN WILKINSON & CO, calico printers, Oakenshaw Printworks, Lancs

Trial book 1857-72, printing and dyeing day book 1864.
Manchester Central Library (M75).

OTHER TEXTILE INDUSTRIES

[862] B & SH ASTARDJIAN, textile merchants, Manchester

Ledgers, accounts and corresp 1896-1977.
Greater Manchester RO.

[863] Number not used.

[864] BELLEEK NEEDLEWORK INDUSTRY, Belleek, co Fermanagh

Letter book 1908, corresp (*c*200 items) 1916-21, ledgers (4) 1916-early 1920s, invoice books (20) 1906, 1910, 1912-27, railway receipts (*c*100) 1918-*c*1920, wages account books, etc (11 vols) of the Belleek Cottage Industry, etc 1905-6, 1913-22, recipe book *c*1912.
Public Record Office of Northern Ireland (D 2149). NRA 31453.

[865] BELLEEK SPRIGGING INDUSTRY, Belleek, co Fermanagh

Wages and sales books (14) 1908-24 incl Castlecaldwell and Cornahilta 1917-23, workers' pass books (8) 1916-18 and employment cards *c*1920.
Public Record Office of Northern Ireland (D 2149). NRA 31453.

[866] BENTLEY, SMITH & CO LTD, bookbinders' cloth and leathercloth mfrs, Manchester

Minute book 1908-71, register of members.
Courtaulds Spinning. Enquiries to the Company Secretary. NRA 30126.

[867] BOOTHROYDS (SOUTHPORT) LTD, drapers, carpet mfrs, venetian blind mfrs and cabinet makers, Southport, Lancs

Partnership agreements and leases from *c*1834, annual balance sheets, corresp, etc from *c*1880, cash and sales ledgers from mid 19th cent, reference book late 19th cent, wages books from *c*1880, catalogues, price lists, etc.
Broadbents of Southport Ltd: see *Business Archives* 38, June 1973, pp18-21, and 42, Nov 1976, pp15-21.

[868] JOHN BOYD & CO LTD, haircloth mfrs and upholsterers, Castle Cary, Somerset

Records 1872-*c*1969 incl minutes, share records, balance sheets, private ledger, journal, cash books, sales and day books, stock lists, patent, and photographs.
John Boyd Textiles Ltd. NRA 28631; BAC *Company Archives* no 421.

[869] **THOMAS BROWN & SON (CHURCH FURNISHERS) LTD**, Manchester

Designs (1 vol and 16 loose sheets) for ecclesiastical embroidery late 19th cent.
Victoria & Albert Museum, Department of Designs, Prints & Drawings (E.4946-1968).

[870] **CHAMBERLINS LTD**, furnishers, drapers and carpet warehousemen, Norwich, Norfolk

Articles and deeds of partnership 1847-66, 1903, share records (16 vols, 3 bundles) 1903-42, private ledgers (7) 1877-1932, general ledgers (5) 1851-1904, silk and cloth account ledger 1864-85, journals (3) 1877-1928, misc cash books (3) 1856, 1891-1907, 1914-30, weekly stock and profit books (2) 1897-1906, stocktaking ledgers (2) 1852-71, inventory and valuation, etc 1903-4.
Norfolk RO (BR 25). NRA 27680.

[871] **CHAMPION, DICKASON & CO**, wholesale weavers and general merchants, London

Business records c1773-c1819 incl account of stock in the looms and inventory of silk goods, velvets, etc 1773, licences for payment of bills of exchange in Europe late 18th cent, papers rel to French investments 1792-1818, letters rel to American debts nd, Excise Office permits 1794-1819, and papers rel to merchant vessels late 18th-early 19th cent.
Northamptonshire RO (Overstone Collection). NRA 4952.

[872] **WILLIAM ALFRED COOPER & SON**, haircloth mfrs, Norwich, Norfolk

Pattern books (2) early 20th cent.
Bridewell Museum, Norwich. NRA 30575.

[873] **DONALD BROS LTD**, furnishing fabric mfrs, Dundee

Standard pattern books (37) 1896-1964, fabric books (15) nd.
Scottish College of Textiles, Galashiels. NRA 31124.

General meeting reports and papers (1 bundle) 1934-47, abstracts of accounts (5 bundles) 1914-62, balance sheets, financial statements, papers rel to insurance and trade mark registration, valuations of factories and plant, etc (9 bundles) 1880-1970, misc staff records (2 bundles) 1916-61.
The Company. Enquiries to NRA (Scotland) (NRA(S) 2018). NRA 22997.

Sample book of woven fabrics c1930.
Victoria & Albert Museum, Department of Textile Furnishings & Dress (T.357-1970). NRA 30151.

[874] **TS DONNE & CO LTD**, haircloth mfrs, Castle Cary, Somerset

Records 1877-c1960 incl memorandum and articles of association, minutes, annual reports, accounts, balance sheets, stock lists, receipt book, catalogues, and inventory.
John Boyd Textiles Ltd. NRA 28631; BAC *Company Archives* no 421.

[875] **ELDERTON & HALL**, cloth factors, London

Letter book 1763-9.
Somerset RO: see *Accessions to repositories 1956*, p29.

[876] **HENRY FREMONT**, embroiderer, London

Ledger 1779-83, expenditure account 1779-82, list of debtors, catalogue of stock and bankruptcy accounts 1783.
Westminster City Libraries Archives Section (Acc 36/ 105-7). NRA 27156.

[877] **HEAL & SON LTD**, bedding, quilt and mattress mfrs, cabinet makers and upholsterers, London

Board minutes (19 vols) 1915-49, directors' attendance register (3 vols) 1929-41, profit and loss accounts (2 vols) 1875-1906, ledgers (4) 1834-51, 1863-89, departmental ledgers (6) 1865-1943, private ledgers (3) 1890-1906, 1926-36, private ledger account (1 vol) 1924-31, journals (3) 1907-45, cash books (5) 1907-43, departmental receipts (5 vols) 1935, nd, order and sales books (6) 1938-56, furniture cost and stock books (120) 1855-89, 1897-1955, stocktaking records (9 vols) 1876-1919, 1924-41, textile samples (26 vols) 1893-1945, wages books (5) 1901-46, misc administrative and staff records 1885-1954, deeds and papers rel to premises 1840-1925, catalogues, price lists, advertisements, photographs, etc (c145 vols, files, etc) 1844-1940, nd, notebooks (11) of Ambrose Heal nd.
Victoria & Albert Museum, Archive of Art & Design (AAD 2-1978). NRA 21362.

Misc records 19th-20th cent incl patents 1836, 1858, 1860, day book 1824, cash book 1870-9, receipts (22) for goods 1850s-1860s, memoranda book mainly rel to carriage of goods c1867-76, staff book 1858-60, and time book 1871-4.
The Company. Enquiries to the Business Archives Council. NRA 21362.

[878] **JOHN HEYWOOD & SON**, counterpane and quilting mfrs, Bolton, Lancs

Business corresp and misc papers (18 bundles) 1805-22 mainly letters from firms and individuals in Britain, Gibraltar and Jamaica, business letter book 1830-40, personal corresp of John Heywood (1 bundle) 1791-1804, corresp and misc papers of Robert Heywood mainly rel to national politics and local affairs (47 bundles) 1823-69, diaries of Robert Heywood and other family papers (c56 vols, 2 bundles) 1803-1938.
Bolton Metropolitan Borough Archives (ZHE). NRA 27113.

[879] **RB HOVELL & CO LTD**, haircloth mfrs, Norwich, Norfolk

Pattern books (2) 1857-8, c1904.
Bridewell Museum, Norwich. NRA 30575.

[880] **ARTHUR H LEE & SONS LTD**, furnishing fabric mfrs, Birkenhead, Cheshire

Records mainly 20th cent incl minutes, albums of fabric designs, point papers, fabric samples, personnel records, catalogues, photographs, and press cuttings.
Williamson Art Gallery & Museum, Birkenhead.

Card cutting account books (2) 1903-8, pattern books (3) 1888-1905, point papers (79 items) 1888-1907.
Victoria & Albert Museum, Department of Designs, Prints & Drawings (E.1117-1316-1970).

Pattern book of woven textiles 1897-1905.
Victoria & Albert Museum, Department of Textile Furnishings & Dress (T.423-1970). NRA 30151.

[881] **GEORGE P LEE LTD**, furnishings mfrs and general warehousemen, Manchester

Minute book 1888-92.
National Library of Wales (Cambrian News Salvage Collection). NRA 26130.

[882] **ALEXANDER McNAB & CO LTD**, cloth mfrs, Glasgow

Memorandum and articles of association 1900, share register 1901-23, private ledger 1901-48, private journal 1900-48, cash book 1901-30.
Coats Viyella plc. Enquiries to the Company Secretary. NRA 32374.

Directors' minute book 1957-70
Lancashire RO (DDVc). NRA 30810.

[883] **JAMES MILLIGAN & CO**, cloth merchants, Glasgow

Journal, cash book, ledger and index (4 vols) 1788-93.
Scottish Record Office (CS 96/1023-6). *Court of Session Productions*, List & Index Society, special series vol 23, 1987, p96.

[884] **J MOON**, children's bedlinen mfrs, London

Books and papers (2 boxes) 1849-57.
Public Record Office, Chancery Lane (J 90/918-19).

[885] **MORRIS & CO**, pre-raphaelite furnishers, London and Merton Abbey, Surrey

Minute book 1862-74, day book 1862-3, dye book 1882-91, misc corresp 1887-98, nd.
Sanford and Helen Berger Collection, California: see Linda Parry, *William Morris textiles*, 1983. Photocopies of the minutes and letters are in Hammersmith and Fulham Archives (DD/235).

Manager's corresp and memoranda (1 vol) 1866-9, embroidery day book 1892-6, William Morris notebook rel to tapestry, textiles, hours worked, etc c1879, bills and corresp 1880-96.
Victoria & Albert Museum Library (L.2636-2637-1939, L.687, 691-1958). NRA 13466.

Account book of Philip Webb 1861-77.
Birmingham Museum & Art Gallery: see C Harvey & J Press, 'William Morris and the marketing of art', *Business History* XXVIII, 1986, pp36-54.

Account book of Edward Burne-Jones 1861-98.
Fitzwilliam Museum, Cambridge: see Harvey & Press, ibid.

Designs (over 400 items), pattern and sample books (9 vols), misc corresp (c170 items) 1848-96.
William Morris Gallery Library, Walthamstow: see *Catalogue of the Morris collection*, 1969.

Designs for printed and woven fabrics, carpets, tapestries, embroidery, etc 19th-20th cent.
Victoria & Albert Museum, Department of Designs, Prints & Drawings (E.65-1898; E.633-858-1915; E.144, 441-608, 5012-1919; E.287-405, 543, 620-621, 889-1939; E.27-67, 117, 426, 571-572, 1166-1167, 1169-1172-1940; E.955-962-1954).

Wallpaper and textile pattern books 1864-c1940.
Arthur Sanderson & Sons Ltd. Access restricted. Enquiries to the Company Archivist. NRA 30127.

Sample book of patterned textiles 19th cent, sample book of printed velveteens c1910.
Victoria & Albert Museum, Department of Textile Furnishings & Dress (T.660-1919, T.30-1940). NRA 30151.

Pattern book nd.
Art Gallery of South Australia, Adelaide: see Linda Parry, ibid.

Sketches, plans and notes (1 vol) 19th cent, William Morris journals (5) 1881-96, Morris family papers and corresp c1853-1938, some rel to business.
British Library (Add MSS 45298-45353, 45407-12).

[886] **MORTON SUNDOUR FABRICS LTD**, textile mfrs, Darvel, Ayrshire, Carlisle, Cumberland and Edinburgh

Legal papers and corresp rel to formation of company, its acquisition by Courtaulds, etc (14 files) 1913-67, directors' minutes (13 vols) 1928-63, policy statements and lists of shareholders 1924-64, balance sheets, reports and accounts incl subsidiary and associated companies 1903-69, ledger 1920-5, corresp (c60 files) 1928-66 rel to trading and investment policies, promotional plans and overseas marketing activities, technical notes 1930, 1941-62, papers rel to tariffs 1948-65, plans (5) 1925-6, 1937, minutes and corresp of the Furnishing Fabric Federation and Furnishing Fabrics Export Group 1941-67 and the Federation of British Industries 1947-65, personal and business papers of Sir James Morton 1887-1943 and other Morton family papers 1889-1973; Alexander Morton & Co Ltd profit and loss accounts 1903-14, sales statistics 1894-1908, stock books (2) 1907-21, misc corresp and legal papers 1898-1905, 1914, press cuttings and notes on history of company 1917-73.
Scottish Record Office (GD 326). NRA 20588.

Balance sheets, etc 1935-40, 1958-65, patents and assignments 1930-6, press cuttings 1935-65.
Courtaulds plc, Coventry. Enquiries to the Head of Archives. NRA 29343.

Design record books (3) c1900-63, photographs of designs (3 vols) 1943-59, nd, sample books (56) c1909-1960s incl corresp with customers; Oberkampf pattern books (308) 18th-19th cent; Lyon order, sample and scrap books (56) 19th cent.

Courtaulds plc, London. Access restricted. Enquiries to the Design Library, Courtaulds Textiles. NRA 30957.

Corresp, technical notes, patent specifications, trials, samples, drawings of machinery and fabric design and photographs (129 files, etc) 20th cent.
Science Museum, Department 6. NRA 28468.

Testcards, notebooks, corresp, pattern books, samples, photographs of factories, etc and pamphlets (34 boxes) 1828-1970.
Science Museum, Department 2. NRA 28468.

Design record books (2) 1900-5, addresses of designers, etc 1929-31, corresp with E & A Hunter, Letchworth, with memoranda, specimens of fabric, etc 1927-8, corresp between the Morton family and S Mawson, CFA Voysey and other designers 1896-1968.
Victoria & Albert Museum Library (L.449-1973, L.3212-3213-1973, L.4032-4033-1973). NRA 13466.

Papers *c*1896-1963 incl corresp, etc (12 files) between Sir James Morton and designers, diaries and notebooks, textile colour samples, misc catalogues, and pamphlets.
Victoria & Albert Museum, Archive of Art & Design (AAD 4-1978). NRA 28681.

Carpet and textile designs from Alexander Morton & Co Ltd (954 items) 20th cent.
Victoria & Albert Museum, Department of Designs, Prints & Drawings (E.824-1095-1974).

Letters, bills, etc to Alexander Morton & Co Ltd 1912-14.
Cumbria RO, Carlisle: see *Report of the County Archivist*, March 1967, p3.

[887] **J MUNN & CO**, yarn and cloth commission agents and merchants, Manchester

Out-letter books (2) 1853-8, 1878-98, private letter books (2) 1871-5, ledgers (2) 1813-22, day book 1813-19, agreements with employees (1 vol) 1847-78, inventory and valuation 1873.
Manchester Central Library (M386).

[888] **GEORGE OLDLAND**, cloth merchant, Trowbridge, Wilts

Ledger 1859, goods bought and sold books (2) 1859-61, stock book 1859-61, notes of debts, etc *c*1861.
Wiltshire RO (WRO 2153). NRA 32193.

[889] **ARTHUR SANDERSON & SONS LTD**, mfrs and distributors of wallpaper and furnishing fabrics, Uxbridge, Mddx

Directors' minutes (11 vols) 1900-60, 1966-9, general meeting minutes (1 vol) 1909-39, executive committee minutes (3 vols) 1931-4, 1966-9, registers of directors and members, share ledgers, etc (9 vols) 1900-71, annual returns (2 vols) 1948-52, 1958, register of mortgages and bonds 1921, private ledgers (6) 1892-1956, account books (4) 1900-61, textile and wallpaper design log books and pattern books (*c*115 vols) incl subsidiary firms 19th-20th cent, textile and wallpaper samples 18th-20th cent incl printed cottons 18th-20th cent and French jacquard woven textiles 18th-19th cent, piecework prices (1 vol) 1938, wages

books (5) 1912-13, 1920-36, advertising material and photographs 20th cent.
The Company. Access restricted. Enquiries to the Company Archivist. NRA 30127.

[890] **SCHOFIELD & FROGGATT LTD**, candle and lamp wick mfrs, Stalybridge, Cheshire

Day books and ledgers (9 vols) 1901-64, invoices (2 files) 1958-62, wages book 1935-9.
Manchester Central Library (L12).

[891] **ISAAC THORP & SONS LTD**, textile mfrs and warehousemen, Manchester

Articles of association and partnership 1891-1908, papers rel to sale to J & N Philips & Co Ltd 1920-1, minutes 1896-1904, assets and liabilities 1916-44, share records, bank books, etc 1911-21, property deeds, accounts and papers 1869-1922.
Manchester Central Library (M97). NRA 24109.

[892] **BENJAMIN WAINWRIGHT & CO**, haircloth and bagging mfrs, Thurlstone, Yorks

Journal and letter book 1798-1808, journals (4) 1804-25, ledger and sundries account book 1813-19, letter and invoice book (1 vol and loose sheets) 1813-26, order books (2) *c*1812, purchase and sales book 1790-1813, purchase record and other business notes (1 vol) 1836-44, business memoranda book nd, Wainwright family corresp, deeds and papers mainly 19th cent.
Sheffield City Archives (WBC). *Letters from a Yorkshire emigrant . . . A catalogue of the family papers of John Wainwright . . .*, 1967.

[893] **JW & C WARD**, furnishing fabric mfrs, Halifax, Yorks

Production record books (5) 1886-1911.
Courtaulds plc, London. Access restricted. Enquiries to the Design Library, Courtaulds Textiles. NRA 30957.

[894] **WATTS & CO LTD**, church furnishers, London

Records from 1879 incl minutes, share registers, balance sheets, annual returns, cash books, sales day books and other accounting records, order books, stock books, production records, pattern books, wages and salaries books, and premises records.
The Company. NRA 28631; BAC *Company Archives* no 302.

[895] **WINTERBOTTOM BOOK CLOTH CO LTD**, Manchester and Salford, Lancs

General meeting and finance committee minutes, agenda and balance sheets (3 vols) 1892-1961, index of shareholders nd, private ledgers (3) 1943-65, cash book 1960-1, spreading department daily reports 1968-9.
Salford Archives Centre (U150). NRA 25207.

Notebook and misc papers of WD Winterbottom rel to bleaching, dyeing and fabric printing 1875-95.
Derbyshire RO (D 779B/B34-40). NRA 28050.

[896] **YUILL & SON**, cloth mfrs, Glasgow

Stock books (2) 1857-61, despatch book 1857-8, account book (equipment) 1857-60, wages book 1857-61.
Scottish Record Office (CS 96/66-70).

CLOTHING, HOSIERY AND KNITWEAR

[897] **ALLEN & TURTLE LTD**, hosiery mfrs, dyers and finishers, Belfast

Contracts register 1897-1929, order book 1912-32, stock book 1931-2, costing books (2) 1890-1931.
Public Record Office of Northern Ireland (D 3234). NRA 31466.

[898] **DAVID ALLISON**, tailor and draper, London

Accounts (3 vols) 1817-19.
Northamptonshire RO (D10388-90).

[899] **WILLIAM ANDERSON & SONS LTD**, tailors and outfitters, Edinburgh

Directors' minute book 1912-44, papers rel to incorporation 1912, private account book 1871-1900, cash book 1899-1912, sales totals book 1869-1946, cost book 1916-22, inventory 1874, misc balance sheets, agreements, price lists, etc 1862-1913.
In private possession. Enquiries to NRA (Scotland) (NRA(S) 327). NRA 10975.

[900] **ATKINS BROTHERS (HOSIERY) LTD**, hosiery mfrs, Hinckley, Leics

Letter book 1912-15, corresp files (2) 1915-23, ledgers (4) 1800-62, 1936-57, account of monies placed with firm by family and others (1 vol) 1871-*c*1900, day book 1916-58, bill book 1888-1958, sales books (4) 1869-77, 1885-95, 1902-6, *c*1919-21, corresp, etc rel to contracts (1 parcel, etc) 1911-14, 1941-9, order book *c*1931-63, reference book 1888-1900, status reports *c*1907-12, corresp (1 vol) rel to commission accounts 1900-8, price lists (23) *c*1889-98, despatching department weekly totals (1 vol) 1937-62, details of goods supplied to the firm 1880-*c*1916, yarn records (4 vols) 1901-5, 1914-15, *c*1921-27, 1947-*c*1953, stocktaking books (2) 1867-1918 and list 1914, costing book early 20th cent, production returns 1904-41, wages and other staff records (14 vols, etc) 1887-1903, 1915-18, 1926-34, 1946-72, misc business papers, catalogues and photographs 1877-1950s, misc family papers 1864-1945.
Atkins of Hinckley Ltd. Enquiries to the Managing Director. NRA 31899.

[901] **GIDEON BAIRD**, hatters and outfitters, Belfast

Accounts, etc (10 vols) 1902-61.
Public Record Office of Northern Ireland (D 1880).
Deputy Keeper's Report 1960-5, p57.

[902] **JOHN BARRAN & SONS LTD**, clothing mfrs and merchants, Leeds

Directors' and committee minutes 1903-33, registration and share records 1903-59, accounts, ledgers, cash books, etc 1874-1946, sales and purchase books 1906-57, stock inventories and valuations 1845-1948, wages and employment records 1877-1942, deeds and property records 1891-1945, scrapbooks, etc 1856-1954.
West Yorkshire Archive Service, Leeds: see Hudson.

Photographs of boys' fashions (1 vol) *c*1890.
Gallery of English Costume, Manchester.

[903] **WILLIAM BIDE**, glover, Yeovil, Somerset

Ledger and index 1805-22, stock accounts (7 vols) 1851-9, 1863-77, private cash book 1855-64.
Dorset RO (D 128/B). NRA 979.

[904] **WILLIAM BLACKBURN & CO LTD**, clothing mfrs and retailers, Leeds

Balance sheets, profit and loss accounts, etc 1885-1945, ledgers 1903-48, employment records 1904-19, building records 1895-1907, statistics, publicity material, photographs, etc 1890s-1967.
West Yorkshire Archive Service, Leeds: see Hudson.

[905] **MAJOR BLUNDELL & CO**, haberdashers and drapers, London

Business accounts, bills, receipts, agreements and partnership papers (79 items) 1774-1801, private and housekeeping accounts (5 vols) 1779-1801, deeds (4 bundles) 1770-87.
Guildhall Library, London (MSS 10033-10033A). NRA 4597 (Bulletin 28).

[906] **THOMAS BOSTON LTD**, outfitters, boot makers and jewellers, Norwich, Norfolk

Corresp, invoices, receipts, orders, etc (*c*1,800 items) 1887-92, 1913.
Norfolk RO (BR 71). NRA 27688.

[907] **BOULTON BROTHERS LTD**, glovers, Westbury, Wilts

Minutes 1901-75, register of members.
Dents Gloves Ltd. Enquiries to the Company Secretary. NRA 31855.

[908] **GEORGE BRETTLE & CO LTD**, hosiery mfrs, Belper, Derbys

Partnership agreements, etc 1803-34, 1844-1901, directors' minutes (6 vols) 1913-67, balance sheets 1823-33, 1915-64, letter books (3) 1801-23, 1872-87, accounts 1805-20, 1843-1936 incl Edward Brettle's private account book 1843-69, bad debt ledger 1805-37, reference book 1825-37, bought ledger 1816-22, costing book *c*1880, cost accounts 1936-40, pattern book *c*1860, price lists (8) 1827-1930, patent records 1860-72, production notes *c*1912, staff ledgers (3) *c*1813-1913, deeds, leases, building accounts, etc

from 1775, notebook of Walter Bennett c1926.
Courtaulds Hosiery Ltd. Access restricted. NB Harte,
'A history of George Brettle & Co Ltd, 1801-1964',
typescript, 1972-4.

[909] **BROADBENTS OF SOUTHPORT LTD**,
tailors, outfitters and silk mercers, Southport, Lancs

Records from c1896 incl board minutes, share transfer
books, corresp, annual returns, accounts, wages books,
catalogues, and price lists.
The Company: see *Business History* XIII, 1971,
pp64-71, and *Business Archives* 38, June 1973, pp18-21.

[910] **WILLIAM BROCK & CO LTD**, dressmakers,
glovers, hosiers, silk mercers and bedding mfrs,
Exeter, Devon

Partnership deeds 1852-71, partners' cash book
1871-89 incl balance sheets 1871-81, partners' private
cash book from 1899, stock books (3) from 1884, staff
rule book 1876, assistants' engagement book 1884-9
and agreements (4) 1890-6, misc papers rel to premises
1859-1934 incl inventory and valuation 1885, private
ledger of William Brock 1872-83, family history
1812-64.
In private possession. NRA 8197.

[911] **AH BULL LTD**, tailors, outfitters and house
furnishers, Reading, Berks

Private ledgers (3) 1897-1905, 1916-34, 1942-7.
John Lewis Partnership Archives. Access restricted.
Enquiries to the Company Archivist. NRA 31120.

[912] **TG BURRELL LTD**, haberdashers, outfitters
and drapers, Chester, Cheshire

Ledger 1883-90, cash books (6) 1930-63, stock books
(9) 1878, 1882-9, clothing clubs' accounts (1 vol)
1938-60, wages books (5) 1894-1930, 1945-7,
advertisements and photographs 1888-1977.
Chester City RO (CR 529). NRA 30834.

[913] **A CAIRD & SONS LTD**, tailors and drapers,
Dundee

Minute of copartnery 1905, minute book 1919-78,
share register 1919-75, ledgers (2) 1906-69, cash books
(2) 1904-18, directors' and employees' purchases book
1924-5, shop and van sales analysis books (2) 1920-5,
wages and salaries books (7) 1921-38, misc balance
sheets, corresp, property records, etc 1894-1954.
The Company. Enquiries to NRA (Scotland) (NRA(S)
1803). NRA 21937.

[914] **CAMPBELL, PAUL & SONS**, shawl mfrs,
Paisley, Renfrewshire

Shawl print proofs (1 vol) 1840-55.
Royal Museum of Scotland, Queen Street, Edinburgh.

[915] **CASTELL & SON**, tailors and robe makers,
Oxford

Letter book from 1869, ledger 1879-84.
In private possession. NRA 6437.

[916] **CHESTERGATE HAT
MANUFACTURING CO LTD**, Stockport, Cheshire

Minutes (7 vols) 1898-1935, 1940-66, share ledger
1898-1954, balance sheets and accounts 1899-1951,
directors' attendance book 1930-54, deeds and papers
1873-1930.
Stockport Central Library (Christy Collection). NRA
22838.

[917] **CHILCOT & WILLIAMS LTD**, corsetry mfrs
Portsmouth, Hants

Partnership agreements (11) 1879-1952, minute book
1938-65, register of directors and shareholders
1938-65, corresp (5 files) 1861-89, 1938-67, statements
of account 1905-21, 1950-64, general account books
(2) 1860-4, 1883-90, bank books (2) 1874-80, bill
books (2) 1904-39, impersonal ledgers (4) 1934-68,
sales, purchase and bought ledgers, day books, etc
(17 vols) 1921-6, 1935-70, order and stocktaking
records (c30 vols and items) 1940-70, patent records
(c112 items) 1849-1942, misc staff records (1 bundle,
7 items) 1866-1970, corresp, specifications, plans, etc
rel to premises (2 vols, 1 file, 43 items) 1865-1904,
1950-68.
Portsmouth City RO (504A). NRA 30319.

[918] **CHRISTY & CO LTD**, hatters, Stockport,
Cheshire and London

Partnership agreements and related papers 1773-1909,
nd, minutes 1936, 1958-60, directors' attendance book
1887-1936, reports, balance sheets and accounts
1888-1960, corresp rel to shares, etc 1885-1955, misc
general corresp 1830-1939, letter books (26)
1880-1939, ledgers (7) 1889-1958, cash books (23)
1802-14, 1852-1959 and other accounts (17 vols, etc)
1813-1967, order and sales books, etc (44 vols, etc)
1834-1964, stock books (8) and lists 1843-1968,
stocktaking notebooks 1867-87, list of shippers,
agents, etc c1820-41, shipping ledger 1887-1967,
export corresp 1925-62, exhibition papers and corresp
1851-1958, manufacturing cost books, price lists and
catalogues (26 vols, etc) 1821-1962, summary of work
done 1854-5, manufacture record books (8) c1856-60,
1871-96, production ledger 1881-3, book of shapes
1889-1915, patent specifications and corresp
1826-1934, trade marks 1842-c1955, employees'
contracts, agreements, craft membership accounts, etc
1809-1955, wages books, pay sheets, etc (6 vols, etc)
1847-1964, salaries books 1920-39, 1959-63, lists of
apprentices, indentures, etc 1834-1953, job
applications book 1869-72, papers rel to strikes, sick
club and athletic and social club 1830-1963, index of
machines 1865-1905, deeds, valuations, plans, etc
17th-20th cent, family papers.
Stockport Central Library (Christy Collection). NRA
22838.

[919] **EJ CLARK**, tailors and drapers, Bourn, Cambs

Account and order books 1884-1981, trade catalogues
and price lists 1896-1936.
Cambridgeshire RO, Cambridge (R82/102). NRA
25927.

[920] **COLSON & CO**, hosiers, milliners and outfitters, Exeter, Devon

Prospectus, etc 1925, account of Lord Graves with Colsons 1829-32, account of stock purchased (1 vol) 1912-20, inventory (1 vol) 1898, photographs (44) *c*1900-54, sales catalogues (5) 1912-16, press cuttings, notes on firm, etc 20th cent.
Devon RO (68/21). NRA 3506.

[921] **JOHN COLTMAN & SONS**, hosiery mfrs, Leicester

Summary accounts 1782-91, stock books (2) 1792-1814.
Leicestershire RO (7 D 65/LXXV/14,15).

[922] **RICHARD COOPER & CO (ASHBOURNE) LTD**, corsetry mfrs, Ashbourne, Derbys

Minutes (2 vols) 1905-55, balance sheets and accounts 1887-1973, cash book and ledger from 1897, bill book 1923, order book nd, sales and purchases schedule *c*1913, cloth and elastic stocks (*c*35 vols) 1926-51, gauge books (2) 1909, nd, production books (6) *c*1920, nd, pattern books and samples nd, design record book 1929, salaries books (3) 1908-47, details of outwork (1 vol) nd, misc legal and financial papers 1897-1969.
Coats Viyella plc. Enquiries to the Company Secretary. NRA 32375.

[923] **CORAH LTD**, clothing and hosiery mfrs, Leicester

Board, general meeting and committee minutes (9 vols, 6 folders) 1919-76, board papers (3 folders) 1971-5, papers rel to a legal dispute with Wm Buckler & Co Ltd (1 bundle) 1904, share records (5 vols) 1919-40, partnership balance sheets and statements of account (1 vol) 1832-55, balance sheets and profit and loss accounts (1 vol) 1928-31, weekly abstract, etc (1 vol) 1884, accounts and working papers (4 parcels) 1955-62, private ledgers (4) 1863-93, 1919-36, class ledger 1896-1911, journals (2) 1881-1917, cash books (5) 1890-1918, bill books (2) 1869-77, 1901-15, travellers' ledger 1899-1909, private memoranda books (2) 1876-85, Christmas gifts book 1903-9, employees' income tax records (1 vol) 1950-7, photographs of St Margaret's Works (1 vol) *c*1939, title deeds (1 folder) 1924-35, misc family corresp and papers (1 box, 1 packet) *c*1862-1953, printed papers late 19th-early 20th cent.
Corah plc. Enquiries to the Company Secretary. NRA 31055.

[924] **CORNISH & CO**, outfitters, Exeter, Devon

Daily sales, receipt and expenditure record (1 vol) 1902-15, wages book 1912-16, deeds (22) 1619, 1851-1931, photographs.
The Company; NRA 3506 (68/16).

[925] **SAMUEL CORRY & CO LTD**, tie mfrs and hemstitchers, Newtownards, co Down

Ledgers, cash, invoice and stock books, sales journal, corresp, etc (*c*100 vols and items) 1910-60.
Public Record Office of Northern Ireland (D 1965): see *Ulster textile industry*.

[926] **RJ COUSINS**, tailor and outfitter, Kendal, Westmorland

Stock book 1890-1903, day book 1911-20.
Cumbria RO, Kendal: see *Report of the County Archivist* Sept 1980, p10.

[927] **THOMAS CREWDSON & CO**, hosiery and linsey mfrs, Kendal, Westmorland

Ledgers (3) 1759-1800, day book 1781-7, bank books (2) 1784-1805, abstract order book 1784, stocktaking account books (5) 1767-89, stocktaking and cash accounts (1 vol) 1784-5, 1794-5, 1821-5, Crewdson family personal and financial papers 1684-1930.
Cumbria RO, Kendal (WD/Cr). NRA 30978.

[928] **WH CULLEN & SON**, tailors and outfitters, Bury St Edmunds, Suffolk

Business and personal diaries (4) 1900, 1913, 1916, 1918, account book 1915-18, day books (2) 1918-19, 1926-8, bank book 1905-9, stock book 1912, misc bills, receipts, advertisements, etc *c*1909-1939.
Suffolk RO, Bury St Edmunds (HC 513). NRA 25697.

[929] **DAVIES & SON (LONDON) LTD**, tailors and breeches makers, London

Ledgers and journals (*c*75) 1861-1973, day books (*c*93) 1927-77, customers' accounts (*c*91 vols) 1822-9, 1867-1974, branch accounts (*c*21 vols) 1912-40, ledger indexes and log books (*c*28) *c*1900-70, corresp with customers (*c*391 items) 1914-50, order, measurement, pattern, tailoring and other manufacturing records (*c*316 vols, etc) 1825-9, 1880-1979, salaries books (7) 1890-1974, tax and insurance records, advertising material, price lists, etc 1877-1973.
Westminster City Libraries, Marylebone Archives and Local Studies (Acc 1043). NRA 32481.

[930] **THOMAS DAVIES & CO**, hatters, London

Partnership deeds (3) 1773-85, letter books (2) 1771-87, corresp incl orders and misc accounts (*c*120 items) *c*1770-95, title deeds (7) 1756-84.
Public Record Office, Chancery Lane (C 107/104).

[931] **SAMUEL DAVIS & SONS LTD**, hosiery mfrs, Hinckley, Leics

General ledgers (6) 1884-1914, private ledger 1913-24, sundries ledger 1907-19, day books (2) 1897-1903, 1924-6, cash book 1909-14, bought ledgers (5) 1897-1924, sales ledgers (6) 1900-26, sales analysis 1930-48, invoices (2 vols) 1926-9, shipping day book 1918-27, yarn contract book 1926-9, agents' accounts 1933-6, machinery stock book *c*1905, wages books (3) 1924-6.
Leicestershire RO (DE 2544). NRA 26412.

[932] **DENT, ALLCROFT & CO LTD**, glovers, London and Worcester

Cash account book 1781-94, stock accounts 1803-6, corresp, accounts and papers (1 bundle) 1839-53 incl inventory 1846.
In private possession. Enquiries to Gloucestershire RO. NRA 6429.

Minutes 1964-75, register of members, photographs, etc 1890s-1930s.
Dents Gloves Ltd. Enquiries to the Company Secretary. NRA 31855.

[933] **DICKSONS & LAINGS**, hosiery mfrs, Hawick, Roxburghshire

Wages ledger 1848-1907, tweed pattern book 1830-50, diploma 1851, plans, drawings and photographs 1813-1902, 1978, nd.
Hawick Museum. NRA 17662.

[934] **DODDS & CO**, tailors and drapers, Alnwick, Northumb

Ledgers and indexes (11 vols) 1805-21, 1827-32, 1838-81, journals (8) 1865-83, outstanding accounts, cash credit and cash books (7) 1834, 1843-54, 1864-86 incl customers' orders *c*1864-86, sales day books (9) 1788-91, 1801-4, 1845-6, 1875-86, drapery sales account book 1873-7, dressmaking and millinery day books (5) 1876-85, suppliers' accounts, invoices and order books (10 vols) 1788-92, 1813-39, 1849-82, 1887, stocktaking book 1846, 1878.
Northumberland RO (NRO 808). NRA 31041.

[935] **DONN family**, glovers and mercers, Yeovil, Somerset and Exeter, Devon

Account and order books (5) probably of William and Henry Donn 1752-62, business corresp, account books, bill book and other papers (6 vols, 3 files, over 80 items) of Robert Donn 1761-1809.
Somerset RO (DD/PR/34-8, 44-5). NRA 12405.

[936] **J & JC DORWARD**, clothing mfrs, Galashiels, Selkirkshire

Directors' minute book 1920-47, corresp and papers (9 bundles) 1890-1971 incl certificates of registration, contracts, minutes of agreement and leases (1 bundle) 1891-1966, balance sheets 1898-1908, private ledgers (8) 1890-1970, nominal and general ledgers (9) 1926-75, cash books (3) 1935-57, private cash books (3) 1900-78, bill book 1890-1912, finishing entries book 1896-1913, customer credits cash book 1944-63, sales cash book 1953-6, inventories and valuations of Tweed Place and Waukrigg Mills (44 items) 1890, 1910, 1918, specifications for new spinning mill, etc 1866, 1890, plans (33) 1866-1971, misc corresp and accounts (3 bundles, 44 items) 1873-1935, notes on history of Dorward business and family nd.
Scottish Record Office (GD 396). NRA 23737.

[937] **EDE & RAVENSCROFT LTD**, robe makers and wig makers, London

Customers' ledgers (6) 1741-63, 1887-1951, general ledger 1834-49, tradesmen's ledger 1907-24, journal 1837-8, sales day book 1834-6, estimates (2 vols) 1834-1928, descriptions of robes supplied (8 vols) 1761-1955, advertisement register 1872-1931, corresp and papers (17 envelopes) rel to royal warrants 1860-1926, misc corresp, specifications, estimates and printed papers (24 envelopes) 1809-1915.

Guildhall Library, London (MSS 21685-21715). NRA 31283.

Bills, specifications, catalogues, etc (151 groups) rel to design and supply of court dress *c*1850-*c*1939.
Court Dress Collection, Kensington Palace.

[938] **F & J ELLIS LTD**, glovers, Leicester

Papers rel to purchase of business from R Harris & Sons 1887, balance sheets 1901, 1902, 1928, order books (3) 1876-1900, 1907-10, pricing book 1894-1950, Berlin glove price list 1854-95, machinery book 1899-1954, outdoor work book 1908-19, wages books (2) 1904-44, notes on history of firm and Ellis family.
Leicestershire RO (8 D 69). NRA 13886.

[939] **EMANUEL, JOSEPH, HARRIS & CO**, clothiers, London

Day book, bill books, sales and bought ledgers and journals, wages book, etc 1867-73.
Public Record Office, Chancery Lane (J 90/1538-42).

[940] **DANIEL EVANS**, milliner, Sheffield, Yorks

Sales books (4) 1898-1930, lease of premises 1903 and related corresp 1917-28.
Sheffield City Archives (MD 1392-9). NRA 23246.

[941] **EXPRESS RUBBER CO LTD**, waterproof clothing mfrs, London

Minute books (3) 1911-71, share ledger and register of transfers 1911-49, copies of annual returns 1939-70.
Aquascutum Group plc. Not available for research.

[942] **FORBES & HUTCHINSON**, shawl mfrs, Paisley, Renfrewshire

Designs, samples, etc *c*1843-8.
Paisley Museum & Art Gallery. NRA 16052; see also M Lochrie, 'The Paisley Shawl Industry', *Scottish textile history*, ed J Butt and K Ponting, 1987, p111.

[943] **FOSTER BROTHERS CLOTHING CO LTD**, clothing mfrs, tailors and outfitters, Solihull, Warwicks

Minutes (5 vols) from 1894, registers of members, annual summaries, etc (3 vols) 1894-1920, 1927-48, registers of seals (2) 1954-64, 1972-80, directors' papers 1970s, share registers (3 vols) 1927-38, 1951-64, annual reports and accounts, etc from 1965, papers rel to takeover of Adams Group *c*1973, Horne Brothers 1987, etc, private ledgers (10) 1894-1922, 1929-58, 1961-71, cash books (*c*5) 1913-1970s, manufacturing statistics 1970s, salaries books (6) 1941-68, property ledger *c*1939-52, forms rel to tenancies (1 box) *c*1956-71.
Foster Brothers Clothing plc. Enquiries to the Assistant Company Secretary. NRA 32270.

[944] **FOWNES BROTHERS & CO**, glovers, London and Worcester

Register of members, legal papers, income tax returns, etc 1895-1935.
Dents Gloves Ltd. Enquiries to the Company Secretary. NRA 31855.

Staff record book (London) 1877-93, family papers 1670-1898.
Hereford and Worcester RO, Worcester (705:723). NRA 15930.

[945] **FRASER, SONS & CO LTD**, tailors, drapers and house furnishers, Glasgow

Minutes (2 vols) 1909-47, registers of members (2) 1909-17, 1936-8, private ledgers (5) 1866-79, 1910-48, journal 1935-48, balance book 1969-71, current account book 1946-7.
Glasgow University Archives (UGD/98). NRA 19964.

[946] **WILLIAM FRASER**, merchant and glover, Inverness

Waste books (3) 1772-84, account books (3) 1773-84, cash book 1781-3, notebooks (2) 1779-80, 1782.
Scottish Record Office (CS 96/1162-3, 1443-8). *Court of Session Productions*, List & Index Society, special series vol 23, 1987, p66.

[947] **WILLIAM GIBSON & SON LTD**, hosiery mfrs, Nottingham

Records 1862-1977 incl minutes, directors' attendance book, annual reports and accounts, private ledgers and cash book, price lists, stocktaking summary, photographs, and press cuttings.
The Company. NRA 28631; BAC *Company Archives* no 395.

[948] **GIEVES LTD**, tailors and outfitters, Portsmouth, Hants and London

Memorandum and articles of association 1904-71, partnership deeds, agreements, etc (c45 items) 1865-1951, directors' minutes (4 vols) 1904-28, shareholders' minutes (2) 1905-71, board papers 1966-77, seal book 1931-61, charge book 1974-6, registers of members, share ledgers and other share records (c20 vols and bundles) 1912-66, annual reports and accounts, financial statements and other accounting records (c30 bundles) 1905-81, ledgers, journals and cash books (32 vols) 1911-74, nd, sales ledgers, price lists, etc (c13 vols and files) c1912-80, staff records (10 vols) 1916-63, misc legal, registration and insurance records 1903-16, 1942, deeds, agreements, inventories and corresp rel to property 1890-1960.
Gieves Group plc. Enquiries to the Business Archives Council. NRA 27130.

[949] **GLASGOW CLOTHING CO**, tailor, Glasgow

General ledger 1906-21, printed papers (5 vols) 1909-20.
Strathclyde Regional Archives (TD 275), NRA 19952.

[950] **D GURTEEN & SONS LTD**, mfrs of clothing and mats, Haverhill, Suffolk

Minute books (7) from 1917, corresp, agreements, etc (1 box) mainly 20th cent, constitution and rules 1950s-1977, day books (7) 1784-1825, 1900-58, ledgers (13) 1885-1974, journals (4) 1892-1915, 1950s, 1972,

cash accounts (2 vols) 1870-1924, analysis book 1885-99, memoranda of costings (1 vol) 1884-9, misc accounting records (1 box, 21 vols) 1927-1960s, order books (19) 1893-c1971, sales ledgers (6) early 20th cent-1964, area sales analysis books (5) 1928-1960s, customer address and index books (2) c1908-40, despatch book c1911-17, shipping book 1911-21, stock books (3) 1893-1951, stock lists (1 bundle) 1915-17, making accounts (4 vols) 1892-8, 1914-54, production notebook c1863, factory diaries (3) 1889-c1911, pattern and sample books (6) 1912-13, 1922-42, salaries book 1889, salaries, wages and staff records (26 vols) mainly 1931-59, deeds 17th-20th cent and other property records 19th-20th cent, Gurteen family financial, property and misc papers 19th-20th cent, trade catalogues, design cards, circulars and other printed material 19th-20th cent.
The Company. Enquiries to the Managing Director. NRA 30699.

[951] **J & H HADDEN & CO LTD**, hosiery mfrs, Nottingham

Ledgers (7) 1787-1886 incl European and American trade, account book mainly rel to German and Italian trade 1799-1804, travellers' order book 1786, deeds (54) 1685-1915.
Nottingham University Library (Ha). NRA 768.

[952] **H HAINGE**, tailors and drapers, Portmadoc, Caerns

Corresp (12 bundles and items) 1902, 1913-50, nd, letter book 1942, balance sheets 1930-9, trading accounts (2 vols) 1920-44, ledgers (9) 1910-44, rough account books (9) 1891-8, 1931-48, day books (4) 1927-43, nd, bank books (3) 1903-34, misc bills, vouchers and other financial papers (20 vols, bundles and items) 1917-49, customers' account books (32) 1922-43, order books (2) 1908-11, stocktaking book 1931, misc printed and personal papers 1891-1937.
Gwynedd Archives and Museums Service, Caernarfon (XM 2841). NRA 30926.

[953] **HALL BROS LTD**, tailors, Oxford

General account books (13) 1894-1951, customers' account books (9) 1909-51, misc account books (3) 1898-1954, day books (23) 1895-1968, measurements books (4) 1900-28.
Oxfordshire RO (Misc Hall). NRA 26472.

[954] **HANDLEY SEYMOUR LTD**, court dressmakers, London

Designs (51 vols) for court gowns, fancy dress and theatrical costumes 1910-40.
Victoria & Albert Museum, Department of Designs, Prints & Drawings (E.1-5105-1958). NRA 29140.

[955] **HASKINGS & MULLEN**, tailors, Eastbourne, Sussex

Accounts ledger 1881-91, receipted bills 1874, 1878, indenture 1869.
East Sussex RO (Add MSS 3412-15). NRA 7797.

[956] HENRY HEATH LTD, hatters, London

Balance sheets 1898-1949, registers of debentures (2) 1898-1928, general ledgers (4) 1899-1923, cash books (2) 1929-43, agreements and leases 1914-48.
West Yorkshire Archive Service, Leeds (Burton Archives). NRA 21633.

Minutes, corresp and misc papers 1944-66.
Stockport Central Library (Christy Collection). NRA 22838.

[957] HEATONS (LEEDS) LTD, rainwear and costume mfrs, Leeds

Balance sheets 1897-1901 and misc partnership and corporate records 1895-1957, desk diary 1903, corresp rel to accounts, sales, suppliers, etc 1901-12, 1931-3, ledgers (9) 1895-1912, 1929, bank books (5) 1899-1968, travellers' expenses sheets 1919-24, materials order book 1897-9, cloth sales order book 1954-72, stock records 1897-1900, 1922-3, costing records 1901-2, nd, output figures 1922-3, progress report statistics 1951-6, trade mark file 1960-75, staff engagements 1901-5, misc agreements, insurance records, inventories, papers rel to factory extension, etc 1896-1975.
West Yorkshire Archive Service, Leeds (Acc 2538). NRA 27290.

[958] WILLIAM HEDDLE, outfitter and linen draper, Southend, Essex

Customers' account books (2) 1881-99, sample books (2) of calicoes and sheetings 1902, wages book 1890-1901, misc papers 1882-1931.
Essex RO, Southend (D/F 39). NRA 21778.

[959] HEELAS LTD, tailors, outfitters and drapers, Wokingham, Berks

Memorandum and articles of association 1897, 1946, minute books (2) 1912-36, directors' reports and statements of account 1900-48, annual lists and summaries 1901-5, misc papers, corresp with solicitors, etc 1898-1923, balance sheets and profit and loss accounts 1910-46, private ledgers (4) 1854-66, 1897-1924, cash books (4) 1854-1912, journal 1897-1934, stock, sales and purchase sheets and summaries of trading accounts 1904-46, corresp and papers rel to properties 19th-20th cent, catalogues c1870-1949.
John Lewis Partnership Archives. Access restricted. Enquiries to the Company Archivist. NRA 31120.

Ledgers (10) 1798-1867, 1890-1919.
Berkshire RO (D/EHS/B1-10).

[960] J HEPWORTH & SON LTD, clothing mfrs and retailers, Leeds

Directors' minutes 1911-48, balance sheets, accounts and share records 1891-1937, journals 1895-1956, ledgers 1922-66, cash books 1931-56, sales and retail shop records 1935-53, stock books 1896-1909, misc papers 1907-56.
West Yorkshire Archive Service, Leeds: see Hudson.

[961] HINE, PARKER & CO LTD, hosiery mfrs, London

Minutes, annual reports and accounts 1897-1950.
William Gibson & Son Ltd. NRA 28631; BAC *Company Archives* no 395.

[962] HOADLEYS LTD, tailors, outfitters, drapers and furnishers, Burgess Hill, Sussex

Memorandum and articles of association 1900, 1950, 1973, minutes (2 vols, 1 bundle) 1900-56, 1965-71, register of members 1900-55, registers (5) of share certificates 1900-60, annual reports, accounts and returns 1923-79, private ledgers (2) 1899-1974, misc staff records 1954-73, misc plans, photographs and leaflets 20th cent.
West Sussex RO (Add MSS 30116-30250). NRA 27370.

[963] JACK HODGSON & CO LTD, shirt makers, Londonderry

Ledger 1908-10, journal 1902-19.
Public Record Office of Northern Ireland (D 3054). *Deputy Keeper's Report 1983*, p25.

[964] HORNE BROTHERS LTD, clothing mfrs, tailors and outfitters, London

Shop ledgers (9) 1885-1923, misc agreements, papers rel to the estate of George Horne, etc (2 bundles, 5 items) 1891-1953, catalogues, photographs and other printed material (44 vols, bundles and items) c1900-50.
In private possession. Enquiries to the Business Archives Council. NRA 22642.

Corporate records (8 vols, etc) 1923-87.
Foster Brothers Clothing plc. Enquiries to the Assistant Company Secretary. NRA 32270.

[965] DAVID HUGHES & SONS, tailors and drapers, Aberdovey, Merioneth

Ledgers (5) 1878-1946, day books (19) 1888-9, 1895, 1901, 1903-8, 1913, account books (3) 1870-1906, bank book 1937-43, bills and invoices (1 file) 1927.
National Library of Wales (A1982/54). NRA 26130.

[966] HUNTER & DONALDSON, shawl mfrs, Alva, Clackmannanshire

Cash books (11) 1877-89, 1903-10, 1913-50, journal 1903-8, day book 1929-34, sales ledgers and day books (7) 1881-1936, purchase ledgers and journals (6) 1903-55, order books (19) 1927-56, misc orders and corresp 1927-59, wages books (11) 1890-1946.
Central Regional Archives Department (PD14). NRA 24591.

[967] J HUTHART & CO LTD, tailors, hosiers and linen drapers, Carlisle, Cumberland

Nominal ledgers (2) 1894-1906, 1923-52, town and country ledgers 1901-42, cash books (8) 1885-1949, petty cash books (8) 1924-56, invoice ledgers (4) 1924-52; Jackson & Sons, Brampton day books, cash books, invoice books, etc (30 vols) 1925-61; Huthart

or Jackson account books, day books, invoice books, etc (23 vols) 1902-59.
Cumbria RO, Carlisle (DB/18). NRA 17337; *Report of the County Archivist Sept 1978, p5.*

[968] **INNES, HENDERSON & CO LTD** (afterwards **BRAEMAR KNITWEAR LTD**), hosiery and knitwear mfrs, Hawick, Roxburghshire

Minutes (4 vols) 1920-46, journal 1920-35, price lists, brochure and sketches nd, plans and photographs 1891-1970s; James Henderson & Co monthly ledgers (2) 1885, 1892.
Hawick Museum. NRA 17662.

Papers rel to amalgamation of AP Innes & Co and James Henderson & Co 1920, balance sheets from 1896 and misc corporate records from 1930, private ledgers (3) 1931-70, cash books (2) 1948-70, staff benevolent fund records (6 vols) 1922-73.
Pringle of Scotland Ltd. Enquiries to NRA (Scotland). NRA 32092.

[969] **JAEGER CO LTD**, clothing mfrs and retailers, London

Records from 1883 incl board, committee and general meeting minutes, corresp, share records, annual reports and accounts, cash book, catalogues and other printed material.
Jaeger Holdings Ltd. NRA 28631; BAC *Company Archives* no 446.

[970] **JAMES JEFFREY**, cloth merchant and haberdasher, Edinburgh

Ledger 1816-26, day book 1819-26.
Scottish Record Office (CS 96/1932-3). *Court of Session Productions*, List & Index Society, special series vol 23, 1987, p277.

[971] **FRANCIS & WILLIAM LAING**, hatters, hosiers and cloth merchants, Newburgh, Fife

Day books (2) 1818-23, stock and debts book 1823.
Scottish Record Office (CS 96/1837-8, 3005). *Court of Session Productions*, List & Index Society, special series vol 23, 1987, p296.

[972] **R & FE LAMB (NOTTINGHAM) LTD**, shirt makers and outfitters, Nottingham

Day and cash books (11) 1920-52, measure books (10) 1907-45, order, sales and invoice records (9 vols) 1929-55, deeds (15) of premises 1632-1819, advertisements (4 items) *c*1832.
Nottingham University Library (Lb). NRA 9939.

[973] **CHARLES LEWIN**, hosiery mfrs, Wigston, Leics

Making-up or sales books (4) 1866-1937, yarn stock book 1871-82, work record books (3) 1872-85, wages books (5) *c*1865-96.
Leicestershire RO (3 D 63). NRA 21764.

[974] **JB LEWIS & SONS LTD** (MERIDIAN LTD), hosiery mfrs, Manchester and Glasgow

Board and general meeting minutes, company register (3 vols) 1893-19 (3) 1893-1966, nominal ledger 19 account books (2) 1939-47, pension fund records 1939-70.
Courtaulds plc, Coventry (MER). Enquiries to the Head of Archives. NRA 29343.

Articles of partnership 1878, memorandum and articles of association 1893, 1951, account notebooks (2) 1878-91, misc letters, balance sheets, etc 1864-1929.
Nottinghamshire AO (DD 1103). NRA 6885.

Wages books, etc 1913-77.
Nottinghamshire AO (Acc 3660). *Accessions to repositories 1988, p32.*

[975] **LIBERTY & CO LTD**, designers, mfrs and importers of dress fabrics, silks, shawls, furnishing fabrics, carpets, etc, London

Papers rel to Liberty printworks at Merton Abbey incl printers' price list and rules *c*1855, work diary 1910 and photographs *c*1900-60, jewellery department records (6 vols) 1904-67, antique and reproduction furniture department records (*c*210 vols, files, etc) 1926-81, nd, papers and photographs rel to branches *c*1890-*c*1977, catalogues 1883-1980, corresp, reports, advertisements, fabric samples, etc rel to sales and publicity 1877-1982, misc staff records 1889-1971, visitors' books (2) 1926-54, 1971-5, schedule of deeds 1880-94, Liberty family corresp and papers *c*1831-1975, articles and other papers rel to firm's history 1876-1976.
Westminster City Libraries Archives Section (Accs 788, 1166, 1286). NRA 26036.

[976] **W EADEN LILLEY & CO**, haberdashers, outfitters, drapers and furnishers, Cambridge

Stock inventories 1782-1839, agreements, plans, etc 1818-1919, history of firm *c*1950.
The Company. Photocopies are in Cambridgeshire RO, Cambridge (R82/62: TR991). NRA 25927.

[977] **LIMERICK CLOTHING FACTORY CO LTD**, clothing mfrs and wholesalers, Limerick and London

General meeting minute books (2) 1885-1984, directors' minute books (2) 1958-84, registers (5) of members and shareholders 1941-69.
Aquascutum Group plc. Not available for research.

[978] **LINCOLN, BENNETT & CO LTD**, hatters, Stockport, Cheshire and London

Articles of partnership, memorandum and articles of association, etc 1863-1954, agenda and draft minutes 1897-1907, directors' attendance book 1949-54, share ledgers (4) 1897-1910, *c*1914-27, *c*1939-42, 1947-53, balance sheets, deeds and papers 1863-1959, cash book 1889-92, private ledger 1946-51.
Stockport Central Library (Christy Collection). NRA 22838.

[ ] **DAVID LITTLE & CO LTD**, clothing mfrs and woollen merchants, Leeds

Copies of copartnership deed, etc (1 bundle) 1895, balance sheets, profit and loss accounts, trading accounts, etc (8 vols) 1870-1937, bank books (2) 1874-81, 1905-8, reference book 1893-1931, stocktaking book 1921-44, pattern book 1891, particulars of purchase of warehouse (1 vol) 1900-2, machinery and plant valuations and inventories 1900-37, income tax records 1915-42, David Little's account book 1868-81, executorship accounts (4 vols) 1878-1936, price lists and misc papers (52 bundles and items) 1897-1968.
West Yorkshire Archive Service, Leeds (Accs 1416, 2316, 2874). NRA 12951.

[980] **JAMES LOCK & CO LTD**, hatters, London

Ledgers (17) 1796-1914, tradesmen's ledgers (3) 1796, 1819-21, ledger indexes (4) 1809, 1848, nd, day books (45) 1786-1942, waste books (17) 1798-1819, cash books (13) 1809-68, bank books and related records 1860-1922, order books (105) 1805-1950.
Greater London RO (B/LK). NRA 10811.

[981] **JR LOGAN & SON**, tailors and hatters, Easington Lane, co Durham

Customers' ledgers and other accounts (3 vols) 1875-95, 1904-20.
Tyne and Wear Archives Department (Acc 1063). NRA 22512.

[982] **F LONGDON & CO LTD**, elastic fabric and surgical hosiery mfrs, Derby

Records 19th-20th cent.
Nottingham University Library (Acc 908).

[983] **ROBERT H LOWE & CO LTD**, hosiery mfrs, Congleton, Cheshire

Memorandum of agreement 1888, debenture deed and issue 1925, trading accounts, balance sheets and misc papers (1 file) 1904-34, cash book 1870-1905, misc accounts 1912-14, stock sheets (1 bundle) 1911, trade mark certificates, corresp and papers 1920s-1950s, plans, building accounts, etc 1907-1970s, family and legal corresp and papers 1862-1919.
The Company. Enquiries to the Chairman. NRA 32461.

[984] **LYLE & SCOTT LTD**, knitwear mfrs, Hawick, Roxburghshire

Directors' minutes and trading accounts.
The Company: see C Gulvin, *The Scottish hosiery and knitwear industry 1680-1980*, 1984.

Yarn store work book 1903, photographs 1904-12, nd.
Hawick Museum. NRA 17662.

[985] **EDWARD MACBEAN & CO LTD**, waterproof clothing mfrs, Kirkintilloch, Dunbarton

Minute book 1903-23, share register 1903-47.
The Company. Enquiries to NRA (Scotland) (NRA(S) 2158). NRA 23659.

[986] **J & D McGEORGE LTD**, glove, hosiery and knitwear mfrs, Dumfries

Private ledgers (2) 1903-68 and ledger cards 1968-72, private journal 1928-68, cash books (3) 1947-69, sales and purchase books (6) 1938-69, misc financial and premises records (7 vols) 1948-69.
The Company. Enquiries to NRA (Scotland) (NRA(S) 2164). NRA 23732.

[987] **McINTYRE, HOGG, MARSH & CO LTD**, shirt makers, London

Board and general meeting minutes (9 vols) 1888-c1970.
Manchester Central Library (M127).

Londonderry factory order books (2) 1877-9, 1892-1946, price lists and catalogues 1884-1918, apprenticeship contract book 1862-78, wages and salaries book 1889-1900, wages sheets 1933-54, photographs 1919.
In private possession. Photocopies are in the Public Record Office of Northern Ireland (T 3231). NRA 31800.

[988] **McKERRELL & MORGAN**, shawl mfrs, Paisley, Renfrewshire

Sales corresp of John Morgan 1842-4.
Paisley Museum & Art Gallery (74). NRA 14820.

Pattern book c1840.
Paisley Museum & Art Gallery (782/1977).

[989] **MARSHALL & SON LTD**, tailors, outfitters and drapers, Bodmin, Cornwall

Day books (12) 1889-1917, ledgers (4) 1889-1920, country ledgers (2) 1913-25, tailoring account books (3) 1895-6, 1903, 1911-16, measurements book 1909-11.
Cornwall RO (X 81(3)).

[990] **THOMAS MARSHALL (MARLBECK) & CO LTD**, clothing mfrs, Leeds

Memorandum and articles of association 1922, directors' reports 1904-5, purchase and order books 1906-36, circulars and committee reports, etc 1906-61.
West Yorkshire Archive Service, Leeds (Acc 1231): see Hudson.

[991] Number not used.

[992] **MELTON & CO LTD**, hatters, London

Memorandum and articles of association 1908-54, minutes 1898, 1918, 1920-66, register of members, etc 1898-1928, balance sheets and accounts 1898-1951, trade marks 1890-1948.
Stockport Central Library (Christy Collection). NRA 22838.

[993] **ANDREW MICKLE**, tailor, Edinburgh

Account books (3) 1799-1807 and related papers 1804-7, day book 1804-7, cash book 1807, work book 1806-7.
Scottish Record Office (CS 96/1699-1705). *Court of Session Productions*, List & Index Society, special series vol 23, 1987, p140.

[994] **MILLER & CO**, tailors, dressmakers, hosiers and drapers, Sutton-in-Ashfield, Notts

Day books (6) 1853-5, 1863-72, 1889-92, misc papers 1850s, 1886-8.
Nottinghamshire AO (DD 726). NRA 30737.

[995] **MG MOONEY**, clothier and outfitter, Belfast

Ledgers (2) 1892-5, bank book 1892-6, paid cheques (2 bundles) 1892-3, stock book 1896, misc printed papers c1894-7.
Public Record Office of Northern Ireland (D 2585/16). NRA 31461.

[996] **WILLIAM MORLING LTD**, hosiers, tailors and outfitters, Maidstone and Canterbury, Kent

Copartnership agreement 1873, memorandum of association and certificates of incorporation 1908-9, 1947, directors' minutes (2 vols) 1909-81, share ledger, registers and certificates (4 vols) 1909, 1934-7, annual reports, accounts and balance sheets 1873-1979, stock books (2) late 19th cent, wages books (2) 1955-78, photographs, press cuttings and other misc papers c1890-1978.
In private possession. Enquiries to Kent AO, Maidstone. NRA 29611.

[997] **MORRIS & SON, CAMBRIAN ESTABLISHMENTS**, tailors, dressmakers and drapers, Barmouth, Merioneth

Letter book 1889-1928, day books (15) 1860-1916, 1920-39, draft day books (16) 1891-1929, ledgers (7) 1889-1920, journals (3) 1855-1904, petty cash books (3) 1874-1903, cashiers' check books (6) 1874-94, 1901-11, customers' account book 1847-89, supplies account books (4) 1899-1903, 1919-34, dressmaking bill books (2) 1905-10, dressmaking order book 1896-7, visitors' order books (2) 1878-1900, tailoring log book 1890-1901, misc papers (1 box) 19th-20th cent.
National Library of Wales.

Ledgers (5) 1901-45, tailoring day book 1896-1907, post order book 1890-1928, misc accounting records (4 vols) 1915-36, 1942-9, measurements book 1903-8, stocktaking book 1894-8, wages books (2) 1901-27.
Gwynedd Archives and Museums Service, Dolgellau (M/824). NRA 16425.

[998] **MOSS BROS & CO LTD**, tailors, clothiers and outfitters, London

Board minute books (4) 1914-82, general meeting minute book 1943-83, directors' attendance books (3) 1947-82 and papers 1980-4, misc corporate and share records (c12 files and items) 1914-79, annual accounts 1899-1911, 1918-47, comparison of accounts c1910-20, misc accounting records (4 vols) 1916-48, analysis of sales 1899-1900, price lists and misc production and sales records 1943-68, salary and pension fund records (11 vols and files) 1947-76, misc legal and insurance records 1895-1976, publications, press cuttings and photographs c1931-83.
Moss Bros plc. Enquiries to the Business Archives Council. NRA 28363.

[999] **S MOULTON & CO**, india rubber and protective clothing mfrs, Bradford-on-Avon, Wilts

Business and misc letters to Stephen Moulton from customers, suppliers, agents, etc (over 15,000 items) 1848-60.
In private possession. NRA 1245.

[1000] **F & H NEWCOMB**, military and naval tailors and outfitters, Chatham, Kent

Sales ledgers (5) 1835-9, 1919-45, bought ledger 1936-45, sales day books (3) 1938-82.
Kent AO, Maidstone (U 2822). NRA 29066.

Sales ledger 1859-63, private ledger 1863-79, tax and investment record book 1919-21, insurance policy journal nd, misc bills, agreements, leases, press cuttings, etc (5 vols, c70 items) 1845-1985.
Newcombs (Gentlemen's Outfitters). Enquiries to Kent AO. NRA 29066.

[1001] **NOTTINGHAM MANUFACTURING CO LTD**, hosiery and lace mfrs, Nottingham

List of members attending meetings (1 vol) 1873-1957, misc corporate records 1899-1956, letters patent and related notes 1853, 1861, nd, scrapbooks (2) 1864-1956.
Ruddington Framework Knitters' Museum (88/8-15).

Minutes (2 vols) from 1976, articles, accounts and seals.
Coats Viyella plc. Enquiries to the Company Secretary. NRA 32377.

[1002] **E & T OWENS**, tailors, Abergele, Denbighs

Accounts (4 vols) 1876-1928, diaries 1882-1912.
Clwyd RO, Hawarden (270, 303). *Guide to the Flintshire Record Office*, 1974, p121.

[1003] **PALMER BROS LTD**, hosiery mfrs, Leicester

Patent specifications and related legal papers (19 items) 1886-1919, prices for various work 1891, valuation of machinery and plant 1941, lists of machinery 1945, misc papers 1905-49.
Leicestershire RO (DE 2523). NRA 26410.

[1004] **PAQUIN LTD**, court dressmakers, London

Designs for costumes and accessories and reference collection of fashion plates (110 vols) c1865-1939.
Victoria & Albert Museum, Department of Designs, Prints & Drawings (E.18-23047-1957, E.23052-23053-1957).

Designs for dresses (19 vols) c1917-40, press cuttings (44 vols) rel to collections 1909-56.
Costume & Fashion Research Centre, Bath.

Photographs of dresses and costumes.
Victoria & Albert Museum, Archive of Art & Design (AAD 1-1982).

[1005] **EDWARD PARRY & SON**, tailors, Tynygongl, Anglesey

Ledgers and accounts 1870-1950.
Gwynedd Archives and Museums Service, Llangefni: see *Accessions to repositories 1985*, p47.

[1006] **DG PATTERSON**, tailors and drapers, Chesham, Bucks

Ledgers (47) 1876-1946, invoice books 1889-1900, commercial diary 1898, rent book 1885-96.
Buckinghamshire RO (D 141). *Annual report 1982*, p7.

[1007] **JOHN PECK & CO LTD**, protective clothing mfrs, Liverpool

Private ledger 1900-5, trade catalogues and photographs (1 box, 1 file) 1894-1973.
Liverpool RO.

[1008] **JOHN PHILLIPS**, hatter, Bishop's Stortford, Herts

Sales cash book 1758-75.
Hertfordshire RO (71246). NRA 7214.

[1009] **PHILLIPS & PIPER LTD**, clothing mfrs, Ipswich, Suffolk

Partnership agreement 1859, board, general meeting and committee minutes 1900-77, register of members and share ledger 1900-73, annual returns of members 1900-54, reports, balance sheets and accounts 1889-1981, ledgers 1910-61, misc cash books and other accounting records 1863-1966, patent and trade mark records 20th cent, staff and wages records 1901-9, 1946-77, plant and machinery registers 1930-c1959, inventory 1941, trade literature and other printed papers 1931-66.
Suffolk RO, Ipswich (HC 414). NRA 30269.

[1010] **PIKE & RAIKER**, tailors and army clothiers, London

Books and papers (1 box) 1850-7 incl printed catalogue of stock.
Public Record Office, Chancery Lane (J 90/888).

[1011] **FW PLAISTOWE & SON**, tailors, Folkestone, Kent

Ledgers 1884-1917, day book 1896-1900, bills 1898-1922, wages book 1897-1918.
Kent AO, Folkestone: see *Guide to the Kent County Archives Office, Second Supplement 1969-80*, p203.

[1012] **HENRY POOLE & CO LTD**, tailors, London

Reports and accounts (1 vol) 19th cent, private ledgers (5) 1871-1940, petty ledgers (5) 1851-1941, indexes to ledgers (107) nd, journals (5) 1871-1937, misc accounting records (6 vols) c1870-c1915, papers rel to Russian accounts c1918, purchase ledgers (2) c1870, c1920, sales and purchase analysis books (2) 1871-1941, customers' ledgers (128) 1846-c1960, measurements books (25) c1840-1917, cutting room records, pattern books and drawings (c19 vols) 1854-c1940, private memoranda book 1876-98, address books nd, deeds, family papers, etc 19th-20th cent.
The Company. Enquiries to the Business Archives Council. NRA 22524.

[1013] **THOMAS PRATT & SONS LTD**, clerical tailors, London

Nominal ledgers (2) 1900-61, balance sheet 1890, legal and other corresp (10 bundles) 1879, 1895-1901, 1911-46, measurements book 1905-31, deeds (3) 1871, 1883.
Westminster City Libraries Archives Section (WBA 1082). NRA 30961.

[1014] **W PRESTON & SON LTD**, elastic web mfrs, Leicester

General corresp and papers mainly rel to trade mark registration 1901-63, notebooks (4) 1877-1919 incl inventory of machinery and fixtures 1919, insurance papers 1939-42, certificates, etc 1884-1906.
Leicestershire RO (3 D 72). NRA 18790.

[1015] **THOMAS PRICE**, wholesale hosier and yarn and flannel mfr, Llanrhystud, Cards

Ledger 1873-93, sales account book 1894-1903, pocket diaries containing personal and business entries (5 vols) 1879, 1881, 1886, 1892, 1894.
National Library of Wales (MSS 19359-61).

[1016] **W RAVEN & CO LTD**, hosiery and knitwear mfrs, Leicester

Ledger 1926-32, cash books (4) 1933-50, sales day book 1923-56, stock books (9) 1926, 1929, 1931, corresp (1 box) rel to patents, service agreements, insurance, etc 1902-c1950, staff welfare records (1 box) 1885-c1965.
Leicestershire RO (23 D 68). NRA 31952.

[1017] **BURTON RAVENSCROFT**, wig maker, London

Customers' registers (14 vols) 1827-1964, register of wigs supplied 1902-34, customers' ledger 1898-1920, journal 1902-28.
Guildhall Library, London (MSS 21716-25). NRA 31283.

[1018] **RH REYNOLDS BROS LTD**, underclothing mfrs, Manchester

Directors' minutes (2 vols) 1934-62, share books (2) 1903-52, balance sheets and accounts 1930s-1950s, private ledgers (3) 1903-46, nominal ledgers (7) 1914-46, travellers' ledgers (2) 1932-42.
Coats Viyella plc. Enquiries to the Company Secretary. NRA 32376.

[1019] **RHODES BROS SONS LTD**, shawl mfrs, Hucknall, Notts

Sales ledgers (6) 1869-1938, quotations ledger 1899-1921, wages ledgers (3) 1886-1915, misc financial papers and corresp 1849-1916, photographs 1948.
Nottinghamshire AO (DD 607). NRA 30736.

[1020] **J & J ROBERTSON**, shawl mfrs, Paisley, Renfrewshire

Pattern books 19th cent.
Paisley Museum & Art Gallery: see M Lochrie, 'The Paisley shawl industry', *Scottish textile history*, ed J Butt and K Ponting, 1987, p111.

Pattern book 1840-52.
Courtaulds plc, London. Access restricted. Enquiries to
the Design Library, Courtaulds Textiles. NRA 30957.

[1021] **ROGERS & CO (MILITARY
OUTFITTERS) LTD**, London

Ledgers and pattern books (20) with details of
uniforms supplied to named regimental officers
1825-1930.
National Army Museum (5909/247-56, 8303/15).

[1022] **ROMANES & PATERSON**, tweed and
knitwear merchants, Edinburgh

Inventory of stock 1808, wages book 1889-1919.
The Company. Enquiries to NRA (Scotland) (NRA(S)
250). NRA 10796.

[1023] **EP ROSE & SON LTD**, outfitters,
dressmakers and carpet and woollen merchants,
Bedford

Memorandum and articles of association and related
papers 1913-64, share register 1913-52 and transfers
1922-47, balance sheets and accounts 1913, 1919-73,
dissertation of stock book 1878-1905, trading returns
1955-7, departmental abstracts 1923-43 and accounts
1971-3, fabric samples 1938, wages books (3) 1930-6,
1943-72, staff agreements and misc related records
(1 vol, 28 items) 1910-14, 1933-c1966, insurance
policies (17) 1946-71, corresp, leases and other papers
rel to premises (30 files and items) 1904, 1921-73,
press cuttings, photographs, etc 1924-1970s.
Bedfordshire RO (X 679). NRA 27091.

[1024] **ROWANS LTD**, tailors and clothiers,
Birmingham and Glasgow

General ledgers and other accounting records (12 vols)
1912-64, salaries books (7) 1915-56, advertising
material for Rowans and other firms (1 box, 53 vols)
1909-63.
Strathclyde Regional Archives (TD 275). NRA 19952.

[1025] **BENJAMIN RUSSELL & SONS LTD**,
hosiery and knitwear mfrs, Leicester

Directors' meeting minutes (6 vols) 1928-75 and papers
1941-80, register of directors' holdings 1948-66, share
records (740 items) 1936-78, balance sheets, profit and
loss accounts, directors' reports and related papers
1851-1980, letter book 1865-81, private ledgers (9)
1886-1958, class ledgers (8) 1903-51, cash books and
other accounting records (16 vols) 1934-85, record of
bills of exchange 1825-1937, bought ledger 1890-3,
sold ledger 1870-6, shipping books (2) 1931-49, corresp
mainly rel to agency agreements and the Board of
Trade 1906-74, notes on clients c1880-1922, status
enquiry book 1931-49, yarn contracts c1924-50,
millinery making-up books (2) 1932-44, stock sheets
1935, 1939, price lists and Christmas present books
c1850, 1894-1908, wages books (6) 1914-63, pay
records 1964-78, register of young employees 1866-7,
age certificate books 1866-78, general registers (14)
1883-4, 1902-32, certificates of fitness 1908-21,

personnel records incl Russell Benevolent Fund
1913-77, memoranda book 1919-45, machinery books
(8) 1865-1938, agreements, valuations, etc rel to
machinery and property 1911-71.
Leicestershire RO (27 D 56, DE 3189). NRA 6943.

[1026] **SCOTTS LTD**, hatters, London

Memorandum and articles of association 1890-1950,
minutes 1890-1944, registers of members, shares, etc
1898-1956, order book 1934-6, misc corresp, etc
1935-63.
Stockport Central Library (Christy Collection). NRA
22838.

[1027] **JOHN SHANNON & SON LTD**, clothing
mfrs, Walsall, Staffs

Corporate and accounting records 1924-78, pattern
numbers record books (2) 1895, 1900, staff and salary
records 1946-76, insurance policies and related papers
1967-78, deeds, legal opinions, corresp, etc (c50 items)
rel to Tamworth property 1831-1931.
Walsall Local History Centre (Acc 599). NRA 32064.

Tamworth factory summary account book 1906-11,
catalogues (c100) c1880-c1960 and fashion plates (1
box file) c1900-20, woven and printed labels (1 vol)
1920s-1960s.
WA Goold (Holdings) Ltd. Enquiries to the Chairman
and Managing Director. NRA 32064.

[1028] **SHEPHERD & MANNING LTD**, milliners,
dressmakers and ladies' outfitters, Northampton

Records 1867-1951 (107 vols, 67 bundles) incl credit
cash books (9) 1914-45, fur stocks, sales and returns
(1 vol) 1867-84, daily sales record (2 vols) 1899-1933,
stock book 1885-1928, details of funerals (2 vols)
1903-28, and salaries and insurance books (6) 1912-50.
Northamptonshire RO (Shepherd & Manning). NRA
31897.

[1029] **JOHN SMEDLEY LTD**, hosiery mfrs,
Matlock, Derbys

Records 18th-20th cent.
The Company.

[1030] **SMITH & GILLETT**, outfitters, London

Ledgers (2) 1811-15, cash book 1811-15, petty cash
book 1811-14, journal 1811-15, day book 1811-15,
waste book 1812-15, bill book 1811-15, bank book
1813-14, invoice books (7) 1811-15, invoices and
receipts 1814-15, monthly sales totals 1813-14, pattern
book 18th cent.
Public Record Office, Chancery Lane (C 217/68, 70, 77,
78, 80, 84, 87).

[1031] **SOUTH MOLTON SHIRT & COLLAR
MANUFACTURING CO LTD**, South Molton,
Devon

Certificate of incorporation 1895, memorandum of
association 1898 and related papers, minute books (2)
1890-1909, share records (3 vols, c7 bundles)
1891-1926, balance sheets 1895-1943, letter book

1890-1900, private ledgers (2) 1897-1914, cash book 1945-64, bank book 1909-14, misc corresp, agreements, etc (*c*24 bundles and items) 1895-1965, deeds of premises (58) 1754-1868.
Devon RO (TD 190B). NRA 23519.

[1032] **WALTER SPENCER**, hatter, Bury, Lancs

Sales ledger 1878-92, notes of orders (2 vols) 1878, 1882, proofing and dyeing book 1881-4.
Greater Manchester Museum of Science & Industry (TX 2/7). NRA 29510.

[1033] **SPIRELLA CO OF GREAT BRITAIN LTD**, corsetry mfrs, Letchworth, Herts

Minute books (10) 1910-76 and index, annual returns, reports and accounts 1975-9, seal book 1953-70, directors' commissions ledger nd, document register nd, pension fund minutes, etc (2 vols, etc) *c*1950-78, statistics nd, wages books (3) 1961-81, Samaritan Fund cash book nd.
Coats Viyella plc. Enquiries to the Company Secretary. NRA 32377.

Nominal ledgers, cash book and plant registers 1934-1970s.
Coats Viyella plc (Hollins Collection). Enquiries to the Company Secretary. NRA 32374.

Memorandum and articles of association 1909, annual reports and balance sheets 1911-56, corresp nd, photographs from 1910, press cuttings nd, pamphlets, catalogues, etc from 1908.
First Garden City Heritage Museum, Letchworth (FGCHM 100). NRA 30793.

[1034] **STAMMERS LTD**, clothing mfrs, Walsall, Staffs

Register of returns of allotments 1906-7, annual summaries book 1927-35, private ledgers (2) 1907-38, nominal ledger 1919-38.
Foster Brothers Clothing plc. Enquiries to the Assistant Company Secretary. NRA 32270.

[1035] **HENRY STOCKER & CO**, tailors, Exeter, Devon

Ledgers (4) 1825-55, 1877-83, 1901-44, cash book 1932-42, order book 1873-4, pattern books (3) *c*1873-1933, measurements books (2) 1915-29, family account book 1827.
Devon RO (Exeter City Library 62/2). NRA 3506.

[1036] **SUTTON & TORKINGTON LTD**, hatters, Stockport, Cheshire

Summaries of capital, share transfers and other share records 1896-1961, corresp (*c*32 files) 1937-64, balance sheets 1880-1929, private ledgers (13) 1891-1941, nominal ledgers (7) 1901-54, cash books (10) 1870-3, 1933-60, loan ledgers, deposit books, bank pass books, etc 1904-65, bill book 1845-82, misc financial records 1872-9, order books (32) 1871-2, 1950-64, sales ledgers, etc (7 vols and bundles) 1923-61, invoices, bills of lading, etc (*c*40 bundles) 1940-64, receipts

(16 bundles) 1948-57, commission agents' corresp and accounts (8 bundles) 1946-61, stock records (2 vols, 8 packets, etc) 1871-9, 1896-1901, 1920-64, sample books (3) and misc related papers 1903-61, millinery designs (2 packets) 1937-8, wages books (21) 1872-81, 1910-60, apprenticeship papers and other staff records 1885-1964, misc agreements, patents, insurance and property records 1874-1963.
Stockport Central Library. NRA 27964 (vol 3).

[1037] **R & WH SYMINGTON & CO LTD**, corsetry mfrs, Market Harborough, Leics

Certificate of incorporation 1898, memorandum and articles of association 1965, reports of directors and balance sheets 1920-66, patent books 1887-1967, patent specifications 1900-70, corresp rel to trade marks 1946-69 and related papers, pattern books (7) 1892-1915, wages book 1896-1917 and misc staff records 1922-46, misc family and business corresp, photographs, press cuttings, etc *c*1850-1980.
Leicestershire RO (DE 2262). NRA 18785.

Sales ledger 1898-9.
Courtaulds plc, Coventry (SYM). Enquiries to the Head of Archives. NRA 29343.

[1038] **S TEMPEST & CO**, clothing mfrs, Bradford, Yorks

Production and employment records 1906-36.
Brotherton Library, Leeds University: see Hudson.

[1039] **THORPE & CO LTD**, tailors and cloth mfrs, Carlisle, Cumberland

Letter book 1894-6, financial, sales and purchase records (*c*100 vols, etc) 1922-64, sample books 1938-9, salesman's expenses book 1915-30, time book 1924-36, Thorpe family papers *c*1890-*c*1940.
Cumbria RO, Carlisle (DB/60). NRA 30976; *Report of the County Archivist* Sept 1976, p3.

[1040] **THRESHER & GLENNY LTD**, hosiers, shirt makers and outfitters, London

Business corresp (9 bundles and items) 1785-6, 1800-1, 1831-1946, bills, estimates, valuations and extracts from salary books (17 bundles and items) 1772-1943, price lists, outfit lists, etc (8 bundles and items) 18th-20th cent, personal and estate papers of Richard Thresher (*c*18 bundles) 1776-1806.
Westminster City Libraries Archives Section (WBA 301). NRA 10705.

[1041] **TISSIMANS & SONS**, tailors, Bishop's Stortford, Herts

Day books or journals (7) 1776-*c*1793, 1836-54, 1877-98, customers' ledgers (10) 1787-1912, cash book 1880-90, order books (14) 1819-50, 1867-99, pattern books (2) 1935.
Hertfordshire RO (D/ETs). NRA 103.

[1042] **TUBBS, LEWIS & CO LTD**, elastic mfrs, Kingswood, Wotton-under-Edge, Glos

Letter books, day books, cash books, etc (4 boxes) 1879-94.
Gloucestershire RO (D3129).

[1043] **ARCHIBALD TURNER & CO LTD**, elastic web and hosiery mfrs, Leicester

Letter books (19) 1891-1954, ledgers (22) 1892-1939, cash books (20) 1899-1946, day books (41) 1913-30, purchase books, ledgers, etc (25 vols) 1870-1946, sales ledgers and day books (23) 1902-46, agents' orders, etc (10 vols) 1889-1941, foreign orders (4 vols) 1889-1935 and making-up book *c*1906-8, credit books (2) 1913-49, invoice books 1936-47, shippers' advice notes 1916-20, stocktaking books (51) 1906-37, samples and patterns (20 vols, *c*3,200 items) 1860-1962, patents and specifications 1841-75, make books (6) 1865-75, registers of yarn measurements (8 vols) 1874-1920, work books (30) 1862-1935, daily output record (1 vol) 1909-28, time books (7) 1869-1935, wages books (19) 1911-38.
Leicestershire RO (18 D 58). NRA 26151.

[1044] **WILLIAM TURNER (STOWMARKET) LTD**, dressmakers, drapers, glovers and hosiers, Stowmarket, Suffolk

Ledger 1900, funeral furnishings book 1861-79, stocktaking book 1886-1944, staff engagement books 1873-1908, deeds 1719-1909, photographs *c*1897-1930s.
Suffolk RO, Ipswich (HC 425). *Annual report 1986-7.*

[1045] **HC WAKEFIELD & SON**, clothiers, Tiverton, Devon

Day books (6) 1896-1931, cash books (5) 1888-1900, cash analysis book 1913-17, invoice book 1888-94, discount book 1890-7, diaries and price lists (6 vols) 1889-96.
Devon RO (3514 B). NRA 25134.

[1046] **WALLIS & LINNELL LTD**, clothing mfrs, Kettering, Northants

Memorandum and articles of association 1913, 1954, directors' minutes (2 vols) 1913-47, share ledger and other share records 1913-60, balance sheets and profit and loss accounts 1920-61, private and misc ledgers (7) 1903-54, 1962-73, day books (4) 1898-1971, record of bad debts 1874-1939, weekly turnover 1893-1973 and other stocktaking records 1957-66, misc staff and wages records 1894-1973, misc letters, price lists, photographs, etc 1890-1976.
Northamptonshire RO (ZB 57). NRA 22296.

[1047] **WATSON, MALCOLMSON & CO**, blouse mfrs, Belfast

Accounts, etc (5 vols) 1894-1937.
Public Record Office of Northern Ireland (D 837): see *Ulster textile industry.*

[1048] **WELCH, MARGETSON & CO LTD**, menswear mfrs, London

Agreements, memorandum and articles of association, special resolutions and misc legal papers 1865-1952, minutes 1941-62, annual balances *c*1950-62, price lists and advertising material (2 vols, etc) early 20th cent, memoranda rel to products (1 file) 1950s, deeds and

other premises records 1865-1980, visitors' books (3) 1951-76, sports and social club records *c*1921-77, photographs, press cuttings.
Guildhall Library, London. NRA 32386.

[1046] **WELCH & STALKER**, military and naval tailors, London

Pattern books (2) and misc bills 1795-1809.
Victoria & Albert Museum Library (L.2993-1934, L.1486-1958).

[1050] **WILLIAMS & WHYTE**, hatters, London

Agent's ledgers (4) 1809-15.
Scottish Record Office (CS 96/3978-81). *Court of Session Productions*, List & Index Society, special series vol 23, 1987, p203.

[1051] **ISAAC WILSON**, hosier, Kirkland, Westmorland

Ledger 1811-38, cash account book 1826-40, bank book 1809-43, purchase and sales journal 1822-43, misc personal and family papers 1771-1843.
Cumbria RO, Kendal (WD/MM, box 69). NRA 30980.

[1052] **WILSON & WATSON**, hosiery mfrs, Hawick, Roxburghshire

Day book of William Wilson (1764-1832).
Hawick Museum. NRA 17662.

[1053] **J WIPPELL & CO LTD**, clerical outfitters, robe makers and church furnishers, Exeter, Devon

Articles of association 1902, share records 1902-23, 1940s-1950s, annual accounts and working papers from 1902, corresp and papers rel to income tax (2 boxes) 1901-19, ledger 1834-58, private ledgers (3) from 1902, nominal ledgers (5) 1896-1943, expenses ledger *c*1929-37, cash books (4) 1865-74, 1891-1939, journal 1931-5, bank book 1865-71, order books (11) 1834-9, 1873-94, 1897-1901, 1923-40, 1960s, record of costs and sales (1 vol) 1886-1922, stock book 1891-1929 and stocktaking records 1934-45, nd, corresp and papers mainly rel to government contracts and American trade 20th cent, price lists and catalogues 1821, 1878-20th cent, pattern books 20th cent, memoranda book rel to printing blocks *c*1927-36, wages books and other staff records (7 vols, 1 bundle, *c*50 items) *c*1880-1965, premises records (1 box, 2 vols, *c*80 bundles and items) 19th-20th cent, scrapbooks, press cuttings and photographs from *c*1860.
The Company. Access restricted. Enquiries to G Miller Esq. NRA 31421.

[1054] **WORTH OF PARIS LTD**, court dressmakers, London

Designs for costumes and accessories and reference collection of fashion plates (100 vols) 1921-56.
Victoria & Albert Museum, Department of Designs, Prints & Drawings (E.18-23047-1957, E. 23052-23053-1957). NRA 29140.

Photographs of dresses and costumes.
Victoria & Albert Museum, Archive of Art & Design (AAD1-1982).

Photographs of dresses and costumes (36 vols) 1902-12, *c*1920-50, press cuttings (12 vols) rel to collections 1926-48.
Costume & Fashion Research Centre, Bath.

LEATHER

[1055] **JAMES ALLAN & SON LTD**, shoe mfrs, Edinburgh

Board minutes from 1897, ledger 1864-5, monthly sales and day book 1880-97, ladies' order books (2) 1864-72, statement of business 1870, wages books 1881-1934, offer and conditions rel to acquisition of R Greenoak's business 1853, 1856; Edinburgh Master Boot and Shoemakers' Association minutes (2 vols) 1890-1932.
In private possession. Enquiries to NRA (Scotland) (NRA(S) 251). NRA 10795.

[1056] **ALLINSON & CO**, footwear mfrs, Northampton

Out-letter book 1881-1909, bill books (2) 1899-1909, bank book 1879-81, receipts and payments books (2) 1915-24, travellers' order and account notebooks (4) 1873-1909, customers' address book *c*1890, stock books (2) 1889-1952, shoe costing book 1896, costing sheets incl army boots 1914-18, summary and analysis book 1890-1915, wages book 1902-4, photographs, catalogues, price lists, show cards, brochures and press cuttings 20th cent.
Northamptonshire RO (S357, 1983/78, ML4049). NRA 22287.

[1057] **ALSOP BROTHERS LTD**, leather merchants, Northampton

Directors' minute books (5) 1923-34, 1950-81, private ledgers (11) 1900-57, typescript history of firm 1896-1981.
Northamptonshire RO (AB). NRA 31748.

[1058] **GEORGE ANGUS & CO LTD**, leather and india rubber mfrs, etc, Newcastle upon Tyne, Northumb

Records from *c*1851 incl minutes, attendance book, registers of directors and members, reconciliation and other share books, corresp, private ledgers, journals and cash books, receipts, price lists, catalogues and sales literature, photographs, and plans; F Reddaway & Co Ltd misc corporate records, catalogues and price lists, etc 1896-1956.
The Company. NRA 28631; BAC *Company Archives* no 625.

[1058A] **AVALON LEATHERBOARD CO LTD**, leatherboard mfrs, Street, Somerset

Memorandum and articles of association 1900, 1938, directors' minutes 1901-29, 1946-67, managers' minutes 1931-6, summaries of capital and shares 1904-29, papers rel to family shares (1 file) 1926-38,

reports, memoranda and corresp 1930s-1971, private ledger 1900-39, ledgers 1914-70, cash books and other accounts 1926-75, credit rating book 1905-32, receipt books *c*1930, nd, wages and bonus list 1889-1945, pensions and insurance papers, etc 1937-73, valuations 1900, 1923, 1931-41, corresp and bills for new engine, buildings, etc 1885-92, 1896, 1906, reports to Board of Trade (1 file) 1913-31, patents, trade marks, samples, recipes, price lists, advertising leaflets, etc 19th-20th cent, historical notes, corresp and papers rel to effluent 20th cent.
C & J Clark & Co Ltd. Enquiries to the Public Relations Officer. NRA 29606.

[1059] **JOHN BAIN**, boot maker and leather seller, Edinburgh

Account books (2) 1835-7 waste books (2) 1836.
Scottish Record Office (CS 96/3861-4). *Court of Session Productions*, List & Index Society, special series vol 23, 1987, p497.

[1060] **JAMES BAIRD & SONS LTD**, boot makers, Great Yarmouth and Norwich, Norfolk

Sales ledgers (6) 1909-46, ledger index early 20th cent, order books (2) 1907-21, account statements 1922-6, 1946, customers' fitting book early 20th cent.
Norfolk RO (D98). NRA 27669.

[1061] **CW BARRON & CO LTD**, boot and shoe mfrs, London

Directors' minutes 1908-53, register of members 1908-49.
Leicestershire RO (DE 2357). NRA 25479.

[1062] **BARROW, HEPBURN & GALE LTD**, tanners, curriers, hide and skin merchants, London

General meeting and committee minutes (17 vols) from 1936, monthly balances, analysis books, etc (13 vols) 1930-71, private journals, cash books and other accounts (10 vols) 1956-81; Harvey & Sons Ltd misc corporate and financial records, etc 1899-1977.
Barrow Hepburn Group plc. Not normally available for research. Enquiries to the Company Secretary. NRA 30986.

Papers rel to amalgamation 1920, subsidiary companies' liquidations nd, minutes from 1920, share records from 1922, register of seals from 1928, annual returns, balance sheets, etc 1938-70, corresp 1939-*c*1970, private ledgers 1903-62, private journals 1920-68, patents and trade marks nd, employment records 1915-80, papers rel to properties and tenants, etc from 1930; Alexander Ross & Co Ltd minutes from 1899.
Originals destroyed. A microfilm is held by Barrow Hepburn Group plc. NRA 30986.

[1063] **J & T BEAVEN LTD**, leather dressers, Holt, Wilts

Records (8 boxes, 112 vols) 1613-1970 incl rough ledger *c*1808-20, petty ledger 1886-1917, private ledgers (4) 1871-1932, ledger 1891-1910, cash books (10) 1911-61, investment register 1896, bank book

1874-6, wool sales records (3 vols) 1877-1949, wool purchase books (5) 1845-57, 1891-1964, fellmongering purchase day books (3) 1877-88, 1928-37, bought fleece books (2) 1862-79, woolstapling department bought day book 1869-1918, odd wool account 1881-1940, trial stocktakings 1883-93, stocktaking books (2) 1912-65, wages books (5) 1895-1958, savings bank and sick club records 1863-1912, insurance book 1874-1919, and deeds 1613-1919.
Wiltshire RO (WRO 1272). NRA 32291.

[1064] **BEVINGTONS & SONS LTD**, leather mfrs and merchants, London

Minute books (17) 1859-1922, 1924-31, rough minute books (2) 1869-73, 1885-98, journal 1921-49, purchase register 1923-46, stock and sales record book 1862-1973, copy invoices 1912-16, stock book c1837-50, price lists (1 bundle) 1909-14, attendance books (2) 1860-4, 1875-7, inventory of Neckinger Mills 1910, deeds 1792-1928.
Greater London RO (Acc 1616). NRA 21405.

[1065] **BISHOP BROS (PORTSMOUTH) LTD**, shoe mfrs and retailers, Portsmouth, Hants

Balance sheets 1890-1959, corresp 1872-1911, stocktaking book 1879-82, daily and weekly takings books for retail branches (27 vols) 1882-1958, weekly journals (2) 1948-54, deeds and legal papers 1874-1949, James Bishop executory accounts incl trading accounts (5 vols) 1879-86, ephemera and misc family papers 1872-1962.
Portsmouth City RO (530A). NRA 30320.

[1066] **BOLTON HIDE, SKIN & FAT CO LTD**, hide and skin merchants, Bolton, Lancs

Records 1872-1944 incl directors' and general meeting minutes, agenda, and reports and accounts.
WD Mark & Sons Ltd. NRA 28631; BAC *Company Archives* no 136.

[1067] **BOUGHTON family**, saddlers and harness makers, Woburn, Beds

Ledgers (3) 1870-1944, day books (8) 1870-1902, 1914-42, cash book 1878-1908, bank books (3) 1871-1902, stock, harness and note books (6) c1867-1925, GR Broughton's diary 1861-81, bills, receipts, misc personal and printed papers 1805-1928.
Bedfordshire RO (DDX 171). NRA 8198.

[1068] Number not used.

[1069] **JOHN BRANCH LTD**, shoe mfrs, Northampton

Minute book 1894-5, cash book with balance sheet and account 1893-4, shoe order book c1891, stocktaking balances 1888-9, 1892-4, list of machinery nd.
Northamptonshire RO (ZA9649-51). NRA 4039.

[1070] **BRISTOL & WESTERN COUNTIES BUTCHERS' HIDE, SKIN, FAT & WOOL CO LTD**, hide and wool brokers, Bristol

Register of members, etc 1869-1958, lease 1861.
Bristol RO. NRA 28631; BAC *Company Archives* no 102.

Directors' and general meeting minutes 1927-77.
The Company. NRA 28631; BAC *Company Archives* no 102.

[1071] **BRITISH BELTING & ASBESTOS LTD**, Cleckheaton, Yorks

Secretary's letter book 1908-14, balance sheets (1 vol) 1915-25, ledgers (9) 1885-1925, journals, day books and account books (26 vols) 1914-69, export and foreign ledgers and journals (13 vols) 1892-1956, purchase, sales and freight records (c40 vols) 1919-58, works journals (3) 1913-41, manufactured goods (15 vols) 1929-49, pay roll and other employment records (1 box, 14 vols) 1926-51, nd, maintenance books 1920-42.
West Yorkshire Archive Service, Kirklees (KC 227).

[1072] **GB BRITTON & SONS LTD**, shoe mfrs, Kingswood, Bristol

Memorandum and articles of association 1951, minute book 1952-3, registers of members and share records (5 vols) 1951-2, annual reports and accounts 1951-73, balance sheets 1884-98, statement of account on dissolution of partnership 1899, ledgers and other financial records 1930-63, sickness benefit register 1964-5, advertisements, press cuttings; misc minute and account books for subsidiaries 20th cent.
GB Britton. Enquiries to GAM Wells-Cockburn Esq. NRA 32004.

Private ledgers (5) 1884-6, 1904-34, day book 1944-51, summaries of production, wages and sales (5 vols) 1914-43, sales ledger 1930-45, 1963.
Bristol Polytechnic Library, St Matthias, Oldbury Court Road, Fishponds, Bristol. NRA 32305.

[1073] **BRUNSWICK & CO**, furriers, London

Papers 1782-1830 of Joseph Dickenson Croskey, partner, incl balance sheets (1 file) 1820-2, 1824-9, private ledgers 1813-29, private monthly accounts with Charles Brunswick 1824-31, bank book, insurance policies, bills and receipts (1 file, etc) 1816-30, stock books (2) 1813, business and personal corresp (2 files) 1788-1830, and deeds 1782-1830.
Guildhall Library, London (MSS 11552-62).

[1074] **BUCHANAN & CARRICK**, tanners, Glasgow

Ledgers (2) 1784-6, cash and hide book 1783-6.
Scottish Record Office (CS 96/3965-7). *Court of Session Productions*, List & Index Society, special series vol 23, 1987, p82.

[1075] **JOHN CARTER & SONS LTD**, leather merchants and shoe mercers, London

Agreement rel to sale of business (2 items) 1896-7, memorandum and articles of association 1896, 1919, directors' and shareholders' minutes (1 vol) 1896-1942, directors' minutes (5 vols) 1924-70, balance sheets and

accounts (3 bundles) 1872-1945, annual returns (1 vol) 1960-74, seals register (1 vol) 1950-69, private ledgers (2) 1897-1918, 1935-50, cash account books (2) 1847-53, 1900-10 and other account books (4 vols) 1923-71, sales registers (2 vols) 1862-78, 1897-8, order and commission records (4 vols) 1925-73, wages books (2) 1887-98, wages ledger 1871-90, salaries book 1916-45, pensions book *c*1907-46, corresp and papers rel to premises 1879-1937, Carter family account book 1912-18 and misc corresp and papers (5 bundles) 1897-1918.
Hackney Archives Department (D/B/CAR). NRA 29014.

[1076] **CHARLES CASE & SON LTD**, tanners and leather mfrs, Westbury, Wilts

Records (101 boxes, 177 vols) 1890-1983 incl balance sheets (1 vol) 1890-9, corresp mainly with other firms (82 boxes) 1908-67, bought ledger *c*1910-30, stock books (11) 1913-49, wages books and pay lists (29 vols) 1909-1960s, and general factory registers 1898-1920, 1927-48.
Wiltshire RO (WRO 2146). NRA 32292.

[1077] **CHURCH & CO LTD**, footwear mfrs, Northampton

Deeds of partnership, memorandum and articles of association, etc 1873, 1892, 1926, minutes (10 vols) 1926-77, agenda book 1926-42, balance sheets and profit and loss accounts (1 vol, 1 file, etc) 1899-1925, annual reports and accounts from 1925, share certificate books (8) from 1926, partnership share assessments, etc 1920s, partners' interest book 1898-1905, ledgers (14) 1915-65, private cash book 1908-24, private journal 1926-54, monthly account book 1894-1904, trading agreements, accounts and corresp (1 vol, 7 files, etc) 1898-1960s, customers' book 1912-23, journey books (2) nd, order book 1905, export ledger and sales analysis (10 vols) 1910-29, 1948-63, stock lists and accounts (2 boxes, 1 file, *c*100 packets, etc) 1884-1986, price lists and catalogues 1907-34, nd, rough shop and grindery accounts 1881-97, costing books for leggings, gaiters, etc (4 vols) *c*1900-56, weekly production and wages accounts, etc (6 vols) 1926-62, nd, inventories and valuations (3 vols, etc) 1920, 1942, 1951, insurance record (1 vol) 1925-*c*1946, deeds incl some for Joseph Cheaney & Sons, memoranda books (2) 1893, *c*1909-14 and misc papers *c*1914-1940s, Alfred Church's private accounts (4 vols, etc) 1876-1924.
The Company. Enquiries to the Chairman. NRA 32017.

[1078] **C & J CLARK LTD**, shoe mfrs, Street, Somerset

Partnership deeds and agreements, etc from 1849, minutes 20th cent, profit and loss accounts, etc 19th cent, dividend accounts 1904-33, letter books and corresp from mid 19th cent, ledgers 1823-20th cent, order books from 1834, invoice record books from 1824, trade reports, catalogues, price lists and advertising material 20th cent, stock accounts 1833-20th cent, production records from mid 19th cent, patents and trade marks files, factory output statistics 1920s-1940s, staff records incl salary and

bonus schemes 20th cent, pension fund minutes, registers and ledgers 20th cent, deeds and schedules of deeds 19th-20th cent, power plant files 1920s-1940s, valuations 20th cent, reports on boilers and machinery 1913-52, 125th anniversary celebrations files, Clark family history and local history collections incl WS Clark's notes on the financial crisis of the 1860s and R Clark's memoirs, files rel to the firm's museum and shoemaking history collection; misc corporate deeds and accounting records 19th-20th cent of Bayne & Duckett Ltd, Craddock Bros Ltd, J Halliday & Sons Ltd, Alan MacAfee and Mayfair Shoe Co; National Union of Boot and Shoe Operatives, Street branch records 1908-77.
The Company. Enquiries to the Public Relations Officer. NRA 29606.

Dundalk factory corresp, accounts, etc (*c*40 feet) 1936-82.
Public Record Office of Ireland.

[1079] **HENRY F COCKILL & SONS LTD**, curriers, leather merchants and general mill furnishers, Cleckheaton, Yorks

Order book 1898-1902, wages book 1897-1908, catalogues (*c*3 vols) 20th cent.
West Yorkshire Archive Service, Kirklees (KC 116). NRA 26729.

[1080] **WILLIAM COOK**, shoe mfr, Stafford

Ledger 1815-29, accounts (2 vols: one labelled 'Richard Ash') 1827-9 principally for copper, small debts book 1818-29, bills receivable book 1824-8, invoice book 1822-9, letters, invoices, bills of lading and misc papers (*c*600 items) 1819-30.
Public Record Office, Chancery Lane (J 90/73).

[1081] **J CROGGON & SON LTD**, tanners, Grampound, Cornwall

Corresp of JT Croggon rel to hides, etc (1 bundle) 1804-17, stock book 1862-1901, cost book 1897-1942, tannery building and improvement account book from 1885, deeds and family papers *c*1720-1893.
In private possession. NRA 4200.

[1082] **JAMES DALLAS**, saddler, Golspie and Dornoch, Sutherland

Ledger and index 1812-17, day books (2) 1812-16, cash book 1814-15.
Scottish Record Office (CS 96/1540-4). *Court of Session Productions*, List & Index Society, special series vol 23, 1987, p231.

[1083] **WILLIAM DEARDS**, saddler and harness maker, Welwyn, Herts

Ledgers (3) 1899-1907, 1921-5, 1931-41, day books (4) 1867-8, 1896-9, 1912, 1921-2, order books (2) 1864, nd.
Hertfordshire RO (D/EX 418). NRA 3507.

[1084] **DOLCIS LTD** (formerly **UPSONS LTD**), shoe mfrs, London

Minutes (4 vols) 1921-57, register of directors 1951, registers of members and share records (3 vols) 1921-57, private ledgers (3) 1905-30, press cuttings 1946-7.
Leicestershire RO (DE 2357). NRA 25479.

[1085] **GEORGE DUTTON & SONS (NORTHWICH) LTD**, roller leather dressers, Northwich, Cheshire

Minutes 1929-69, balance sheets and profit and loss accounts (1 vol) 1904-20, annual returns 1927-58, letter book 1873-80, corresp (1 file) c1921-8, ledgers (8) 1851-1970, day books (4) 1934-57, cash books (20) 1851-1968, bill books (2) 1871-c1878, 1886-98, bank books (14) 1856-94, order books (4) 1895-1950s, customers' or suppliers' books (2) late 19th cent, purchase, sales, invoice and consignment books (16) 1919-1950s, address book nd, contract books for lamb pelts (4 vols) 1902-37, pelt accounts and corresp (5 vols, 1 file) 1902-1950s, commission book 1924-53, hat leather commission (1 parcel) 1905-31, stock records (3 vols, 1 file) 1916-1960s, gloving and dye samples (2 vols) 1930s, nd, weekly production records, notebooks, etc (12 vols, etc) 1915-1960s, wages books (4) 1857-97, 1912-41, c1960, salaries book 1920-44, employees' holiday scheme 1928-48, inventory and valuation 1923, deeds and agreements (1 vol) 1882, misc papers incl plans, photographs, samples, price lists, and trade reports c1896-1960s.
Cheshire RO (DDN/2094). NRA 31655.

[1086] **WILLIAM EDWARDS**, saddler, Bridgnorth, Salop

Ledger 1902-7, account book 1902-7, day books (2) c1899-1901, misc family accounts 1899-1901.
Shropshire RO (SRO 2239). NRA 11563 (Accessions June-September 1969).

[1087] **THOMAS EVANS & SON LTD**, parchment and vellum mfrs, Sawston, Cambs

Letter books and registers 1932-49, ledgers 1884-1970, accounts 1881-1965, stock books 1932-46, wages accounts 1880-1900, 1936-54.
Cambridgeshire RO, Cambridge (R82/22). *Annual report 1982*, p14.

[1088] **TS & D EVANS**, tanners, Oswestry, Salop

Balance sheets, profit and loss accounts, stock lists and plant valuations (1 vol) 1882-1910, sales ledgers (2) 1909-36, summaries of cash transactions (1 vol) 1920-35, description of machinery in tannery and cost of new plant (1 vol) 1924-36.
Shropshire RO (SRO 5091).

[1089] **JOHN H FLEMING & CO LTD**, tanners, Warrington, Lancs

Memorandum of association 1895, revised articles of association 1947, directors' reports and accounts, etc 1930-62, register of members 1896-1910, papers rel to stock and shareholders (1 box) c1947-59, ledgers (2)

1899-1905, 1927-35, bank books (2) 1944-54, staff wages and income tax papers (1 box, 2 vols) 1936-60, misc deeds and papers (1 box, 1 bundle) 1742-1949.
Warrington Library. NRA 30860.

[1090] **FORRES BOOT & SHOE MANUFACTURING CO**, Forres, Moray

Register of directors or managers 1901-14, letter books (2) 1908-20, cash books and ledgers (5 vols) 1897-1914, sample book 1902-14; with further ledger entries in the books of Leask, solicitors, Forres, late 19th-20th cent.
Elgin Library (DBA BS, DBA, A). NRA 31771.

[1091] **FREEMAN, HARDY & WILLIS LTD**, shoe mfrs and retailers, Leicester

Directors' minutes (5 vols) 1876-1930.
British Shoe Corporation Ltd. Enquiries to the Company Secretary. NRA 25479.

Directors' minutes (3 vols) 1928-40, register of shares and transfers 1953-7, balance sheets and profit and loss accounts 1912-46, trading accounts, etc 1933-9, shop accounts and expenditure 1939-46, war damage accounts 1940-5, pension scheme members' register 1962-5, agreement rel to competition with S Hilton & Son 1897, deeds and papers rel to property mainly in Leicester 1698-1945.
Leicestershire RO (DE 2357). NRA 25479.

Copies of minutes rel to purchase of shoe shop in Wellingborough 1888-92.
Northamptonshire RO (1977/376). NRA 4039.

[1092] **GARDINER BROS & CO**, curriers and leather and grindery merchants, Gloucester

Letter books, ledgers, accounts and stock books (27 boxes) 1877-1964.
Gloucestershire RO (D3044).

[1093] **TH GEARY LTD**, leather dressers and tanners, Kettering, Northants

Bank books (9) 1910-46, customers' accounts ledger 1910-20, suppliers of chemicals ledger 1910-26, purchase day book 1917-24, sales day book 1910-14, agreements (4 items) 1908-19, photographs c1920, c1957.
The Company. Enquiries to Northamptonshire RO. NRA 22283.

[1094] **D GIBBONS & SON**, shoe mfrs, Northampton

Invoice book 1908-25, ledger (made work) 1919-30, making book 1911-22, repairs and petty cash book 1916-17, receipts and labels for repairs 1920s, photographs 1906-1930s.
Northampton Central Museum. NRA 9196.

[1095] **JAMES GOODMAN**, harness maker, Great Wakering, Essex

Customers' account ledgers (4) 1875-93, day book 1891-2.
Essex RO, Southend (D/DS 71). NRA 21778.

[1096] **JOHN C GOTCH & SONS**, shoe mfrs and bankers, Kettering, Northants

Corresp rel to shoe contracts (c30 items) 1799-1816, stock totals 1778-1806, private stock book 1795-1825 and other stocktaking records 1794-1805, family corresp 1790-1885 incl some references to the shoe business.
Northamptonshire RO (GK). NRA 18845.

[1097] **GREAT GRIMSBY HIDE, SKIN & FAT MARKET CO LTD**, hide and skin merchants, Grimsby, Lancs

Records 1877-1982 incl directors' and general meeting minutes, registers of directors, members and transfers, list of shareholders, and annual reports and accounts.
The Company. NRA 28631; BAC *Company Archives* no 272.

Deeds 1694-1915.
South Humberside Area RO. NRA 28631; BAC *Company Archives* no 272.

[1098] **WILLIAM GREEN & SON (GRENSON) LTD**, shoe mfrs, Rushden, Northants

Letter book 1900-22, history of firm 1966.
Northamptonshire RO (S357). NRA 22288.

[1099] **HANDFORD, GREATREX & CO LTD**, tanners, Walsall, Staffs

Directors' minutes (1 vol) 1940-60 with memorandum and articles of association and reports and accounts, share records (3 vols) 1898-1965.
Barrow Hepburn Group plc. Not normally available for research. Enquiries to the Company Secretary. NRA 30986.

[1100] **HARDING family**, saddlers, harness makers and wheelwrights, Great Claybrooke, Leics

Ledgers (6) 1859-95, 1920-35, day books (11) 1851-1922, order books (4) 1922-49, memoranda books (12) 1887-1905.
Leicestershire RO (12 D 64, 4 D 69). NRA 13885.

[1101] **F HEARN LTD**, leather merchants, Exeter, Devon

Bank book 1887-99, notebook rel to leather processing c1910, wages book 1895-7, account book of rents collected 1899-1909, letters (2) 1898, 1901, catalogue nd.
Devon RO (Acc 63/18). NRA 32168.

[1102] **DAVID HENDERSON**, tanner, Newburgh, Aberdeenshire or Fife

Ledger 1794-5, waste books (2) 1790-4, hide book 1792-6.
Scottish Record Office (CS 96/1998-2001). *Court of Session Productions*, List & Index Society, special series vol 23, 1987, p103.

[1103] **TOM HILL (KNIGHTSBRIDGE) LTD**, makers of leggings and hunting and polo boots, London

Pattern books (11) 1903-8.
Kensington and Chelsea Central Library (66). NRA 10808.

[1104] **RICHARD HODGSON & SONS LTD**, tanners, Beverley, Yorks

Records 1896-1900, 1915-17.
Humberside RO: see *Accessions to repositories 1977*, p29.

Minutes from 1967, annual returns, balance sheets, etc from 1959.
Originals destroyed. A microfilm is with Barrow Hepburn Group plc. Enquiries to the Company Secretary. NRA 30986.

[1105] **HOLT & SON**, boot and shoe mfrs, Bridport, Dorset

Ledgers (2) 1880-1913, day book 1903-13, order book 1890-1913.
Dorset RO (D 1004).

[1106] **J & J HOWE**, saddlers, Alyth, Perthshire

Cash book 1868-74, specifications book 1905-46, notebook of recipes for polishes and remedies 1929-46, catalogue c1890, price lists 1932-7, photographs c1900.
In private possession. Enquiries to NRA (Scotland) (NRA(S) 1699). NRA 19459.

[1107] **HOWLETT & WHITE** (afterwards **NORVIC SHOE CO LTD**), shoe mfrs, Norwich, Norfolk

Memorandum and articles of association 1935, 1949, minutes (2 vols) 1899-1956, registers of members, shares and directors 1899-c1949, stock and share registers (4) 1902-35, private ledgers (5) 1899-1927, ledgers (5) 1952-8, cash books (23) 1899-1969, bank ledgers (6) 1900-47, stores accounts 1971-3, cash paid bought ledger 1962-3, customers' invoice numbers and valuers 1968, pattern and design books c1938-64, salaries and wages books (6) 1955-70, pension fund deed 1936 and associated employment records (17 vols) 1937-70, misc property, executorship and other papers, press cuttings and advertisements 20th cent.
Norfolk RO (BR 114). NRA 27700.

[1108] **GEORGE HUDSON**, saddler and harness maker, Burnham Market, Norfolk

Customers' account ledger 1862-73 incl balance sheet 1863-6, sales account books (7) 1862-75, 1882-5.
Norfolk RO (BR 69). NRA 27687.

[1109] **WL INGLE LTD**, boot and shoe mfrs and tanners, Leeds

Ledger 1868-93, private ledgers (3) 1895-1966 incl balance sheets 1896-1935, misc business corresp and papers 1899-1969.
West Yorkshire Archive Service, Leeds (Acc 2040). NRA 20660.

Ledger 1849-66 incl personal memoranda.
In private possession. A copy is in West Yorkshire
Archive Service, Leeds. NRA 20660.

[1110] **E JEFFRIES & SONS LTD**, saddlery mfrs,
Walsall, Staffs

Wages book 1861-70, notebook *c*1938 (formerly profit
and loss account book 1872-97 of Shutt & Marshall,
lorimers, Walsall).
WA Goold (Holdings) Ltd. Enquiries to the Chairman
and Managing Director. NRA 32064.

Corresp, circulars, accounts, etc (1 bundle) 1912-28,
cash book 1941-4, stamp book 1950-6.
Walsall Local History Centre (Acc 249). NRA 21950.

[1111] **JOHN JORDAN**, tanner, Kelso,
Roxburghshire

Account books (2) 1768-75.
Scottish Record Office (CS 96/3835-6). *Court of Session
Productions*, List & Index Society, special series vol
23, 1987, p58.

[1112] **K SHOEMAKERS LTD** (formerly
SOMERVELL BROS LTD), Kendal, Westmorland

Memorandum and articles of association 1915,
registers of members and share ledgers (8 vols) 1865-7,
dividend account book and warrants 1865-7, special
resolutions 1920-30, directors' appointments file
1966-75, futures committee minutes 1957, travellers'
and foremen's half-yearly conference minutes (2 vols)
1927-51, annual reports and accounts 1958-75, letter
books (6) 1885-1958, private ledger 1842-7, misc
ledgers (2) 1861-1950, day book 1846-8, bought ledger
1842-7, sales ledger 1842-51, overseas sales records
(7 vols) 1847-90, 1920-8, journey book 1844-7,
customers' accounts ledgers (5) 1925-47, bad debts
notebooks (2) 1889-1963, cash book for sales of
grindery and sundries 1899-1925, agents' account
books, diaries and despatch record book (13 vols)
1884-1968, travellers' reports and agents' sales
1954-66, shoe descriptive books (6) 1886-1935, grading
books (8) 1933-41, salaries books (4) 1847-1918, wages
books (8) 1881-1934, plant ledger 1886-1932,
inventories and valuations 1920, 1941, summary of
leases and freeholds 1909-79, insurance schedule 1961,
specification 1967, assignments of trade marks 1886,
1893, royal warrants 1969, expired purchase
agreements 1888-1918, advertising sales and analysis
books (6) 1925-50, advertisements and press cuttings,
Somervell family ledger 1877-92; John Bird Ltd
minutes 1908-56; HE Randall Ltd book of leases and
freeholds of shops 1900-66.
The Company. Enquiries to the Honorary Secretary,
K Archives. NRA 30985.

[1113] **KETTERING BOOT & SHOE CO LTD**,
shoe mfrs, Kettering, Northants

Memorandum and articles of association 1879, trust
deed 1900, resolution of change of name 1913,
directors' and general meeting minutes (2 vols)
1879-1935, statements of accounts 1894-1912.
Leicestershire RO (DE 2357). NRA 25479.

[1114] **WJ KIDD & SONS LTD**, leather merchants
and handicraft suppliers, Belfast

Ledgers (2) 1892-3, account book 1890-2, day book
1909-11, cash book 1900, bank book 1894, wages book
1907-9.
Public Record Office of Northern Ireland (D 2201).
NRA 31799.

[1115] **DAVID & JAMES KIRKLAND**, tanners,
Cumnock, Ayrshire

Waste books (2) 1807-17, account book 1807-26, hide
and skin books (2) 1807-17, tanyard book 1807-17.
Scottish Record Office (CS 96/4750-5). *Court of Session
Productions*, List & Index Society, special series vol
23, 1987, p187.

[1116] **KITCHIN & CO LTD**, tanners, Leeds

Purchase ledger 1867-81, sales ledger 1901-8, order
book 1909-10.
West Yorkshire Archive Service, Leeds (Acc 1640). NRA
31026.

[1117] **KNIGHT & LAWRENCE**, footwear mfrs,
Rushden, Northants

Boot and shoe costing books (3) 1907, 1909, *c*1912,
printed ephemera.
Northamptonshire RO (Knight & Lawrence; S352).
NRA 21290.

[1118] **LANCASHIRE BUTCHERS' HIDE &
SKIN CO LTD**, hide and skin merchants,
Manchester

Records 1894-1969 incl register of members, share
ledger, annual reports and accounts, private ledgers,
day books, and cash books.
Markendale Lancashire Ltd. NRA 28631; BAC
Company Archives no 72.

[1119] **WJ & W LANG LTD**, tanners, Paisley,
Renfrewshire

Letter books (16) 1921-42, ledgers (14) 1837-47,
1872-1935, day books (10) 1837-1916, cash books (20)
1844-52, 1872-1963, order books (8) 1919-58, purchase
books (13) 1894-1961, sales books (6) 1883-1952, hide
costing books (3) 1955-60, weight books (2) 1914-15,
1957-8, time and wages books (5) 1871-1940.
Paisley Museum & Art Gallery. NRA 32084.

[1120] **JJ LAW & CO LTD**, football boot mfrs,
Leicester

Memorandum and articles of association 1925-54,
certificate of incorporation 1926, register of liabilities
and assets 1914-39, balance sheets and profit and loss
accounts 1906-82, cash and payments books (41)
1933-81, bills account book 1908-38, order, purchase,
sales and returns books (21 vols) 1934-82, pattern
cutting book 1905, pattern books (2) 1952-80,
machinery and fixtures valuation book 1910, wages
records (3 vols, etc) 1937-53, 1963-77, misc corresp,
circulars, pamphlets, etc 20th cent.
Leicestershire RO (DE 2420). NRA 26159.

[1121] **JE LAWSON**, saddler, Sheffield, Yorks

Ledgers (2) 1902-13, cash book 1906-23, catalogues
(2) nd.
Sheffield City Archives (MD 6086-8). NRA 23246.

[1122] **FWH LEES & CO**, tanners, Newent, Glos

Business corresp mainly rel to orders for and enquiries
about hides (541 items) 1898-1905, bills and vouchers
(65 items) 1897-1901, advertisements, catalogues,
reports, etc (142 items) 1878-1911.
Gloucestershire RO (D2263). NRA 19428.

[1123] **THOMAS LEGG & SON**, dealers in
sheepskins, Rye, Sussex

Corresp and papers c1820-80.
East Sussex RO (Acc 4276).

[1124] **LEICESTER 'SELF-HELP' BOOT &
SHOE MANUFACTURING SOCIETY** (afterwards
TOY TOWN SHOES LTD), footwear mfrs,
Leicester

Committee minutes (4 vols) 1931-68, reports and
balance sheets 1904-20, 1955-67, draft financial reports
1931-41, papers (1 bundle) rel to copartnership
managers 1956-7, legal case papers 1912, liquidation
papers 1970, account book 1940-59, cash books (4)
1944-66, misc financial papers 1901-69, sales and order
records (9 vols, etc) 1919-70, stock books (5) 1902-70,
clicker's costing sheets 1970, notebooks (9) of shoe
styles c1950-65, register of defective shoes 1963-4,
wages books (10) 1896-1964 and other staff records
(12 vols) 1921-66, plans, inventories and valuations
1930-62, advertising material, press cuttings and
printed ephemera 20th cent.
Leicestershire RO (6 D 70). NRA 30672.

[1125] **THOMAS LINLEY, SONS & CO**, bellows
makers, Sheffield, Yorks

Letter book 1829-30, order and despatch books (2)
1829.
Sheffield City Archives (MD 3526). NRA 23246.

[1126] **LOAKE BROS LTD**, boot and shoe mfrs,
Kettering, Northants

Certificate of incorporation (photocopy) 1895, annual
reports and accounts 1903, ledgers (11) 1894-1910,
transfer ledger 1910-27, cash books (12) 1880-1940,
bank ledger 1894-9, bank day book 1931-5, bought
ledgers (7) 1880-1914, invoice books (21) 1884-1910,
1914-35, sales ledgers (10) 1883-1910, order books
(10) 1915-26, despatch books (15) 1880-1900, 1907-8,
1922-6, 1930-3, discount books (10) 1884-1922, sales
returns 1932-5, carriage account book 1922-35, reports
on creditworthiness of companies and shops 1909-23,
agency agreements 1893-1914, costing book c1910-12,
wages books (6) 1925-9, 1933-5, 1943-4, holiday fund
account books (4) 1919-36, specifications, bills,
receipts and insurance documents rel to firm and
premises c1890-1930.
Northamptonshire RO (Loake 1-116). NRA 24547.

[1127] **JOHN LOBB & CO**, boot makers, London

Cash book 1961-4, order books (41) 1914-67, sales
ledgers and customers' account books (22) 1899-1956,
sales journal 1961-4, index to ladies' lasts 1959, sales
representative's notebook 1970s, catalogues nd,
corresp file rel to takeover of H Peen 1947-75; Joseph
Box measurements books, order books and customers'
accounts (18 vols) c1900-1955.
Westminster City Libraries Archives Section. NRA
10810.

Draft books with outlines of feet from 1912.
The Company. NRA 10810.

[1128] **THOMAS LOVEDAY & SONS**, horse collar
mfrs, Islip, Northants

Ledgers (5) 1853-91, day books (2) 1875-6, 1882-7,
account of manufacture of rush matting by the firm
1925.
Northamptonshire RO (X4600-2). NRA 4039.

[1129] **JOHN McAFEE & SON**, boot makers and
shoe fitters, Belfast

Corresp, accounts, etc (3 vols, c80 items) 1858-1954.
Public Record Office of Northern Ireland (D 3247).

[1130] **RICHARD MARKENDALE & CO LTD**,
hide and skin brokers, tanners, fellmongers and curers,
Manchester

Records 1865-1986 incl memorandum and articles of
association, directors' and committee meeting minutes,
share transfer register, ledgers, journal, day and cash
books, weekly balances, hide weight registers, wages
books, price sheets, and photographs.
Markendale Lancashire Ltd. NRA 28631; BAC
Company Archives no 72.

[1131] **AE MARLOW LTD**, boot and shoe mfrs,
Northampton

Sole stamps memoranda book c1900-c1930, price lists
(1 folder) 1904-5.
Northampton Central Museum. NRA 9196.

[1132] **W & J MARTIN LTD**, tanners, curers,
footwear mfrs and merchants, Bridge of Weir,
Renfrewshire

Articles of association 1946, minute books (2) 1946-52,
balance sheets and accounts 1936-78, corresp (1 file)
1976-80, ledgers, journals, day books and other
accounting records 1932-80, process notebooks (4)
1897-1913, 1922-6, 1939-40 and other production
records (20 vols and files) 1922-67, salaries and wages
books (5) 1965-75, staff wages and bonuses file
1930-51, trade marks, trade journals and membership
records 1929-79.
Glasgow University Archives (UGD/167). NRA 25309.

[1133] **MASON & MARSON LTD**, shoe mfrs,
Stafford

Private ledger 1907-19 with balance sheets 1906-18,
general ledgers (2) 1914-34.
Staffordshire RO (D 4338/A/33). NRA 29538.

[1134] **D MEREDITH & CO LTD**, fellmongers, Dolgellau, Merioneth

Ledger, day book and account book 1878-1900.
Gwynedd Archives and Museums Service, Dolgellau: see *Accessions to repositories 1976*, p47.

[1135] **MERRY & CO**, saddlers, London

Letter books (7) 1931-43, corresp file 1951, ledgers (16) 1883-1950, annual receipt books or combined ledgers (2) 1901-18, account book 1940-51, customers' accounts (2 vols) 1920-30, 1939-42, order books (111) 1863-1943, designs for monograms (1 bundle) 1926-38, wages books (3) 1912-30.
Greater London RO (B/MR). NRA 10895.

[1136] **MERRYLEES, PUGH & CO LTD**, leather belting mfrs and oil merchants, Gloucester

Ledger 1912-13, cash book 1905-14, purchase ledger and journals (4 vols) 1899-1918, sales ledgers and journals (9 vols) 1873-1920, monthly summary of sales invoices (1 vol) 1904-5, price lists (1 vol) 1874.
Gloucestershire RO (D4085). NRA 24223.

[1137] **GL MICHEL & SONS**, leather merchants, knife mfrs and machine repairers for the footwear industry, Northampton

Letter books (8) 1920-44, corresp incl bills and orders (c11 boxes, 1 bundle) 1906-16, 1929-30, 1947-62, rough private ledger 1904-15, cash books of payments out (16) 1917-56, petty cash and expenses books (3) 1923-50, bank books and papers (1 box, etc) 1892-1971, receipts and payments books (14) 1892-1972, purchase day book 1914-17, bought ledgers (4) 1891-1967, orders ledger 1924-43, corresp rel to orders, etc (1 box, 9 bundles) c1906-61, bills and invoices (2 boxes, etc) 1929-78, goods on approval books (2) 1931-56, sales ledgers and day books (22 vols) 1912-c1970, despatch books (8) 1929-77, customers' accounts ledgers (6) 1907-71, stock books (6) 1922-70, leather notebooks (8) incl prices late 19th cent-1951, leather measurements 1907-17, DO Michel notebooks and diaries (4 vols) 1950-3, press cuttings, advertisements and misc corresp and papers c1906-57.
Northamptonshire RO (Acc 1972/D83, 1986/345). NRA 21312.

[1138] **JOHN & JAMES MITCHELL**, tanners, Kirriemuir, Angus

Letter book 1796-8, ledger 1786-98, bill and receipt book 1787-97, journals (2) 1789-96, memoranda books (2) 1789-96, waste book 1792-8, hide book 1797-8, wages books (2) 1789-96.
Scottish Record Office (CS 96/244-53, 1510). *Court of Session Productions*, List & Index Society, special series vol 23, 1987, p92.

[1139] **JOHN & JAMES MUIRHEAD**, skinners and tanners, Glasgow

Ledger and index 1807-8, journals (2) 1805-8, day book 1807-8.
Scottish Record Office (CS 96/1027-31). *Court of Session Productions*, List & Index Society, special series vol 23, 1987, p169.

[1140] **FRANCIS MURGATROYD & SONS**, tanners, curriers and leather merchants, Shelf, Yorks

Trading and profit and loss accounts, balance sheets, etc 1916-45, day books (2) 1911-23, cash books (2) 1916-33, 1945-57, accounts and notebooks (8 vols) 1912-24, bank books (2) 1902-6, stocktaking account books (2) 1870-1906, rent book 1889-1900, plans of proposed extension to Carr Wood tannery 1944, North American travel diary of Francis Murgatroyd 1949.
West Yorkshire Archive Service, Calderdale (FM). NRA 25503.

[1141] **RICHARD NEWLAND**, harness maker, Stratford-upon-Avon, Warwicks

Account books, cash book and bank book 1837-52, general corresp, bills and papers c1836-54.
Shakespeare Birthplace Trust RO, Stratford-upon-Avon (DR 325/1832-4). NRA 28046.

[1142] **NICKOLS & RHODES**, leather mfrs, Leeds

Letter books 1830-45.
West Yorkshire Archive Service, Leeds: see *West Yorkshire Archive Service Report 1982-3*, p25.

[1143] **SE NORRIS & CO LTD**, curriers and leather mfrs, London

Deeds of partnership, etc 1882-1933, nd, papers rel to processes, working drawings, etc 1895-1957, nd, schedule of deeds 1903 and other premises records 1870-98, nd, price lists, photographs and misc family papers c1852-1964.
Museum of Leathercraft, Northampton. NRA 31125.

[1144] **JOHN ORMEROD & SONS LTD**, tanners and leather dressers, Rochdale, Lancs

Memorandum and articles of association 1954, dividend book 1919-48, ledger 1871-5, private ledger 1919-31, prices book 1881-1913, order book 1877-80, stock books (2) 1877-98, skins books (2) 1884-7, 1902-10, tests, etc (1 vol) 1892-1910, strap butts 1898-1906, 1915-21, work book 1909-14, wages books (5) 1887-1921, inventory 1916, plans of works 1887-1949, Roller Leather Manufacturers Association corresp 1940-65, press cuttings 1877-9, 1907.
Rochdale Local Studies Department (C/IND/LEA/ORM). NRA 31057.

[1145] **R & H OWEN**, tanners, Caernarvon

Account books (2) 1845-66.
University College of North Wales, Bangor (Bangor MSS 601-2).

[1146] **MARK PALFREY & CO LTD**, sheepskin rug mfrs, Stourbridge, Worcs

Memorandum and articles of association 1924, 1937, letter book 1925-6, private ledgers (5) 1884-8, 1904-61, day books (10) 1871-1953 and other accounting records (21 vols, etc) 1928-74, order and sales books (8) 1884-7, 1931-73, stock books (2) 1939-73, costing analysis books (5) 1936-67, samples of dye trials book 1918, wages and time books (5) 1926-67.
Hereford and Worcester RO, Worcester (705:829). NRA 19702.

[1147] **PALMER'S BOOT & SHOE WAREHOUSE**, shoe mfrs and retailers, Sturminster Newton, Dorset

Ledger 1937-55, order books (6) 1882-1936, bills, etc (12) 1948-55, wages book 1950-5.
Dorset RO (D 477). NRA 20484.

[1148] **C PARAGREEN & CO**, shoe wholesaler and repairer, Bicester, Oxon

Accounts, price lists, repairs, etc (5 vols, etc) 1909-62.
Northampton Central Museum. NRA 9196.

[1149] **PARKER, HUNTER & SMITH & CO**, shoe mfrs, Kilmarnock, Ayrshire

Letter book 1780-6, journal 1785 incl trade with America.
In private possession. Enquiries to NRA (Scotland) (NRA(S) 905). NRA 17389.

[1150] **WILLIAM PAUL LTD**, tanners, Leeds

Ledger 1898-1919, cash book 1919-22, piece work rate books (4) 1961-6, employees' address book 1863-1942.
West Yorkshire Archive Service, Leeds (Acc 1438). NRA 31031.

[1151] **PEAL & CO LTD**, boot makers, London

Letter book 1855-99, ledgers (29) 1811-39, 1925-58, cash book 1828-52, American trade ledgers (12) 1929-48, summaries of customers' orders (2 vols) 1933-52, notes on American boot factories 1903, feet books (*c*700) containing outline drawings and records of orders 1873, 1890s-1964.
Greater London RO (B/PEL). NRA 10704.

[1152] **PETTIT & SONS (NORTHAMPTON) LTD**, tanners, Northampton

Directors' minutes 1920, annual reports 1930-46, lists of shareholders 1927-62, private ledgers (2) 1896-1919, sales and stock ledger 1882-93, 1915-31, stock book 1945-59, costing ledgers (2) 1913-64, inventories and valuations 1920-30, papers and plans rel to rebuilding of premises 1923, misc corresp and papers (5 files) rel to the Board of Trade and the United Tanners Federation 1940-9.
Northamptonshire RO (ZA2270-2312). NRA 23255.

[1153] **PHILPOT & SONS**, saddlers and leather goods mfrs, Walsall, Staffs

Letter book *c*1908-10, corresp (9 bundles) *c*1893-1946, day book 1907-60, expenditure account book 1907-60, petty cash and postage book 1924-60, order books (2) 1905-7, 1919-56, day books (16 bundles) of orders taken by salesmen 1929-30, stock book 1927-50, price lists, publicity material, etc.
Walsall Local History Centre (Acc 140). NRA 26577.

[1154] **CW PITTARD & CO LTD**, leather mfrs, Yeovil, Somerset

Corporate records from *c*1943, account book 1909-*c*1914, wages book 1826-*c*1844, deeds and premises records 19th-20th cent.
Pittard Garnar plc. Enquiries to the Company Secretary.

[1155] **PETER RAYMOND POLAND & SON**, fur and skin merchants, London

Foreign accounts ledger 1871-8, cash book 1886-90.
Guildhall Library, London (MSS 11563-4).

[1156] **POLLARD & SON**, shoe mfrs, Northampton

Ledgers 1886-1923, journals 1897-1948, petty cash books 1903-36, bill book 1895-1932, monthly purchase and sales figures 1929-45, bought ledgers 1912-24, sales day books, ledgers and cash books 1883-1950, invoice books 1891-1901, 1911-48, shipping invoices, etc 1900-27, customers' ledgers, address books, etc 1869-1900, 1903, 1915, 1917, 1930, despatch records 1901-7, 1915-17, empties account book 1916-28, price lists 1868, 1909-40, details of goods returned 1891-1944, special and bespoke order books 1902-16, stock lists and books 1869-1932, finishing and making rooms and stitching department production records 1911-19, production log books and other records 1908-42, repairs book 1938-46, lists of employees 1909-33, wages books 1889-93, 1912-44, war bonus books 1915-19, insurance and misc records, family and printed material late 19th-20th cent.
Northamptonshire RO (Pol 1-319). NRA 18912.

[1157] **PORTLAND SHOES LTD**, shoe mfrs, Leicester

Private ledger 1872-89, sales ledger 1895-1900, style books *c*1915-60, wages ledger 1879-1919 and other employment records 1879-1946, catalogues, press cuttings and misc printed material 20th cent.
Leicestershire RO (DE 2113). NRA 1283.

Private ledgers from 1889, costing book 1890-6, description book 1890-6, deeds 19th-20th cent.
Portland Shoes Ltd. Enquiries to the Managing Director. NRA 1283.

[1158] **THOMAS, JAMES & THOMAS POWELL**, leather, hide and bark factors, London

Files of brokers' trade circulars, tables of prices current, and produce and sales reports, with manuscript additions, 1848-90.
Guildhall Library, London (MS 10825).

[1159] **FREDERICK PUCKRIDGE & NEPHEW LTD**, goldbeaters' mould and skin mfrs, London

Letter books (11) 1892, 1895-7, 1905-20, purchase day book 1936-50.
Hackney Archives Department (D/B/PUC). NRA 29016.

[1160] **QUANT & SON LTD**, shoe mfrs and retailers, Bury St Edmunds, Suffolk

Copy articles of partnership, etc 1920-1, balance sheets and monthly returns 1919-70, corresp rel to stocks, shares and trade marks 1920, 1927-37, letter books (2) 1903-10, 1971-7, ledgers (9) 1886-1975, day books (4) 1918-19, 1938-69, cash books (8) 1906-75, monthly cash sales and orders record (1 vol) 1890-1975, order books (2) 1911-57, sales ledger incl stock and salaries 1958-76, customers' records (3 vols, etc) 1879,

1906-74, Bury and Newmarket shops records (15 vols) 1936-77, wages books (25) 1944-76, deeds 1803-1955, inventories and insurance policies, etc 1894-1976, brief history of the firm 1800-1933.
Suffolk RO, Bury St Edmunds (HC 512). NRA 31614.

[1161] **HENRY QUICK LTD**, book factors and leather merchants, Exeter, Devon

Letter book 1902-12, cash books (12) 1854-66, 1888-1916, summary account book 1933-8, bank books (7) 1852-62, 1913-31, customers' and bought ledger debt abstract books (4) 1854-1905, customers' ledgers (5) 1891-6, c1932-49, bought ledger 1922-32, commercial travellers' account book 1916-19, wages books (2) and related papers 1931-54, family account books and misc papers 1897-1953.
Devon RO (D 2766). NRA 25370.

[1162] **THOMAS RADCLIFFE**, buffalo and leather picker mfrs, Halifax, Yorks

Account books (2) 1927-60, cash books (4) 1906-49, purchase and sales ledgers (7) 1905-70, purchase day books (11) 1909-68, invoice book 1899-1920, credits book 1905-64, wages books (6) 1920-60, register of trades cautioned by committee 1915-27, misc corresp nd.
West Yorkshire Archive Service, Calderdale (RAD). NRA 27645.

[1163] **RANDALL & PORTER LTD**, tanners, Ulverston, Lancs

Partnership agreements, etc 1887-98, directors' minutes (2 vols) 1897-1972, register of members (2 vols) 1913-32, balance sheet book 1897-1970, consignment book 1897, hide book 1905-7, deeds, maps, etc (c57 items) 1721-1910.
Cumbria RO, Barrow: see *Report of the County Archivist* April 1985, p10.

[1164] **EDWARD & JAMES RICHARDSON LTD**, leather dressers, Newcastle upon Tyne, Northumb

General purposes meeting minutes (1 vol) 1893-1904, board and committee meeting minutes (1 vol) 1957-8, share ledger and papers (1 vol, c13 bundles) 1859-89, 1922-53, letter books (3) 1806-12, 1871-91, 1904-15, corresp (4 bundles) 1893-1931, private ledgers (8) 1795-1814, 1858-1940, private journals (4) 1817-45, 1928-35, cash books (4) 1802-34, purchase contracts (1 vol) 1847-56, ledger rel to tanning preparations 1805-9, tanning book 1822-35, yard book 1853-8, notes on tanning, etc c1805-1936, dye books (3) 1842-8, notes on dyeing preparations (1 vol, 6 items) 1863, 1931-2, leather samples (5 vols, 7 items) c1933, tanners' journey book 1814-29, apprenticeship indentures (4) 1854-67, deeds rel to premises, etc (12) 1843-1948, valuation books (7) 1788-1893, notes on stock, machinery and building costs (2 vols) 1858-85, photographs (268 items) 1880-1954, misc family corresp and papers (20 items) 1792-1900.
Tyne and Wear Archives Service (Acc 161). NRA 16343.

[1165] **JOHN ROBERTS & CO**, tanners, Llanrwst, Denbighs

Articles of partnership 1891-1927, annual statements of accounts 1954-71, private ledgers 1877-1928, cash and day books 1895-1974, purchase ledgers 1898-1954.
Clwyd RO, Ruthin; see *Annual report 1978*, p37.

[1166] **J H ROGERS & CO**, saddlers and harness makers, Edinburgh

Day books (2) 1795-1800, 1816-22.
The Company. Enquiries to NRA (Scotland) (NRA(S) 2003). NRA 19459.

[1167] **W ROUGHT LTD**, furriers, skin merchants, dressers and dealers, Brandon, Suffolk

Memorandum and articles of association 1924, letter books (15) c1883-5, 1908-25, profit and loss and capital account book 1902-16, private ledgers (3) 1924-39, 1945-50, ledgers (5) 1891, 1900-13, day books (5) 1865-71, 1904-33, 1947-74, journals (4) 1913-60, cash books (7) 1919-26, 1932-65, bank books (2) 1927-37, personal expenses account book 1907-13, receipt and payment account books (4) 1900-19, brought and sold ledgers (7) 1913-59, invoices (8 vols, etc) 1904-59, notes rel to skins bought (1 vol) 1884-1913, price list 1902-3, stock sheets 1894, work book 1937-44, wages books (3) 1917-31, family and estate papers 1838-1966 incl letter books (3) 1909-24, photographs of factory c1920.
Suffolk RO, Bury St Edmunds (HC 521). NRA 30996.

[1168] **SAMPSON & CO LTD**, belting mfrs, Stroud, Glos

Directors' minutes (1 vol) 1899-1911.
Gloucestershire RO (D1347). NRA 4493.

[1169] **F SCHRADER**, leather factors, Liverpool

Corresp, accounts, etc c1850-c1900 incl papers rel to Clarke's tannery, Penrith.
National Museums & Galleries on Merseyside, Merseyside Maritime Museum: see *Merseyside County Archives preliminary brief descriptive guide*, p12.

[1170] **SCHRADER, MITCHELL & WEIR LTD**, leather merchants, Glasgow

Private ledgers (10) 1870-1905, ledger 1879-87, journals (4) 1860-90, misc vouchers and accounts 1870-85, estimates for building new premises (1 vol) 1903, inventory and valuation 1941, legal papers rel to George Schrader's trust 1891-7, corresp, etc rel to the Lockwood leather scouring and setting machine syndicate 1884-5.
In private possession. Enquiries to NRA (Scotland) (NRA(S) 987). NRA 18737.

[1171] **SHEFFIELD BUTCHERS' HIDE & SKIN CO LTD**, hide and skin agents, Sheffield, Yorks

Records 1869-1982 incl directors' and general meeting minutes, register of members, share ledgers and transfers, annual returns, reports and accounts, journal, fellmonger licences, photographs, and company history.
The Company. NRA 28631; BAC *Company Archives* no 104.

[1172] GEORGE SMITH & SONS LTD,
manufacturing furriers, London

Memorandum and articles of association *c*1898-1950s,
board and general minutes (3 vols) 1898-1988, registers
of directors and members and shareholders' ledgers (6
vols) *c*1898-1980s, misc share records 1898-1985,
annual accounts 1949-86, private ledgers (3) *c*1932-87,
journal 1899-1972, private cash books (2) 1942-7,
1977-87, debtors' and creditors' book 1903-60 and
other financial records 1978-88, sales account books
(3) 1873-85, catalogues (*c*40 vols) 1940s-1960s, stock
book 1977-87, salaries book 1941-5, service
agreements, etc 1933-54, leases and related papers
1899, *c*1965-72, prints and photographs *c*1890s-1950s,
press cuttings (12 vols) 1966-79.
Westminster City Libraries Archives Section. NRA
31121.

[1173] SOLLARS family, shoemakers, Evesham,
Worcs

Shoe repair registers (9) 1903-32, foot outlines and
measurements books (2) 20th cent, accounts and wages
books (8) 20th cent, bills, receipts, letters, catalogues,
size charts, indentures of apprenticeship and other
papers (*c*3,000 items) 20th cent.
Hereford and Worcester RO, Worcester (899:251). NRA
12560.

[1174] JAMES SOUTHALL & CO LTD,
(afterwards **START-RITE SHOES LTD**), boot and
shoe mfrs, Norwich, Norfolk

Minutes from 1900, catalogues 1860s.
Start-Rite Shoes Ltd. Enquiries to the Managing
Director.

[1175] G STAYNES & SONS LTD, leather
merchants, Leicester

Letter books (31) 1888-1952, memoranda books (4)
1906-20, ledgers (23) 1849-1948, account books (6)
1855-90, 1899-1903, monthly account books (2)
1872-7, 1896-1912, day books (2) 1898, 1901-3, cash
books (17) 1870-1950, bank books (15) 1865-1931,
invoice books (2) 1877-1928, purchase book 1931-4,
order book 1896-8, price lists and catalogues (*c*80
items) 19th-20th cent, stock books (13) 1862-1922,
yard book 1870-9, tanning progress books (5)
1880-1921, shoe pattern book 19th cent, wages book
1886-96, misc corresp and papers (*c*100 items)
1840-1955.
Leicestershire RO (16 D 69). NRA 26144.

[1176] STEAD & SIMPSON LTD, footwear mfrs
and retailers, Leicester

Memorandum and articles of association 1889,
1939-53, directors' minutes (2 vols) 1879-1932,
management committee minutes (2 vols) 1897-9,
1910-11, register of members and share ledger
*c*1930s-1960s, balance sheets, profit and loss accounts,
etc 1877-1959, letter books (3) 1872-96, corresp and
circulars (3 vols) 1941-9, private ledgers (3) 1878-1953,
ledger 1889-97, private cash book 1901-42, cash book
1861-3, bank books (5) 1872-6, diary or bills due book

1871, diaries and memoranda books (3) 1872-82,
corresp and orders (*c*50 items) 1872-5, shop stocks,
returns and commission 1884-97, 1908, calculations
book *c*1874, price and stock lists *c*1889-1939, wages
book 1870-1, sick and funeral club contributions book
1887-1935 and other employment records 1925-66,
agreement for Belgrave Gate Works 1868, plans 1870,
1889, nd, engine estimate 1880, press cuttings,
catalogues, advertisements, photographs and centenary
histories.
The Company. Enquiries to the Company. NRA 1024.

[1177] GILLYAT SUMNER, fellmonger, Beverley,
Yorks

Letters (3 vols) from the Emmet family of Halifax rel
to wool purchases 1785-1816.
West Yorkshire Archive Service, Leeds (GA/E/12). NRA
19412.

[1178] WILLIAM SUTTON LTD, tanners and
curriers, Scotby, Cumberland

Letter books (20) 1847-8, 1870-1903, corresp (*c*180
bundles) 1846-1908, day books (3) 1837-53, bought
and sales day books (8) 1853-87, copy telegrams (30
bundles) 1879-1908, wages books (10) 1839-95, family
corresp and papers (*c*16 bundles) 1859-1907;
Bermondsey, Leicester, Northampton and Paris
agencies' letter books, orders, accounts, etc (83 vols,
58 bundles) 1885-1909.
Cumbria RO, Carlisle (DB/33). NRA 17337.

[1179] TANNED LEATHER CO LTD (formerly
TURNERS PATENT STRAP CO LTD), tanners,
Greenfield, Yorks

Records 1851-79 incl directors' and general meeting
minutes, private ledger, patents, and licences.
Greater Manchester RO. NRA 28631; BAC *Company
Archives* no 114.

[1180] JOHN TAYLOR, DUNFORD & CO LTD,
leather, rubber and asbestos goods mfrs, Newcastle
upon Tyne, Northumb

Board and general meeting minutes (5 vols) 1906-55,
local directors' meeting minutes (1 vol) 1921-8, sale
papers and agreements 1905-7, register of members
and shares ledgers (2 vols) *c*1906-48, registers of
transfers (2 vols) 1906-52, reports and accounts
1908-25, bank books (2) 1890-1904, price lists 1882,
*c*1917, 1948, nd, wages book 1914-19.
Tyne and Wear Archives Service (Acc 1705). NRA
28367.

[1181] GEORGE THOMPSON & SONS LTD,
leather belting mfrs, Sowerby Bridge, Yorks

Cash/contra ledger 1907, bank books (2) 1910-11,
cheque/payments record book 1902, other accounting
records (16 vols) 1930-74, sales ledger 1962, expenses
journal 1895-1905, customers' account book 1955,
export packing record 1928, particulars for shipment
book 1924-38, curriers' stock book 1904, department
stock record 1915, belt making book 1908, wages
books (2) 1907, 1910.
Bankfield Museum, Halifax. NRA 5855.

[1182] **W & J THORNHILL** (afterwards **F & J HALL**), curriers and leather merchants, Stockport, Cheshire

Ledgers (2) 1815-84.
Stockport Central Library. NRA 9716.

[1183] **JOSEPH TODHUNTER**, boot and shoemaker, Burgh-by-Sands, Cumberland

Day books (4) 1888-1922.
Cumbria RO, Carlisle (DB/32). NRA 17337.

[1184] **W & AJ TURNER LTD**, tanners, Ipswich, Suffolk

Director's minute book 1937-54, letter book 1904-13, account books (3) 1912-70, ledger 1923-33, private journal 1930s, notebook rel to bends ordered and delivered 1930s, contracts (2 vols) 1950s-1980s, price lists 1924-39, catalogue 1932-3.
Museum of Leathercraft, Northampton. NRA 31125.

[1185] **W & E TURNER LTD**, boot and shoe mfrs, Leicester

Directors' minute books (10) 1901-78, registers of directors 1911-46, share registers, etc *c*1900-78, annual returns 1938-47, branch profit and loss accounts 1968-9, private ledgers (6) 1876-1978, bank ledger 1934-77, rents ledgers 1904-45, index to properties rented 1895-1927, centenary celebration photographs 1956.
Leicestershire RO (DE 2835). NRA 28588.

[1186] **TURNEY BROS LTD**, leather dressers and mfrs, Nottingham

Records 1861-1979 incl directors' and general meeting minutes, register of directors and managers, annual reports and accounts, ledgers, journal, cash books, sales books, laboratory book, wages books, staff lists, corresp, drawings and plans rel to plant, photographs, and press cuttings.
Nottinghamshire AO. NRA 28631; BAC *Company Archives* no 615.

Balance sheets 1891-6.
In private possession. Enquiries to NRA (Scotland)(NRA(S) 987). NRA 18737.

[1187] **WJ TURNEY & CO LTD**, leather dressers, Stourbridge, Worcs

Ledgers (3) 1907-18, 1934-41, nominal ledgers (2) 1909-20, 1931-43, cash books (4) 1930-56, bill books (2) 1898-1957, bank books (4) 1890-1902, bought ledger 1910-20, general bought day book 1906-8, purchase, sales and consignment records (13 vols) 1934-57, stock books (5) 1902-37, skivers, basils and pelt books, etc (31 vols) 1924-63, wages books (3) 1894-1903, 1938-43, accident book 1924-54, young employees' register 1935-8, plant repairs ledgers (5) 1910-51, rate book nd, business corresp, market reports, telegrams, samples, price lists and papers (*c*3,150 items) 1942-56.
Hereford and Worcester RO, Worcester (705:702). NRA 15916.

Title deeds and related papers (122 items) 1667-1897.
Dudley Archives and Local History Department (8680).

[1188] **WILLIAM WALKER & SONS LTD**, tanners, Bolton, Lancs

Directors', shareholders' and advisory board minutes (4 vols) 1895-1933, 1955-6, seal register (2 vols) 1919-45, general ledger 1838-95, general account and stock book 1841-55, private ledger 1943-51 and other accounting records (11 vols) 1953-74, register of firms supplied and credit given 1911-29, foreign collections register 1938-48, orders and costings for hides 1972-6, wages books (9) 1946-73 and other staff records 1947-76; records of Dri-Ped Ltd and other subsidiaries 1913-73, nd.
Bolton Metropolitan Borough Archives (ZWK). NRA 27223.

[1189] **W & J WALLACE LTD**, boot mfrs, Rochdale, Lancs

Directors' minutes (2 vols) 1902-33, register of members 1902-35, nominal ledgers (2) 1928-32, cash book *c*1922-3, staff benefit scheme committee minutes 1924-32.
Staffordshire RO (D 4338/C/1). NRA 29538.

[1190] **WARD & SHEFFIELD**, boot mfrs, Earls Barton, Northants

Annual account book 1850-1908.
Northampton Central Museum. NRA 9196.

[1191] **WEBB & SON (COMBS) LTD**, tanners, Stowmarket, Suffolk

Dissolution of partnership 1848, partnership accounts and ledger (12 vols) 1809-17, executorship letters and papers 1864-81, transfers and balances (4 vols) 1916-45, letter books (63) 1841-7, 1898-1911, 1930s, ledgers (26) 1848-1964, journals (8) 1776-1944, day books (25) 1839-1936, cash books (42) 1849-1971, account books (11) 1818-1904, 1935-65, bank books (23) 1830s-1930, purchase and sales books (16) 1927-60, factors' consignments (5 vols, 1 file) 1911-39, John Hayward in account with Webb & Son for sheep (1 vol) *c*1875-87, Stowmarket shop ledgers and stock book (3 vols) 1855-1901, agreements and contracts (3 vols) 1847-99, receipts, invoices, orders, etc (27 bundles) *c*1925-50, details of other firms (2 vols) 1866-84, *c*1909-12, warehouse or despatch books (9) 1877-1940, stock books and ledgers (30) 1817-1947, bark books (9) 1885-*c*1943, works diary 1834-8, account book for piece work 1829-47, fleece wool record (1 vol) 1861-1912, scale book 1933-4, trial, recipe and test books (5) 1830, 1851-65, 1940-57, rough calculations books 1862-1910, inventory and memoranda books (5) 1830s-1896, work account books (5) *c*1833-47, curriers' books (3) early 20th cent, wages books (47 vols, etc) 1848-1968, papers rel to treats, celebrations and festivities *c*1870-20th cent, valuation books (9) 1819-1926, insurance policies, schedules, accounts and corresp (1 box, 1 vol, 3 bundles, etc) 20th cent, maps and plans 19th cent, leather tax papers 1774-1818, government controls and returns *c*1939-45,

Leather Belting Federation corresp 1940s; Model
Farm accounts, stock and wages records, valuations,
etc (c52 vols, 5 bundles) 1823-20th cent; family,
personal, property and local authority and society
papers 19th-20th cent.
The Company. Enquiries to NW Portway Esq. NRA
32010.

[1192] **WELLINGBOROUGH BOOT & SHOE
MANUFACTURING CO LTD**, Wellingborough,
Northants

Directors' minute books (5) from 1890, profit and loss
account books (5) 1946-66, receipts and payments
books (7) 1918-70, purchase, sales, order and
production records (33 vols) 1919-70, wages books (5)
1925-52.
Northamptonshire RO (S355). NRA 21506.

[1193] **E WEST & CO**, shoe mfrs, Northampton

Memorandum of association 1896, overseas orders
despatch ledger 1880-7, letters from travellers 1898-9,
skin room ledger 1902-5, schedule of plant to Mounts
Factory Co 1907, costings of army boots c1916,
memorandum by AE West about welted shoe trade
1896-1957 (1966), misc printed material.
Northamptonshire RO (ZA4106-18). NRA 4039.

[1194] **WHITEHEAD family**, boot makers,
Honington, Warwicks

Account books (2) 1843-1919.
Northampton Central Museum. NRA 9196.

[1195] **WHITNEY & WESTLEY LTD**, shoe mfrs,
Burton Latimer, Northants

Memorandum and articles of association 1928-70,
private ledger 1920-3, cash book 1957-72, purchase
and sales records (3 vols) 1920-56, wages books (16)
1897-1952 incl Mono Shoe Co, Alex Shoe Co and
Relay Shoe Co, price lists and misc papers 20th cent.
Northamptonshire RO (Whitney & Westley 1-4). NRA
22298.

[1196] **T WILKIE & SON LTD**, boot makers,
Leven, Fife

Account books (3) incl purchases and apprenticeship
contracts 1835-63.
In private possession. Enquiries to NRA (Scotland)
(NRA(S) 2131). NRA 19459.

[1197] **H WILLIAMS & SONS**, boot makers and
retailers, Fishguard, Pembs

Accounts 1904-44.
Dyfed Archive Service, Pembroke: see *Accessions to
repositories 1977*, p51.

[1198] **WILLIAM WILSON**, shoemaker, Stirling

Account books (2) 1819-25 and index, waste books (2)
1820-5.
Scottish Record Office (CS 96/1294-7). *Court of Session
Productions*, List & Index Society, special series vol
23, 1987, p314.

[1199] **THOMAS WRIGHT & CO LTD**, leather
dressers, Leeds

Ledgers and other accounting records (29 vols)
1911-64, purchase day books (2) 1925-50, commissions
book and accounts 1940-54, country books and cash
sales (24 vols) 1938-63, inward and outward credits
1939-58, plan account 1889-1916, order books (9)
1907-61, stock books (8) 1939-62, crust books (17)
1935-62, details of skins bought and dyed (5 vols)
1906-57, diaries (5) incl details of skins 1934-63,
quantities of skins under daily headings (1 vol)
1898-1906, 1913, notebooks, samples, etc rel to dyeing
(c5 vols) 1925-8, nd, measuring machine book 1946-53,
nailers' work book 1939-40, wages books (6) 1920-57.
West Yorkshire Archive Service, Leeds (Acc 1242). NRA
31029.

[1200] **G & J ZAIR LTD**, whip mfrs, Birmingham

Ledger 1924-8, day books (16) 1902-52, cash books
(5) 1902-19, petty cash books (6) 1898-1950, purchase
day books and journals (4 vols) 1924-5, nd, prices
books (3) c1920 and price lists nd, order books (5)
1885-91, 1909-11, 1957-63, country, export and Irish
order books (18) 1901-13, upstairs and warehouse
order book 1911-15, sent-in books (7) 1904-31, stock
books (21) 1891-1954, stocktaking sheets 1944-55,
costing books (18) c1921-52, nd, pattern books and
notebooks (10) 1891-1950, nd, wages books (3)
1891-1907, 1941-6, health and unemployment
insurance contributions book 1913-29, corresp and
misc papers (3 boxes).
Birmingham Central Libraries Archives Department (MS
160). NRA 29845.

Index of Businesses

The references are to entry numbers

Holwell Co Ltd 775
Holywell Textile Mills Ltd 305
Hope, Matthew 377
Hornby, WH, & Co 414
Horne Brothers Ltd 964
Horner & Turner 155
Horrockses, Crewdson & Co Ltd 415
Horsfall, Joseph, & Sons Ltd 156
Hounsell, William, & Co 590
Hovell, RB, & Co Ltd 879
Howard, Cephas, & Co 459
Howard, Rivers & Co 842
Howe, J & J 1106
Howlett & White 1107
Hoyle, A & J, Ltd 416
Hoyle, Joshua, & Sons Ltd 417
Hoyle, Thomas, & Sons Ltd 157
Hudson, C 158
Hudson, George 1108
Hudson, Sykes & Bousfield 159
Hughes, David, & Sons 965
Hunt & Winterbotham Ltd 160
Hunter & Donaldson 966
Hutchison & Pollok Ltd 591
Huthart, J, & Co Ltd 967
Hyde, R & N 402

Ibbotson, Thomas 161
Illingworth, Daniel, & Sons Ltd 162
Ingle, WL, Ltd 1109
Innes, AP, & Co 968
Innes, Henderson & Co Ltd 968
Ireland, Edmondson & Co 163
Island Spinning Co Ltd 592
Ives, Basely & Robberds 724
Ivory, James, & Co 593

Jack, James, & Sons Ltd 594
Jack, Ronald, & Co Ltd 164
Jackson, Joseph 165
Jackson & Sons 967
Jackson, Watson & Greig 805
Jaeger Co Ltd 969
Jaffe Brothers & Co Ltd 595
Jeffrey, James 970
Jeffries, E, & Sons Ltd 1110
Jennens, Welch & Co Ltd 806
Jessop Brothers 166
Johnson, Joseph, Ltd 411
Johnston, James, & Co 167
Johnston, Philip, & Sons Ltd 596
Johnston, William 418
Johnston, William, & Son 597
Johnstone, John D, Ltd 168
Jones, Jacob, & Son 169
Jones, John 170
Jones & Morris 598
Jones & Shewell 599
Jordan, John 1111
Jourdain & Ham 700
Jowitt, Robert, & Sons Ltd 171
Julius, Cohen & Josephy 172

K Shoemakers Ltd 1112
Kay, Henry, & Co 419
Kay, James 173

Kaye, Joseph, & Sons 600
Kearns, Allen & Co Ltd 775
Keddie, Darling & Co Ltd 37
Kellett, Brown & Co Ltd 174
Kelly, John 175
Kenworthy, JF & C, Ltd 176
Kenyon, James, & Son Ltd 177
Kerr & Co Ltd 420
Kerr, Pollock & Co 420
Kershaw, Hugh, & Sons Ltd 178
Kettering Boot & Shoe Co Ltd 1113
Kidd, WJ, & Sons Ltd 1114
Kidderminster Spinning Co Ltd 63
Kilwee Bleaching Co Ltd 807
Kinder Printing Co 778
Kirk & Steel Ltd 179
Kirk, William, & Sons 601
Kirkcaldy Linoleum Co 602
Kirkland, David & James 1115
Kirkpatrick Bros 808
Kitchin & Co Ltd 1116
Knight & Lawrence 1117
Knockcloghrim Flax & Tow Spinning Co 603
Knowles, JH, & Co Ltd 180
Knox & Pollock 604
Kyd, John N, & Co Ltd 605

Laidlaw & Fairgrieve Ltd 181
Laing Bros & Co 532
Laing, Francis & William 971
Lamb, James 606
Lamb, R & FE, (Nottingham) Ltd 972
Lambeg Bleaching, Dyeing & Finishing Co 809
Lamont, Samuel, & Sons Ltd 607
Lanark Spinning Co 421
Lanark Twist Co 421
Lancashire Butchers' Hide & Skin Co Ltd 1118
Lancashire Felt Co Ltd 183
Lancaster Carpets Ltd 183
Lang, WJ & W, Ltd 1119
Larne Weaving Co Ltd 608
Laverton, A, & Co Ltd 184
Law, JJ, & Co Ltd 1120
Lawson, JE 1121
Lawson, William, & Sons 609
Lawton, Ben 44
Lawton, Joseph, & Co 185
Lea, Francis & John 186
Leach, John, Bennett & Co 810
Lean, John, & Sons Ltd 422
Lear, Browne & Dunsford Ltd 187
Learoyd Bros & Co 188
Lee, Arthur H, & Sons Ltd 880
Lee, Daniel, & Co Ltd 778
Lee, George P, Ltd 881
Lees, FWH, & Co 1122
Lees, James 189
Lees, James, Son & Co 423
Lees, John & Richard 190
Legg, Thomas, & Son 1123
Legget, Robert, & Sons Ltd 191
Le Gros & Co 725
Leicester 'Self-Help' Boot & Shoe Manufacturing
    Society 1124
Lerry Mills 192
Lester, T, & Sons 758

Quick, Henry, Ltd 1161

Raceview Woollen Mills Ltd 242
Radcliffe, Thomas 1162
Raffield, Thomas 642
Raistrick, John, & Sons 243
Randall, HE, Ltd 1112
Randall & Porter Ltd 1163
Raphael & Co 643
Ratcliffe, Thomas, & Co Ltd 244
Ratsey & Lapthorn Ltd 644
Raven, W, & Co Ltd 1016
Ravenscroft, Burton 1017
Rawdon Low Mill Co 245
Rawson, WH, & Co 95
Reckitt, Isaac 246
Reddaway, F, & Co Ltd 1058
Reddihough, John, Ltd 247
Reddihough & Murgatroyd 247
Reed, JB, & Co 248
Relay Shoe Co 1195
Rennie, WM, & Co Ltd 249
Reynolds & Gibson 460
Reynolds, RH, Bros Ltd 1018
Rhodes, Albert, & Co Ltd 250
Rhodes & Broadbent 251
Rhodes Bros Sons Ltd 1019
Rhodes, J & S, Ltd 252
Rhodes, William, Ltd 253
Rhydygwystl Woollen Factory 254
Richardson & Co 809
Richardson, Edward & James, Ltd 1164
Richardson, JN, Sons & Owden Ltd 645
Ridgway, Thomas, Bridson & Sons 833
Ridgway, Thomas, & Co Ltd 828
Riley, Edward & Pickles, & Co Ltd 461
Ripley, Edward, & Son Ltd 829
Robb, Hamilton 646
Robb, HM & Co Ltd 647
Roberts, JF & H, Ltd 255
Roberts, John, & Co 1165
Roberts, Richard 648
Robertson, J & J 1020
Robinson & Cleaver Ltd 649
Robinson, George, & Co 462
Robinson, G & R, & Co Ltd 650
Robinson, T, & Co Ltd 830
Rodgett & Brierley 463
Rogers & Co (Military Outfitters) Ltd 1021
Rogers, JH, & Co 1166
Romanes & Paterson 1022
Ronald & Rodger 256
Rose Bank Printworks 805, 850
Rose, EP, & Son Ltd 1023
Rosebank Weaving Co Ltd 651
Ross, Alexander, & Co Ltd 1062
Rought, W, Ltd 1167
Rowans Ltd 1024
Roy Mill Ltd 464
Royal Tapestry Works 257
Royton Spinning Co Ltd 465
Russell, Benjamin, & Sons Ltd 1025
Russell, James 652
Russian Carpet Co 78
Rylands & Sons Ltd 466

St Martins Langdale Linen Industry 653

Salomon, Julius, & Co 654
Saltcoats Ropeworks Co 655
Salter, Samuel, & Co Ltd 258
Salts (Saltaire) Ltd 259
Sampson & Co Ltd 1168
Sandeman, Frank Stewart, & Sons Ltd 656
Sanderson, Arthur, & Sons Ltd 889
Sanderson & Murray Ltd 260
Sanderson, R & A, & Co Ltd 261
Sandford, Benjamin V 467
Saunders, JR 657
Saunders, Laurence 575
Schofield & Froggatt Ltd 890
Schrader, F 1169
Schrader, Mitchell & Weir Ltd 1170
Scott & Fyfe Ltd 658
Scott, H & A, Ltd 659
Scott, James, & Sons Ltd 660
Scott, William C 262
Scotts Ltd 1026
Seelig & Co Ltd 749
Sewing Cotton Agency 356
Shannon, John, & Son Ltd 1027
Shaw, John, & Sons 263
Shaw & Shaw 468
Sheffield Butchers' Hide & Skin Co Ltd 1171
Shepherd & Manning Ltd 1028
Shiers, John Jackson, & Sons Ltd 433
Shiloh Spinning Co Ltd 469
Shirras, Laing & Co Ltd 661
Sim, R, & Co 264
Simpson Brothers 470
Slater & Co Ltd 831
Slater, George & James, Ltd 832
Slater, Samuel, & Sons 471
Smale, Josiah, & Son Ltd 733
Smart, J & J, (Brechin) Ltd 662
Smedley, John, Ltd 1029
Smieton, James, & Son 663
Smith, Dundas, & Co 472
Smith, George, & Sons Ltd 1172
Smith & Gillett 1030
Smith, J, & Co 486
Smith, John, Junior & Co Ltd 833
Smith, Richard, & Sons 265
Smith, Silvester 639
Smith, Thomas & William, Ltd 664
Smith & Wiseman 473
Smylie, Robert 665
Smyth, John A, & Co 666
Sollars family 1173
Somervell Bros Ltd 1112
South Molton Shirt & Collar Manufacturing Co Ltd 1031
Southall, James, & Co Ltd 1174
Southwell, H & M, Ltd 266
Sparrow, Brown, Hanbury, Savill & Co 267
Spence, Bryson & Co 667
Spencer, John, & Son 474
Spencer, John, & Sons 268
Spencer, Walter 1032
Spirella Co of Great Britain Ltd 1033
Spittal Dyeworks 834
Springfield Hosiery Finishing Co Ltd 835
Spur Doubling Mill Ltd 475
Staley & Millbrook Ltd 476

Gazetteer

Business locations given at the head of each entry in the guide are here grouped alphabetically under the pre-1974/5 counties, in accordance with the ninth edition of Bartholomew's *Gazetteer of the British Isles*. The references are to entry numbers.

ENGLAND

BEDFORDSHIRE
Bedford 680, 758, 1023
Woburn 1067

BERKSHIRE
Reading 911
Windsor 257
Wokingham 959

BUCKINGHAMSHIRE
Chesham 1006

CAMBRIDGESHIRE
Bourn 919
Cambridge 976
Sawston 1087

CHESHIRE
Birkenhead 880
Bollington 480
Chadkirk 844
Chester 912
Congleton 703, 983
Edgeley 845
Langley 860
Macclesfield 705, 708, 714, 715, 726, 733
Northwich 1085
Stalybridge 476, 890
Stockport 451, 452, 459, 916, 918, 978, 1036, 1182
Strines 840
Styal 402

CORNWALL
Bodmin 989
Falmouth 669
Grampound 1081
Truro 99

CUMBERLAND
Alston 299
Brampton 967
Burgh-by-Sands 1183
Carlisle 54, 389, 886, 967, 1039
Cummersdale 837
Dalston 54
Harrington 571A
Millbeck 89
Scotby 1178
Whitehaven 583

DERBYSHIRE
Ashbourne 470, 922
Belper 478, 908

Calver 485
Cromford 331
Darley Abbey 387
Derby 748, 754, 982
Dinting Vale 826
Great Longstone 424
Hayfield 802
Matlock 1029
Matlock Bath 331
Tideswell 731
Wirksworth 348, 492

DEVON
Exeter 187, 910, 920, 924, 935, 1035, 1053, 1101, 1161
Great Torrington 248
Plymouth 677
South Molton 1031
Tiverton 756, 1045

DORSET
Bridport 70, 577, 590, 641, 678, 1105
Burton Bradstock 648
Sherborne 744
Sturminster Newton 1147

DURHAM
Darlington 231
Durham 142
Easington Lane 981
Sunderland 688

ESSEX
Bocking 223, 267
Braintree 740
Great Wakering 1095
Southend 958

GLOUCESTERSHIRE
Bisley 17
Blockley 742
Bristol 400, 531, 668, 674, 1070
Cam 160
Dursley 298A
Gloucester 1092, 1136
Kingswood, Bristol 1072
Kingswood, Wotton-under-Edge 1042
Minchinhampton 60, 236
Nailsworth 220, 291
Newent 1122
Painswick 227
Stonehouse 205
Stroud 9, 138, 146, 205, 1168

998, 1004, 1010, 1012, 1013, 1017, 1021, 1026,
1030, 1040, 1048, 1049, 1050, 1054, 1061, 1062,
1064, 1073, 1075, 1084, 1103, 1127, 1135, 1143,
1151, 1155, 1158, 1159, 1172
Staines 612
Uxbridge 889

NORFOLK
Burnham Market 1108
Great Yarmouth 718, 1060
Norwich 175, 704, 723, 724, 737, 743, 870, 872, 879,
906, 1060, 1107, 1174

NORTHAMPTONSHIRE
Burton Latimer 1195
Earls Barton 1190
Islip 1128
Kettering 313, 1046, 1093, 1096, 1113, 1126
Northampton 1028, 1056, 1057, 1069, 1077, 1094,
1131, 1137, 1152, 1156, 1193
Rushden 1098, 1117
Wellingborough 1192

NORTHUMBERLAND
Alnwick 934
Newcastle upon Tyne 579, 664, 1058, 1164, 1180
Tranwell 12

NOTTINGHAMSHIRE
Blyth 312
Cuckney 487
Hucknall 1019
Nottingham 153, 246, 746, 749, 752, 753, 755, 764,
835, 947, 951, 972, 974, 1001, 1186
Radford 496
Sutton-in-Ashfield 994

OXFORDSHIRE
Bicester 1148
Burford 684
Chipping Norton 38
Oxford 915, 953
Witney 92

SHROPSHIRE
Bridgnorth 1086
Oswestry 1088
Shrewsbury 623

SOMERSET
Castle Cary 868, 874
Chard 859
Frome 296
Street 1058A, 1078
Taunton 730
Wellington 110, 240
Yeovil 903, 935, 1154

STAFFORDSHIRE
Fazeley 849
Leek 706, 711, 716, 717, 727, 728, 739, 741, 745, 856
Leekbrook 855
Stafford 1080, 1133
Upper Tean 455
Walsall 1027, 1034, 1099, 1110, 1153

SUFFOLK
Brandon 1167
Bury St Edmunds 928, 1160

Haverhill 950
Ipswich 1009, 1184
Stowmarket 1044, 1191
Sudbury 738

SURREY
Merton Abbey 810, 885

SUSSEX
Burgess Hill 962
Eastbourne 955
Rye 1123

WARWICKSHIRE
Bedworth 729
Birmingham 695, 1024, 1200
Coventry 709, 713, 719, 734
Honington 1194
Solihull 943
Stratford-upon-Avon 1141

WESTMORLAND
Elterwater 653
Holme 568
Kendal 42, 163, 307, 314, 774, 926, 927, 1112
Kirkland 1051

WILTSHIRE
Bradford-on-Avon 10, 838, 999
Devizes 147, 304
Holt 1063
Mere 589
Salisbury 276
Trowbridge 25, 66, 71, 73, 258, 888
Warminster 300
Westbury 184, 907, 1076
Wilton 320

WORCESTERSHIRE
Evesham 1173
Kidderminster 48, 63, 186, 217, 265, 266, 269, 280,
294, 322
Stourbridge 1146, 1187
Stourport 290
Worcester 932, 944
Wribbenhall 616

YORKSHIRE
Almondbury 173, 282, 283
Alverthorpe 321
Armitage Bridge 50
Barnoldswick 438
Barnsley 536
Batley 34, 46, 149, 273, 284, 768, 811
Beverley 1104, 1177
Birkenshaw 253
Bradford 6, 13, 24, 28, 30, 32, 90, 97, 115, 118, 124,
148, 150, 162, 171, 172, 180, 195, 232, 237, 239,
247, 281, 303, 323, 722, 773, 829, 1038
Brighouse 106
Brockholes 279
Burley-in-Wharfedale 107
Calverley 154, 174
Churwell 79
Cleckheaton 123, 1071, 1079
Cullingworth 128

Carnoustie 663
Douglastown 593
Dundee 211, 262, 502, 511, 516, 520, 524, 532, 545,
    550, 555, 559, 566, 575, 581, 585, 595, 605, 609,
    622, 627, 636, 639, 654, 656, 659, 660, 670, 675,
    681, 683, 771, 779, 873, 913
Forfar 521, 546, 548, 617
Kirriemuir 692, 1138
Montrose 634

AYRSHIRE
Cumnock 1115
Darvel 886
Kilmarnock 1149
Kilwinning 58, 783
Saltcoats 655

BANFFSHIRE
Cullen 686

BERWICKSHIRE
Duns 551

CLACKMANNANSHIRE
Alloa 230
Alva 966
Tillicoultry 11

DUMFRIESSHIRE
Dumfries 986
Langholm 29

DUNBARTONSHIRE
Alexandria 852
Kirkintilloch 429, 985
Levenbank 848
Milton 818

EAST LOTHIAN
Saltoun 528

FIFE
Kirkcaldy 510, 602, 615, 629, 671
Leslie 557
Leven 1196
Lower Largo 565
Newburgh 287, 971, 1102
Tayport 658

INVERNESS-SHIRE
Inverness 946

KINCARDINESHIRE
Stonehaven 594

KINROSS-SHIRE
Kinross 31

LANARKSHIRE
Glasgow 33, 289, 330, 356, 361, 392, 418, 422, 431,
    454, 538, 611, 621, 698, 732, 787, 795, 796, 823,
    847, 882, 883, 896, 945, 949, 974, 1024, 1074, 1139,
    1170
Hogganfield 759
New Lanark 421
Wellmeadowfield 825

MIDLOTHIAN
Edinburgh 33, 134, 191, 528, 554, 697, 726A, 834,
    886, 899, 970, 993, 1022, 1055, 1059, 1166
Eskbank 309
Leith 533
Musselburgh 673
Springfield 793

MORAY
Elgin 167
Forres 1090

PEEBLESSHIRE
Peebles 19
Walkerburn 20

PERTHSHIRE
Alyth 1106
Dunblane 319
Huntingtower 814
Luncarty 776
Perth 506, 827
Pitlochry 201

RENFREWSHIRE
Barrhead 676
Bridge of Weir 1132
Elderslie 270
Greenock 108
Houston 373
Johnstone 450, 560
Neilston 328
Paisley 164, 359, 360, 362, 366, 420, 437, 444, 472,
    509, 635, 794, 914, 942, 988, 1020, 1119
Port Glasgow 569

ROXBURGHSHIRE
Hawick 37, 302, 933, 968, 984, 1052
Kelso 1111
Newtown St Boswells 131

SELKIRKSHIRE
Galashiels 8, 52, 53, 85, 181, 190, 260, 261, 936
Selkirk 74, 114, 119, 264

STIRLINGSHIRE
Bannockburn 318
Denny 218
Stirling 61, 288, 816, 1198

SUTHERLAND
Dornoch 1082
Golspie 1082

WIGTOWNSHIRE
Kirkcowan 212
Newton Stewart 377

NORTHERN IRELAND

ANTRIM
Ballyclare 618, 808
Ballymena 21, 22, 527, 638
Ballymoney 580
Ballyweaney 500

Printed in the United Kingdom for HMSO
Dd289399 6/90 C12 G495 10170